Proceedings of the Institution of Mechanical Engineers

European Conference

Developments in Industrial Compressors

3-4 October 1989
The Institution of Mechanical Engineers
Birdcage Walk
London

Sponsored by
Fluid Machinery Committee of the Institution of Mechanical Engineers

Co-sponsored by
PNEUROP (European Committee of Manufacturers of Compressors, Vacuum Pumps and Pneumatic Tools)
Institute of Refrigeration

IMechE Conference 1989-10

Published for the Institution of Mechanical Engineers by
Mechanical Engineering Publications Limited

D
621.51
DEV

The Publishers are not responsible for any statement made in this publication. Data, discussion and conclusions developed by authors are for information only and are not intended for use without independent substantiating investigation on the part of potential users.

Printed by Waveney Print Services Ltd, Beccles, Suffolk

Contents

NO OTHER OIL-FREE COMPRESSOR BRINGS YOU THIS MUCH CONTINUOUS PURE AIR.

This may sound like a mountainous claim, but it's one that's very easily substantiated.

Ingersoll-Rand's Centac oil-free compressors are based on a very simple concept.

There are few moving parts (only three, in fact, in a typical two stage unit), and no close tolerances, nor metal-to-metal contact associated with the compression cycle.

Perhaps not surprisingly, this makes them incredibly reliable.

Rotors matched to static diffusers compress air in volumes of from 500 to over 30,000 cfm.

Each model comes fully packaged, with microprocessor controls and a self-diagnostic facility.

And with pressure outputs of 2-22 bar, they're extremely versatile.

Combine their inherent reliability with an after sales and parts service which can be tailormade to suit the individual user, and you'll appreciate that when it comes to longevity, the sky's the limit.

⊞ INGERSOLL-RAND

FREEPHONE 0800·444222

Please send me further details of your range of Centac air compressors

Name _____

Position _____

Company _____

Address _____

_____

_____

Telephone _____

Return to: Ingersoll-Rand Information Centre, Conrad House, Birmingham Road, Stratford-upon-Avon, Warwickshire CV37 0AZ

Ingersoll-Rand Sales Company Limited, PO Box 2, Chorley New Road, Horwich, Bolton, Lancashire BL6 6JN Telephone: 0204-690690 Telex: 63387 Fax: 0204-691093

The Institution of Mechanical Engineers

The primary purpose of the 76,000-member Institution of Mechanical Engineers, formed in 1847, has always been and remains the promotion of standards of excellence in British mechanical engineering and a high level of professional development, competence and conduct among aspiring and practising members. Membership of IMechE is highly regarded by employers, both within the UK and overseas, who recognise that its carefully monitored academic training and responsibility standards are second to none. Indeed they offer incontrovertible evidence of a sound formation and continuing development in career progression.

In pursuit of its aim of attracting suitably qualified youngsters into the profession — in adequate numbers to meet the country's future needs — and of assisting established Chartered Mechanical Engineers to update their knowledge of technological developments — in areas such as CADCAM, robotics and FMS, for example — the IMechE offers a comprehensive range of services and activities. Among these, to name but a few, are symposia, courses, conferences, lectures, competitions, surveys, publications, awards and prizes. A Library containing 150,000 books and periodicals and an Information Service which uses a computer terminal linked to databases in Europe and the USA are among the facilities provided by the Institution.

If you wish to know more about the membership requirements or about the Institution's activities listed above — or have a friend or relative who might be interested — telephone or write to IMechE in the first instance and ask for a copy of our colour 'at a glance' leaflet. This provides fuller details and the contact points — both at the London HQ and IMechE's Bury St Edmunds office — for various aspects of the organisation's operation. Specifically it contains a tear-off slip through which more information on any of the membership grades (Student, Graduate, Associate Member, Member and Fellow) may be obtained.

Corporate members of the Institution are able to use the coveted letters 'CEng, MIMechE' or 'CEng, FIMechE' after their name, designations instantly recognised by, and highly acceptable to, employers in the field of engineering. There is no way other than by membership through which they can be obtained!

C390/001

Review of preliminary design and performance prediction techniques for centrifugal compressors
Part 1: preliminary design

A WHITFIELD, BSc, PhD, CEng, MIMechE
School of Mechanical Engineering, University of Bath

Synopsis
A procedure is described to design the overall dimensions of a centrifugal impeller. Initial optimisation is carried out by minimising the inlet and discharge Mach numbers. The procedure is developed for a range of possible pressure ratios and the effect of high pressure ratio on the Mach numbers and resultant impeller geometry is discussed.

Notation

A	Flow area
a	Speed of sound
b	Blade height
C	Absolute velocity
h	Enthalpy
i	Incidence angle
M	Mach number
M'	Relative Mach number
$\dot{m}$	Mass flow rate
P	Pressure
R	Gas constant
r	radius
T	Temperature
U	Blade velocity
W	Relative velocity
$\dot{W}$	Power
Z_B	Number of blades
α	Absolute flow angle from the meridional direction. Positive in the direction of rotation of the impeller.
β	Relative flow angle from the meridional direction. Positive in the direction of rotation of the impeller.
γ	Ratio of specific heats
η_I	Impeller efficiency
η_s	Stage efficiency
θ	Non-dimensional mass flow
μ	Slip factor
ν	Inducer hub shroud radius ratio
ρ	Density
τ	Torque

Subscript

o	Stagnation condition
1	Impeller inlet
2	Impeller discharge
3	Stage discharge
h	Hub position
m	meridional component
s	Shroud position or isentropic condition
θ	Tangential component

1 INTRODUCTION

Once a particular performance requirement has been specified and a centrifugal compressor identified as the appropriate machine to meet that requirement the designer has a number of routes he can take in order to develop a suitable design. A design can be derived simply by scaling from an existing one using the appropriate non-dimensional parameters. If, however, a new design must be generated to provide significant improvements in efficiency and/or size then a fundamental aerodynamic design must be undertaken. The objective here is to describe the preliminary aerodynamic design of the compressor and review techniques available to predict the performance of that design at both design and off-design flow rates. The presentation is restricted largely to considerations of the impeller design. This, however, does not imply that other components, such as the diffuser and cross over ducts, are unimportant.

An optimized impeller design should, however, ensure that the aerodynamic problems associated with the downstream components are minimised.

The initial design requirement is to calculate the overall dimensions of the stage, i.e. to lay out a skeleton design from which the detailed shape can be developed. Designing provides an open ended problem, there being no "correct" procedure and considering the compromises usually involved, no "correct" solution. The design requirement is to apply the basic thermofluid dynamics to the determination of the overall dimensions of the impeller. Here the objective is not only to describe a basic impeller design procedure but also to provide insights into the application of the basic thermofluid dynamics.

Precise prediction of efficiencies at the initial design stage, or at any other stage, is difficult, and the designer usually relies upon empirical loss models and correlations, see Coppage et al(17), Rodgers(14) and Whitfield and Baines(24). The predicted efficiencies are then as good as the under lying empirical loss models. Efficiency is maximised when the irreversibilities associated with the

flow process are minimised. The energy loss is generally a function of the square of the velocity relative to the component under consideration, and if the losses are to be minimised it is essential that the flow velocities are no larger than necessary. The procedure developed here assesses the rotor inlet and discharge conditions with a view to minimising the velocities in terms of the absolute and relative Mach numbers. The resultant design should then give minimum losses irrespective of the loss model, and associated uncertainties, used.

2 THE BASIC THERMOFLUID DYNAMICS

Before considering the application of the thermofluid dynamics to the design of compressor impellers it is necessary to recall the basic equations involved.

By considering the rate of change of angular momentum of the fluid passing through the impeller the Euler turbomachinery equation gives the torque and specific work transfer as

$$\tau = \dot{m}(r_2 C_{\theta 2} - r_1 C_{\theta 1})$$

and

$$\frac{\dot{W}}{\dot{m}} = (U_2 C_{\theta 2} - U_1 C_{\theta 1}) \qquad [1]$$

respectively. The application of the steady flow energy equation for adiabatic flow gives

$$\frac{\dot{W}}{\dot{m}} = (h_{02} - h_{01})$$

and by combining these equations it can be shown that the stagnation temperature ratio across the impeller is given by

$$\frac{T_{02}}{T_{01}} = 1 + \frac{\gamma - 1}{\gamma R T_{01}}(U_2 C_{\theta 2} - U_1 C_{\theta 1}) \qquad [2]$$

It is the pressure ratio P_{02}/P_{01} which is of primary interest to the designer. This can be readily calculated for the special case of isentropic flow only. As all real fluid flows are non-isentropic it is necessary to develop techniques which can relate the real flow process to the more tractable

isentropic flow process. The simplest and most direct way to do this is to specify an efficiency which relates the actual flow process to an isentropic one. In practice the designer will wish to calculate the efficiency, not simply specify it; in that case it will be necessary to quantify the irreversibilities which occur in the flow process in order to calculate the entropy gain. The most convenient efficiency definition is that which relates the inlet and discharge stagnation conditions, see Fig.1, then

$$\eta_I = \frac{h_{02s} - h_{01}}{h_{02} - h_{01}} = \frac{(P_{02}/P_{01})^{\frac{\gamma-1}{\gamma}} - 1}{T_{02}/T_{01} - 1} \qquad [3]$$

The stagnation pressure ratio is then given as

$$\left(\frac{P_{02}}{P_{01}}\right)^{\frac{\gamma-1}{\gamma}} = 1 + \frac{\gamma - 1}{\gamma R T_{01}}\eta_I(U_2 C_{\theta 2} - U_1 C_{\theta 1}) \qquad [4]$$

It should be noted that eqn [2] not only gives the stagnation temperature ratio for the impeller, but also gives the overall stage stagnation temperature ratio, for adiabatic flows, as the remaining components do no further work on the gas. Consequently the overall stage stagnation pressure ratio can be determined through eqn [4] provided the impeller total to total efficiency, is replaced by the total to total efficiency of the complete stage.

The difficulties in applying eqn [4] to calculate the stagnation pressure ratio lie in the determination of the efficiency and the tangential components of velocity at impeller inlet and discharge. For the preliminary stage design it is usually acceptable to assume a state of the art efficiency; once a basic design has been derived the efficiencies can then be calculated through the application of appropriate empirical loss models and correlations, see Part 2. However, it is essential that the preliminary design procedure considers the losses involved and attempts to minimise them. To this end the impeller inlet and discharge Mach numbers should, were possible, be minimised.

The tangential component of velocity at inlet to the impeller is usually zero; only if prewhirl vanes are designed into the inlet duct will the incoming air have a tangential component of velocity. For the preliminary design procedure described here it is assumed that there is no inlet swirl.

The calculation of the tangential component of velocity at impeller discharge has been the subject of extensive studies and research papers. The objective of this research was to find a reasonably simple method to calculate the mean tangential component of velocity so that accurate calculations of the pressure ratio developed and power absorbed by the compressor could be made.

The flow at impeller discharge cannot be perfectly guided by a finite number of blades and it is said to slip, leading to the velocity triangles shown in Fig.2. The effect of slip is to reduce the magnitude of the tangential component of velocity from that which is ideally attainable. This then has the effect of reducing the delivered pressure ratio and the compressor power consumption, eqn [1]. The detrimental effect of slip is that the impeller must be larger or run at higher speeds in order to deliver the required pressure ratio. This leads to increased stress levels and to increased relative velocities in the impeller, which will then give rise to increased friction losses and a reduced efficiency.

In order to quantify the slip which occurs a slip factor is defined which usually takes the form of

$$\mu = 1 - \frac{C_{\text{slip}}}{U_2} \qquad [5]$$

$$\mu = 1 - \frac{C_{\theta 2 \infty} - C_{\theta 2}}{U_2} \qquad [6]$$

From the velocity triangle of Fig.2 it follows that

$$C_{\theta 2} = \mu U_2 + C_{m2} \tan \beta_{B2} \qquad [7]$$

It should be noted that the sign convention adopted is such that a backward swept blade is negative.

It should be quite evident that an accurate knowledge of the slip factor is extremely important as it enables the energy transfer between the impeller and fluid to be calculated. Wiesner[1] published an extensive review of the techniques used to calculate impeller slip factors. The review concluded that slip velocities are best correlated through the procedure given by Busemann and described by Wislicenus[2]. This was considered to be an exact theoretical solution for an inviscid fluid and required extensive mathematical treatment. Wiesner was able to approximate

the Busemann results with the equation

$$\mu = 1 - \frac{\sqrt{\cos \beta_{B2}}}{Z_B^{0.7}} \qquad [8]$$

Stanitz, in the discussion to Wiesner's paper, pointed out that his own analysis, Stanitz[3], was also an exact theoretical solution, and provided his resultant equation was not applied to conditions beyond those of the theoretical analysis his results should be identical to those of Busemann. The Stanitz[3] correlation is

$$\mu = 1 - \frac{0.63\pi}{Z_B}$$

and was considered to be satisfactory for blade angles in the range $-45 < \beta_{B2} < 45$.

The correlations of Busemann and Stanitz are based upon theoretical analyses of the flow of an ideal fluid. Consequently they cannot provide an adequate description of the real jet-wake type flow at impeller discharge. Numerous other empirical correlations have been developed in an attempt to allow for flow separation in the impeller. Dean in the discussion to Wiesner's paper pointed out that a given impeller does not have a single value of slip factor, but that it varies with flow rate. This is due to the different degrees of separation which occur within the impeller passage as the flow rate varies. Even at the best efficiency point different impeller designs even with the same number of blades will have different degrees of separation. Dean pointed out that the ideal flow solutions of

Busemann and Stanitz should be applied to the through flow jet only, see Part 2.

3 IMPELLER DESIGN

If the only information available to the designer is the required mass flow and stage pressure ratio, it is clear that further parameters must be assumed before the basic equations can be applied to provide a closed solution to derive the impeller geometry.

State of the art efficiencies will be assumed, however the objective of the design exercise is to maximise efficiency and it is worth giving some qualitative consideration to the sources of energy dissipation even if they are not initially calculated. Perhaps the most familiar source of loss is that due to skin friction which is directly proportional to the flow path length and the flow velocity, relative to the metal surface, squared. A design objective should therefore be to keep both the flow path length and velocity low. A second source of loss is due to overtip leakage for impellers without an integral shroud. This is a function of the clearance gap which must be maintained between the rotating blade tips and the stationary shroud cover. The loss is proportional to the ratio of the tip clearance gap to the height of the blade, and as will be seen this ratio can become quite large for single stage high pressure ratio machines.

The main requirement from an impeller design procedure is the computation of the overall dimensions and the inlet and discharge blade angles. Whilst the impeller design will be considered under the separate headings of inducer and discharge design they should not be viewed as unconnected components. Indeed as will be seen the discharge design is linked critically to the inducer flow parameters.

3.1 Inducer design

Before commencing any design optimisation, prior knowledge of some parameters must be available, whilst others must be assumed and adjusted during the optimisation process. For an inducer design prior knowledge is usually available of:

(a) the inlet stagnation pressure and temperature; the standard atmospheric conditions are often applicable

(b) the degree of prewhirl, here it will be assumed that the flow enters the inducer with zero prewhirl

(c) the mass flow rate of the working fluid.

In addition it will be assumed that the flow enters uniformly so that there is no variation of axial velocity with radius.

Two aspects of inducer operation are usually considered during the design process. The first considers the design point (best efficiency point) and endeavours to ensure that the required mass flow enters the impeller with the minimum possible relative Mach number. This minimises the blade incidence losses and the frictional losses in the following impeller passage. The second considers the flow range between stall and choke. This again leads to a desire to minimise the relative Mach number as the stable operating range between choke and stall decreases significantly as Mach number increases, Rodgers[4].

The main requirements of a design procedure are the hub and shroud radii and the shroud blade angle, see Fig.3. The minimum hub radius needed is usually fixed through considerations of either the minimum cross sectional area to transmit the required torque and avoid critical vibration problems, or the circumferential space needed to accommodate the required number of blades, whichever is the larger. The inducer blade is, with very rare exception, constructed of radial blades fibres, and once the shroud blade angle has been established the blade angles at all other radii can be easily found.

The inducer shroud radius is the position where the blade velocity, and consequently the relative velocity, is greatest. By reducing the inducer shroud radius, Fig.3, the peripheral speed of the blade tip will decrease leading to a reduction in the relative Mach number; however, this also leads to a smaller flow area and consequently the absolute velocity and relative Mach number will increase. Clearly there is a radial position beyond which the increasing absolute velocity has a more significant effect on the relative Mach number than the decreasing peripheral speed. For a flow without prewhirl the inlet velocity triangle, Fig.3, is a simple right angle triangle and

$$W_{1s}^2 = C_{m1s}^2 + U_{1s}^2 = C_{1s}^2 + \omega^2 r_{1s}^2 \qquad [9]$$

With the non-dimensional mass flow given by

$$\theta = \frac{\dot{m}}{\pi r_2^2 \rho_{01} a_{01}} = \frac{r_{1s}^2}{r_2^2}(1-v^2)\frac{\rho_1}{\rho_{01}}\frac{C_{1s}}{a_{01}}$$

and $v = r_{1h}/r_{1s}$

eqn [9] can be rearranged to give

$$M_{1s}'^2 = M_{1s}^2 + \frac{M_u^2 \theta}{1-v^2}\frac{1}{M_{1s}}\left(1+\frac{\gamma-1}{2}M_{1s}^2\right)^{\frac{3\gamma-1}{2(\gamma-1)}} \qquad [10]$$

where $M_u = U_2/a_{01}$

This expression is shown in Fig.4 were it can be seen that a minimum relative Mach number exists for any specified magnitude of $\theta M_u^2/(1-v^2)$. Contours of relative flow angle are also included on Fig.4 from which it can be seen that the minimum relative Mach number occurs at a flow angle between -56 and -64 degrees.

An alternative view to minimising the relative Mach number for any given mass flow is to maximise the mass flow for any given relative Mach number. Stanitz[5] provides a method for designing the inducer to ensure that the maximum mass flow per unit frontal area is achieved. Equation [10] can be rearranged and written in terms of the relative Mach number and flow angle to give

$$\frac{M_u^2 \theta}{1-v^2} = \frac{M_{1s}'^3 \sin^2\beta_{1s}\cos\beta_{1s}}{(1+\frac{\gamma-1}{2}M_{1s}'^2\cos^2\beta_{1s})^{\frac{3\gamma-1}{2(\gamma-1)}}} \qquad [11]$$

The flow angle which will yield the maximum mass flow for any specified relative Mach number can be found by differentiating eqn [11] with respect to β_{1s} and equating the result to zero to yield

$$\cos^2 \beta_{1s} = \frac{3 + \gamma M'^2_{1s}}{2M'^2_{1s}} \left\{ 1 - \left[1 - \frac{4M'^2_{1s}}{(3 + \gamma M'^2_{1s})^2} \right]^{1/2} \right\} \quad [12]$$

This expression is shown graphically on Fig.5 which also shows the data of Fig.4 replotted with the flow angle as the abscissa. For any mass flow the designer can minimise the inlet relative Mach number by selecting the flow angle through eqn [12]. There is no compulsion to apply eqn [12] and Fig.5 shows that the selection of a flow angle 5 degrees away from the minimum point will lead to an increase in the relative Mach number of approximately 1%. This procedure, therefore, provides a means to make a good order of magnitude estimate for the inducer shroud blade angle. For example, Fig.5 shows that an inlet flow angle of -60 degrees is a good initial order of magnitude for a broad range of relative Mach numbers. To transform this flow angle to the required blade angle requires a knowledge of the incidence angle at the design flow rate. An order of magnitude for this incidence angle is -4 to -6 degrees, see Rodgers(4), and the blade angle is then

$$\beta_{B1s} = \beta_{1s} - i$$

Having established the relative flow angle and relative Mach number the continuity equation can be applied to calculate the inducer flow area, and hence the shroud radius if the hub radius is known from the mechanical considerations. The continuity equation can be developed in terms of the relative flow angle and Mach number to

$$\dot{m} = \frac{\rho_{01} a_{01} \pi (r_{1s}^2 - r_{1h}^2) M'^2_{1s} \cos \beta_{1s}}{\{1 + \frac{\gamma - 1}{2} M'^2_{1s} \cos^2 \beta_{1s}\}^{\frac{\gamma + 1}{2(\gamma - 1)}}} \quad [13]$$

from which the shroud radius can be calculated. The magnitude of the relative Mach number, however, is not yet known. This will depend upon the impeller rotational speed, which is a function of the required pressure ratio and impeller discharge radius and blade angle. It will, therefore, be necessary to return to the inducer design when the impeller discharge is considered.

3.2 Discharge design

The geometric parameters required at the impeller discharge are the blade angle, blade height and diameter. The advantages of backward swept blades are well documented by Came et al(9) and Whitfield and Baines(24). Briefly these are:

(a) reduction of the impeller discharge absolute Mach number, thereby reducing the diffusion requirements of the following diffuser system.

(b) An increased negative gradient of the work input and pressure ratio-mass flow characteristic, which leads to a broader stable operating range.

(c) An increased streamline curvature in the blade-to-blade plane, which leads to a reduced blade-to-blade pressure gradient. This in turn leads to a reduction of secondary flows and associated losses.

McCutcheon(10) during an optimization study observed that, aerodynamically, there is no optimum discharge blade angle and the blade backward sweep is limited by mechanical and physical limitations, which are:

(a) increased tip speed leading to increased disc and blade stresses.

(b) The need to construct the blades with non-radial fibres, leading to centrifugal bending stresses.

(c) Increased impeller diameter which leads to increased inertia. This is detrimental to the transient response.

At the initial design stage the only parameters which are known are the mass flow rate and the stage stagnation pressure ratio (not the impeller pressure ratio). The designer must, therefore assign magnitudes to the geometric and aerodynamic parameters he considers most appropriate.

Typical values of the compressor stage total to total efficiency and slip factor will be specified as $\eta_s = 0.8$, and $\mu = 0.85$. These values will be used for illustrative purposes and will remain unchanged in the following section. Strictly these magnitudes are not necessarily satisfactory for the broad range of pressure ratios and impeller designs considered. An efficiency of 80% is probably pessimistic for low pressure ratio compressors, and becomes increasingly optimistic at high pressure ratios. A discussion of the prediction of peak efficiencies for designs covering a range of specific speeds has been presented by Rodgers(11). The slip factor is a function of the number of blades and the discharge blade angle; however for the range of blade angles considered the slip factor does not change significantly, see eqn [8]. The objective here is to describe and illustrate a design procedure, and the effect of assumed geometric and aerodynamic parameters can be more clearly observed by maintaining the assumed efficiency and slip factor constant, these can be refined later if necessary, see Whitfield and Baines(24).

Perhaps the two most important aerodynamic parameters at the impeller discharge are the magnitude and direction of the absolute Mach number. High Mach numbers will impose a heavy burden upon the diffuser system and will lead to high friction losses and possibly shock losses around the leading edges of any diffuser vanes. If the angle of the absolute velocity from the radial direction is large the flow path through the vaneless diffuser will be long and in addition to high friction losses stall and flow reversals back into the impeller may occur, followed by violent surge. Johnston and Dean(12) showed that an optimum swirl angle, for design purposes, lies between 63 and 68 degrees. Similarly Rodgers and Sapiro(13) considered the optimum flow angle to lie between 60 and 70 degrees, and Osborne et al(8) used a magnitude of 70 degrees in the design of an 8 to 1 pressure ratio compressor. A swirl angle of 65 degrees will be adopted, this however will be systematically varied when necessary in order to illustrate the effects of alternative assumptions.

To assess the effect of backward swept blading on the discharge Mach number and flow angle the angles β_{B2} and α_2 will be specified and systematically varied. The stage pressure ratio will also be considered to be a variable so that a range of designs can be assessed. The pressure ratio is related to the impeller speed through eqn [4], with the inlet tangential component of velocity zero in the absence of prewhirl.

The tangential component of velocity at discharge is given by eqn [7] and can be rewritten in terms of the absolute flow angle to yield

$$C_{\theta 2} = \frac{\mu U_2}{1 - \frac{\tan \beta_{B2}}{\tan \alpha_2}} = \lambda U_2 \qquad [14]$$

The pressure ratio is then given by

$$(P_R)^{\frac{\gamma-1}{\gamma}} = 1 + (\gamma - 1)\eta_s \lambda M_u^2 \qquad [15]$$

With M_u systematically varied a range of pressure ratios can be covered. The impeller stagnation temperature ratio also follows from eqn [2].

With the non-dimensional blade speed, flow angle and slip factor specified the discharge velocity triangle can be constructed, and all velocity vectors determined in a form non-dimensionalised by the inlet stagnation speed of sound, a_{01}. Through eqn [2] these non-dimensional velocities can be transformed into Mach numbers.

The impeller discharge Mach number is shown graphically in Fig.6 for an assumed absolute flow angle of 65 deg. Clearly the application of backward swept blades leads to a reduction in discharge Mach number at all impeller speeds. This presentation could be repeated for a series of absolute flow angles, however, Fig.7 illustrates the

variation of M_2 as α_2 is increased for pressure ratios of 8 and 3 to 1. For moderate degrees of backward sweep an increase in flow angle leads to a further reduction in Mach number. However, for discharge blade angles in excess of 30 deg increasing the flow angle leads to an increase in Mach number. The changes, however, are not significant and the detrimental effects of increasing the flow angle possibly outweigh any beneficial effects gained by modifying the Mach number.

Increasing blade backward sweep, therefore, leads to a reduction in Mach number M_2 for any given impeller speed. However, in order to maintain the required pressure ratio the impeller speed M_u must be increased as the blade backward sweep is increased, this, of course, leads to an increase in the discharge Mach number. The stage pressure ratio is given by eqn [15] and for the assumed parameters, α_2 = 65 deg, μ = 0.85 and η_s = 0.8 the pressure ratio can be calculated and added to Fig.6 as constant pressure contours, see Fig.8. The effect of increasing blade backward sweep can now be clearly seen. If a pressure ratio of 5 to 1 is required then increasing β_{B2} from 0 to -40 deg leads to a reduction of the discharge Mach number from 1.18 to 0.96, despite the need to increase M_u from 1.46 to 1.73. The magnitudes of pressure ratio shown are functions of the assumed values of efficiency and slip factor, and as indicated earlier the values used are for illustrative purposes only and may not be applicable over the broad range of pressure ratios shown. They are, however, good order of magnitude values.

The application of backward swept blades can, therefore, be considered desirable as reduced discharge Mach numbers follow. However, the need to increase impeller speed will lead to increased inducer blade speed and the consequences for the inducer conditions must be considered. The inlet shroud blade velocity, U_{1s}, is related to that at the discharge through the radius ratio r_{1s}/r_2. The relative Mach number is then a function of the inlet relative flow angle. Based upon the earlier discussion with respect to the inducer design the inlet relative flow angle will be assumed to be -60 degrees, and will not be modified. With

$$\frac{U_{1s}}{a_{01}} = \frac{U_2 r_{1s}}{a_{01} r_2}$$

it follows from the inlet velocity triangle, with zero prewhirl, that the relative Mach number is given by

$$M'_{1s} = \frac{(U_{1s}/a_{01})/\sin \beta_{1s}}{1 - \frac{\gamma-1}{2}\left(\frac{U_{1s}}{a_{01}}\right)^2/\tan^2 \beta_{1s}}$$

6

© IMechE 1989 C390/001

To apply these expressions the radius ratio r_{1s}/r_2 will be systematically varied from 0.5 to 0.7, with the latter value adopted as the basic magnitude. With these assumed parameters the relative Mach number is a function of M_u only and Fig.8 can be further developed by including the contours of relative Mach number, Fig.9. This figure can also be presented to give the absolute Mach number as a function of the relative Mach number, Fig.10, to show the clear increase in relative Mach number with increasing blade backward sweep. For a pressure ratio of 5 to 1 the inlet relative Mach number increases from 1.23 to 1.47 as the blade angle is varied from 0 to -40 deg. Such a high inducer relative Mach number would probably be unacceptable and a means of effecting a reduction must be investigated.

The main variable available is the radius ratio r_{1s}/r_2. In order to increase M_u to compensate for the blade discharge backward sweep an increase in either the impeller rotational speed or discharge diameter is required. Reducing r_{1s}/r_2 is equivalent to increasing the impeller diameter. As an example from Fig.10 the case of β_{B2} = -40 deg is considered and r_{1s}/r_2 reduced to 0.5. The direct effect on the inlet relative Mach number is clear from Fig.11; for the case of a pressure ratio of 5 to 1 the inlet relative Mach number is reduced from 1.47 to 1.04 by reducing r_{1s}/r_2 to 0.5. A subsonic Mach number could be achieved by reducing the radius ratio further; however, the consequences of this action must be considered. Reducing r_{1s}/r_2 is achieved by increasing the impeller radius r_2 and to maintain a constant flow area the impeller blade height b_2 must be reduced. We must, therefore return to the impeller discharge design to find the precise effect on the non-dimensional blade height b_2/r_2.

The application of the continuity equation will lead to the computation of the discharge flow area, i.e.

$$mi = \rho_1 \pi r_{1s}^2 (1 - r_{1h}^2/r_{1s}^2) C_{m1} = \rho_2 2\pi r_2 b_2 C_{m2} BK_2$$

where BK_2 is a discharge blockage factor

and

$$\frac{2b_2 BK_2}{r_2} = \frac{\rho_1}{\rho_2} \frac{r_{1s}^2}{r_2^2} (1-v^2) \frac{C_{m1} a_{01}}{a_{01} C_{m2}} \qquad [16]$$

Application of eqn [16] requires the specification of the inlet hub to shroud radius ratio, v, and this has been assumed to be 0.4. The actual hub size will depend upon the number of inducer blades to be fitted to the hub surface and/or the stress levels in the hub. The main problem prior to the application of eqn [16] is the calculation of the density at impeller discharge. To calculate the fluid properties at impeller discharge it is necessary to specify an impeller total to total efficiency, this will be assumed to be 0.9 and remain unchanged for the examples given. The impeller discharge stagnation pressure can be calculated through eqn [15] by replacing the stage efficiency with that for the impeller. It should be recalled that for an adiabatic flow the stagnation temperature remains constant through the diffuser and the impeller discharge stagnation temperature is identical to that at the stage discharge.

The non-dimensional blade height b_2/r_2 can then be calculated through eqn [16]. By systematically varying M_u and r_{1s}/r_2, whilst maintaining all other variables constant, the variation of b_2/r_2 with r_{1s}/r_2 for a series of non-dimensional speeds M_u (and hence pressure ratios) can be found. The result of this investigation is shown in Fig.12. As r_{1s}/r_2 is reduced in order to reduce the inlet relative Mach number the non-dimensional blade height b_2/r_2 decreases leading to a long narrow discharge passage. For our example at a pressure ratio of 5 to 1 b_2/r_2 decreases from 0.12 to 0.04 as r_{1s}/r_2 is reduced from 0.7 to 0.5. Also included on Fig.12 are the contours of pressure ratio and discharge Mach number, both of which are vertical lines, and of inlet relative Mach number.

For single stage high pressure ratio compressors a clear choice exists with respect to the impeller design. On the one hand the inlet relative Mach number can be reduced by reducing r_{1s}/r_2, thereby designing a long narrow impeller discharge passage which will lead to increased friction and shroud leakage losses together with additional friction loss on the impeller back face. On the other hand the inducer can be designed for a transonic inlet flow using the knowledge available from transonic axial compressors, with the possibility of increased losses due to shock waves and shock boundary layer interaction, e.g. Osborne et al(8). If neither of these options are acceptable the possibility of introducing prewhirl at impeller inlet can be considered as a means of reducing the inlet relative Mach number, see Morris and Kenny(15). The remaining alternative is to develop the desired pressure over more than one stage.

Design assessment

Rodgers(16) lists the most important design parameters as:

specific speed
Mach numbers
diffusion limitations
exit flow angle.

In the above analysis the Mach numbers and exit flow angle have been employed extensively, and the specific speed and diffusion limitations remain as parameters which can be readily calculated to further assess the design.

Specific speed can be defined as

$$n_s = \frac{\omega\sqrt{Q}}{\Delta h_{os}^{3/4}}$$

and, with the volume flow rate defined as that at impeller inlet, can be developed to

$$n_s = \frac{\left(\frac{r_{1s}}{r_2}\right)^{3/2} \left(\frac{\pi}{\tan\beta_{1s}}\right)^{1/2} (1-v^2)^{1/2}}{(\lambda\eta_s)^{3/4}} \quad [17]$$

see Coppage(17), Galvas(18) and Whitfield and Baines(24). The variation of the specific speed with impeller blade angle and radius ratio is shown in Fig.13. As can be seen the introduction of backward swept blades leads to an increase in specific speed. Whilst the analysis presented is not sufficient to indicate an optimum specific speed the trends shown follow the conclusions given by Rodgers(11), which were

(a) optimum specific speed increases as the blade backward sweep is increased, and

(b) optimum specific speed for a given discharge blade angle decreases with increasing Mach number, i.e. with increasing pressure ratio.

Galvas(18) concluded that maximum efficiency could be expected for backswept impellers with specific speeds in the range 0.705 to 1.018. It is clear that a single optimum specific speed cannot be applied to a wide range of pressure ratio requirements, and it is preferable to work from the fundamental fluid dynamic parameters, see Whitfield and Baines(24).

The internal diffusion limitations have been discussed by many authors, for example, Sheets(19), Dallenbach(20), Balje(21), Dean(22), Rodgers(14,16), and Japikse(23). There are two commonly applied techniques to quantify the internal diffusion, one considers the relative velocity (or Mach number) ratio between the impeller inlet (usually at the shroud radius) and discharge, the other is similar but uses the exit relative velocity based on that of the separated through flow jet. The overall diffusion ratio, DR, is readily available, and by combining the appropriate equations it can be shown that

$$DR = \frac{W_{1s}}{W_2} = \frac{r_{1s}/r_2}{[1 - 2\lambda + \lambda^2/\sin^2\alpha_2]^{1/2} \sin\beta_{1s}}$$

This expression is shown as a function of blade angle in Fig.13b. Clearly the magnitude of DR is a direct function of the radius ratio r_{1s}/r_2, and whilst high diffusion rates are desirable boundary layer separation will occur and high predicted diffusion rates may not be achieved in practice.

Dean(22) compared the required diffusion ratios with those actually attainable over a range of inlet relative Mach numbers, Fig.14, and predicted a maximum attainable for a subsonic inducer of 1.8.

Rodgers(16) showed diffusion ratios between 1.9 and 2.0 at surge flow rates, where the absolute flow angle varied between 75 and 80 deg, for an impeller with $r_{1s}/r_2 = 0.56$ and a blade angle of -40' deg. These diffusion ratios were based upon the relative velocity after the mixing of any jets and wakes at the impeller discharge, whereas those quoted by Dean are prior to separation and are effectively based on the relative velocity of the through flow jet.

4 CONCLUSIONS

The initial skeleton design of the impeller has been developed on a non-dimensional basis based upon a knowledge of the required pressure ratio. The procedure has been developed from the underlying one-dimensional fluid mechanics, and alternative approaches can be developed to accommodate any additional design restraints. A computer procedure for a typical design approach is given by Whitfield and Baines(24).

The further specification of the inlet stagnation conditions and required mass flow enables the absolute dimensions of the impeller to be derived. State of the art efficiencies have been assumed in the analysis and whilst the design procedure endeavoured to minimise relative Mach numbers in order to minimise losses it is necessary to continue the analysis through the inclusion of empirical loss models in order to check the assumed efficiency values. Whilst this could be continued on a non-dimensional basis it is generally better to consider the actual geometric design. The techniques available to do this are reviewed in Part 2.

5 References

(1) Weisner F J 1967
A review of slip factors for centrifugal impellers
Trans ASME J Eng.Pwr V.89 p.558 1967

(2) Wislicenus G F
Fluid mechanics of turbomachinery
Dover press 1965

(3) Stanitz J D
Some theoretical aerodynamic investigations of impellers in radial and mixed flow centrifugal compressors
Trans ASME v.74 p.473 1952

(4) Rodgers C
Typical performance characteristics of gas turbine radial compressors
Trans ASME J. Engng. Pwr. 1964

(5) Stanitz J D
Design considerations for mixed flow
compressors with high flow rates per
unit frontal area
NACA RM E53A15 1953

(6) Connor W A
Design and off-design performance
prediction of high pressure ratio
centrifugal compressors
Von Karman Inst. lecture series 1984-07
May 1984

(7) Howell A R
The present basis of axial compressor
design, Part 1 Cascade theory and
performance
R.A.E. report No E3946 R & M No 2095
Ministry of Supply UK June 1942

(8) Osborne C Runstadler P W and
Stacy W D
Aerodynamic and mechanical design of an
8:1 pressure ratio centrifugal compres-
sor
NASA CR-134782 1975

(9) Came P M   McKenzie I R I and
Dadson C
The performance of a 6.5 pressure ratio
compressor having an impeller with
swept-back blades
NGTE Memorandum 79013, Pyestock UK
1979

(10) McCutcheon A R S
Aerodynamic design and development of a
high pressure ratio turbocharger compressor
Instn. Mech. Engns. Paper No C73/78
1978

(11) Rodgers C 1980
Efficiency of centrifugal compressor
impellers
AGARD CPP 282 Brussels May 1980

(12) Johnston J P and Dean R C
Losses in vaneless diffusers of
centrifugal compressors and pumps
Trans ASME J eng. Pwr. p.49 1966

(13) Rodgers C and Sapiro L
Design considerations for high pressure
ratio centrifugal compressors
ASME Paper No. 72-GT-91 1972

(14) Rodgers C
A diffusion factor correlation for
centrifugal impeller stalling
ASME paper No 78-GT-61 1978

(15) Morris R E and Kenny D P
High pressure ratio centrifugal com-
pressors for small gas turbine engines
AGARD Conf Proc No 31 June 1968

(16) Rodgers C
Impeller stalling as influenced by
diffusion limitations
Trans ASME J. Fluids Engng p.84 1977

(17) Coppage J E   Dallenbach F et al
Study of supersonic radial compressors for refrigeration and pressurization systems
WADC Tech Rept 55-257 1956

(18) Galvas M R
Analytical correlation of centrifugal
compressor design geometry for maximum
efficiency with specific speed
NASA Tech note TN D-6729 March 1972

(19) Sheets H E
The flow through centrifugal compres-
sors and pumps
Trans ASME v 72 p.1009 1950

(20) Dallenbach F
The aerodynamic design and performance
of centrifugal and mixed flow compressors
SAE Tech Progress Series v.3 1961

(21) Balje O E
Loss and flow path studies on centrifu-
gal compressors
ASME paper No 70-GT-12(a) and (b) 1970

(22) Dean R C
The fluid dynamic design of advanced
centrifugal compressors
Creare Tech. Note No 153 1972

(23) Japikse D
Advanced diffusion levels in turbocharger compressors and component
matching
I.Mech.E Conf Turbocharging and Turbochargers paper No C45/82   1982

(24) Whitfield A and Baines N C
The design of radial turbomachines
To be published Longman 1990

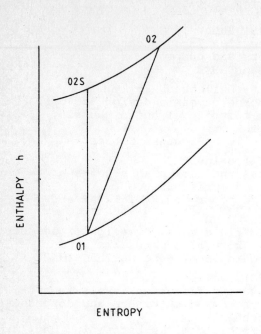

Fig 1   Impeller enthalpy – entropy diagram

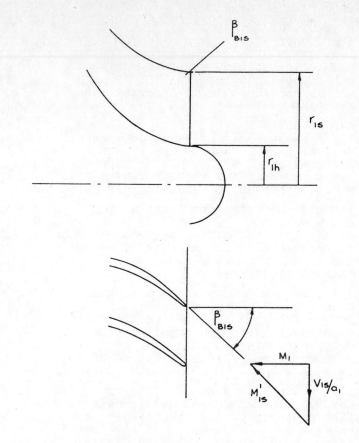

Fig 3   Impeller inducer

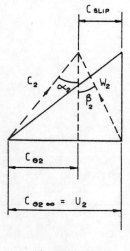

(a)   Radial blade

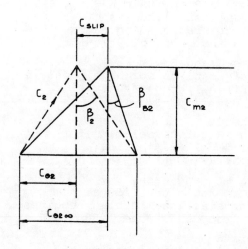

(b)   Backward swept blade

Fig 2   Impeller discharge velocity triangles

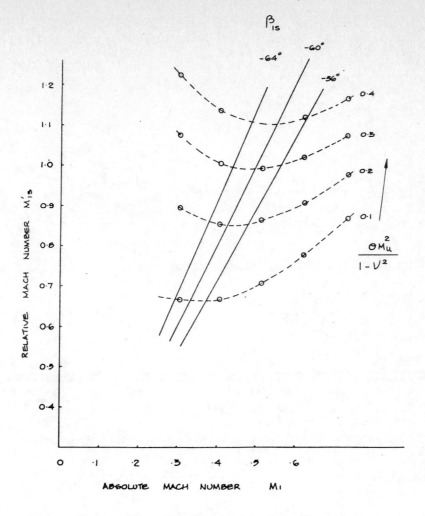

Fig 4   Effect of Mach number on relative flow angle

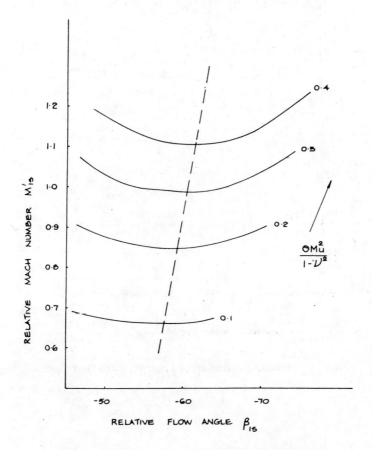

Fig 5   Relative flow angle for minimum Mach number

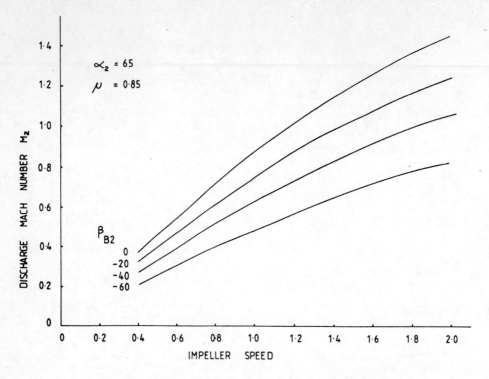

Fig 6   Effect of blade backward sweep on discharge Mach number

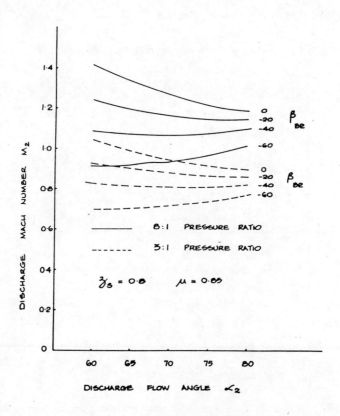

Fig 7   Effect of assumed angle α_2 on discharge Mach number

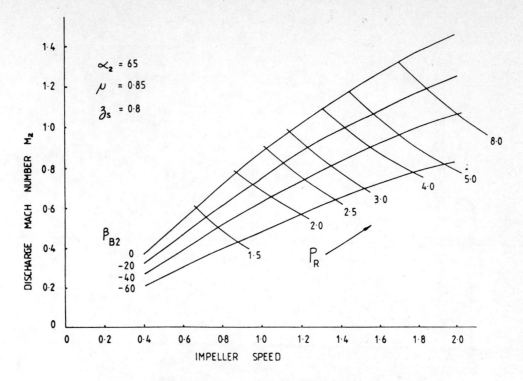

Fig 8   Variation of discharge Mach number with blade angle and
         pressure ratio

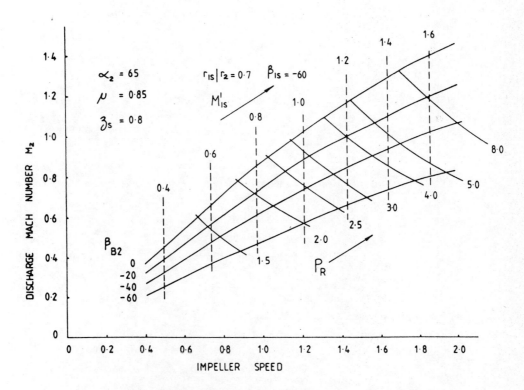

Fig 9   Effect of blade angle and pressure ratio on inlet relative
         Mach number

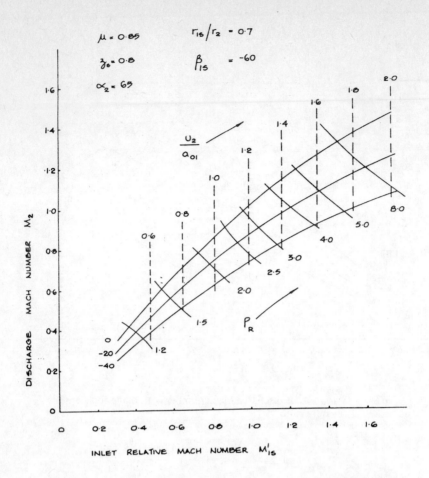

Fig 10   Variation of M_2 and M'_{1s} over a range of pressure ratios

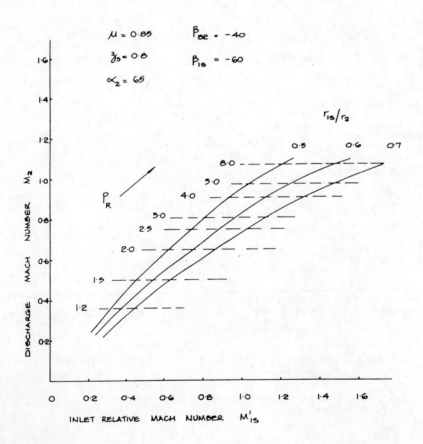

Fig 11   Effect of reducing radius ratio r_{1s}/r_2 on inlet relative Mach number

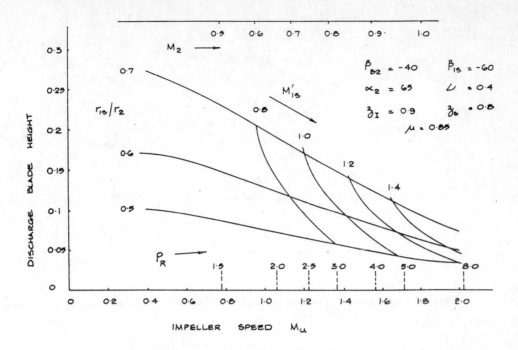

Fig 12   Effect of reducing r_{1s}/r_2 on the discharge blade height b_2/r_2

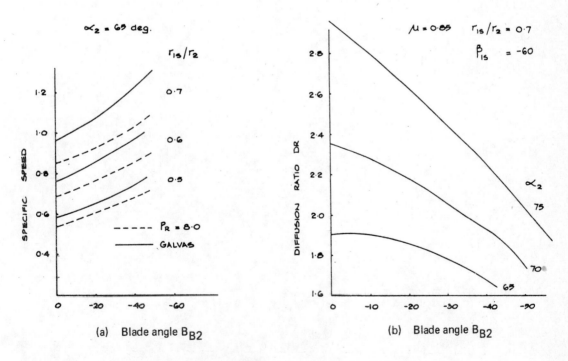

(a)   Blade angle B_{B2}

(b)   Blade angle B_{B2}

Fig 13   Effect of design variables on specific speed and impeller
diffusion ratio

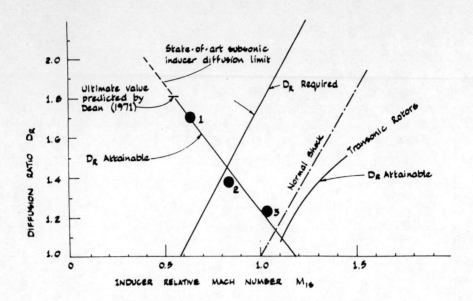

Fig 14   Influence of inducer tip relative Mach number on attainable
inducer diffusion ratios

C390/034

Review of preliminary design and performance prediction techniques for centrifugal compressors
Part 2: performance prediction

A WHITFIELD, BSc, PhD, CEng, MIMechE
School of Mechanical Engineering, University of Bath

Synopsis
The flow through the centrifugal compressor impeller is usually a separated one which forms high and low velocity zones at discharge. As the preliminary design study does not consider the flow process in sufficient detail to allow for separated flow it is necessary to predict the performance of the proposed design and, if required, refine the geometry further before proceeding to the detailed passage design. A generalised prediction procedure is described and the associated empirical flow models and loss correlations available, including incidence models for off-design, are briefly reviewed.

Notation

A	Flow area
b	Impeller blade height
a	Speed of sound
C	Absolute velocity
C_p	Specific heat at constant pressure
DR	Diffusion ratio
h	Enthalpy
M	Mach number
M'	Relative Mach number
$\dot{m}$	Mass flow rate
P	Pressure
R	Gas constant
r	radius
S	Entropy
T	Temperature
U	Blade velocity
W	Relative velocity
$\dot{W}$	Impeller power
$\dot{W}_{DF}$	Power absorbed due to disc friction
$\dot{W}_{RC}$	Power absorbed due to recirculation
Z_B	Number of blades
α	Absolute flow angle from the meridional direction. Positive in the direction of rotation of the impeller.
β	Relative flow angle from the meridional direction

γ	Ratio of specific heats
δ	Wake flow fraction
μ	Slip factor
ρ	Density
σ	Entropy function

Subscripts

o	Stagnation condition
B	Blade
J	jet

Subscripts

o	Stagnation condition
B	Blade
J	jet
m	Meridional component
opt	Optimum
w	Wake
x	Component or flow process inlet
y	Component or flow process discharge
θ	Tangential component

Superscripts

prime	Relative conditions, for example
h'	Relative stagnation enthalpy

1 INTRODUCTION

Before the initial design of part 1 can be accepted for further detailed passage design it is useful to assess some of the assumptions made and predict the off-design performance. In particular the component efficiencies must now be calculated in order to check the assumptions made initially. The implication being that if they turn out to be significantly different from those previously assumed, the preliminary design stage may have to be repeated using the revised component efficiencies.

Any attempt to describe the complex three-dimensional flow in radial turbomachines with a one-dimensional analysis must, by its very nature, contain a large proportion of empirical fluid dynamic models and loss correlations. A satisfactory performance prediction procedure requires the best possible information about the irreversibilities associated with the flow process through the machine. The empiricism involved represents the accumulation of many years experience either directly by the designer, or indirectly through the published literature. It cannot be expected that such empirical correlations will be completely satisfactory for a wide range of applications. Different machines with the same overall dimensions will not necessarily have identical performance characteristics; however, a one-dimensional prediction procedure which cannot fully describe the detail of the passage shape cannot discriminate between such cases. The prediction procedure cannot yield a "correct" answer but will give a solution which can be considered to be of a similar standard to those of known machines which have been used to "tune" the empirical loss models.

Mean line one-dimensional prediction procedures have been described by Balje(1), Coppage et al(2), Galvas(3), Whitfield and Baines(4,8), Frigne and Van den Braembussche(5), Conrad et al (6) and Japikse(7). These prediction procedures consist of a judicious mix of one-dimensional gas dynamics, empirical flow models, and loss correlations. This mixture is in many cases formulated in a manner which makes it difficult for the user of any consequent computer program to appreciate fully the breadth and depth of the assumptions and limitations built into the analysis procedure. If the user is to interpret the results of any computer analysis fully he must have the original assumptions and empiricism clearly in view. Further, if he is to contribute his own experience, or that recently published, he needs to have access to the program code and to be able to make modifications readily. This is particularly important to the designer who needs a clear, comprehensible and flexible design tool which he can use without investing heavily in software modifications and development. By separating the fundamental gas dynamic theory from the empirical models and correlations it is possible to give a clear insight into the models and assumptions used, and this leads to a computer procedure which can be readily developed and extended by another user. Furthermore, the fundamental gas dynamic equations can be formulated so that the same approach can be adopted for each component of the turbomachine, leading to a more efficient and more easily understood procedure, see Whitfield and Baines(4).

2 GENERALISED GAS DYNAMIC ANALYSIS

Performance prediction generally involves the analysis of the gas flow process through the separate components used in the machine construction. The general requirement of the analytical procedure is to predict the component discharge conditions from known inlet conditions and component geometry. The computed discharge conditions then become the known inlet conditions for the next component.

A wide variety of flow types are encountered in radial turbomachines; these can be classified as

(a) straight axial flow in a stationary duct e.g. compressor inlet

(b) guided swirling flow in a stationary duct e.g. vaned diffuser, prewhirl vanes

(c) non-guided swirling flow in a stationary duct e.g. compressor vaneless diffuser

(d) rotating duct e.g. compressor impeller

The approach adopted is to consider all flow conditions as relative to the component under consideration. The relative stagnation enthalpy is then defined as

$$h'_o = h + \frac{W^2}{2} \quad [1]$$

and when applied to a rotating duct the Euler turbomachinery equation becomes

$$h'_{0y} - h'_{0x} = (U_y^2 - U_x^2)/2 \quad [2]$$

where subscripts x and y refer to component, or flow process, inlet and discharge respectively.

The energy equation and continuity equation can be combined with the entropy equation to yield

$$\frac{m\sqrt{(RT'_{0x}/\gamma)}}{A_x P'_{0x}} = \frac{A_y}{A_x}\cos\beta_y M'_y\left(1+\frac{\gamma-1}{2}M'^2_y\right)^{-\frac{(\gamma+1)}{2(\gamma-1)}}$$

$$\sigma\left(1+\frac{\gamma-1}{2\gamma RT'_{0x}}(U_y^2-U_x^2)\right)^{\frac{(\gamma+1)}{2(\gamma-1)}} \quad [3]$$

The entropy gain which occurs during the flow process is given by

$$\Delta S/R = -\ln(P'_{0y}/P'_{0E})$$

then

$$\sigma = e^{-\Delta S/R} = \frac{P'_{0y}}{P'_{0E}} = \frac{P'_{0y}}{P'_{0x}}\left(\frac{T'_{0x}}{T'_{0y}}\right)^{\frac{\gamma}{\gamma-1}} \quad [4]$$

see Fig.1. This applies equally to stationary and rotating ducts.

Equation [3] combines the equations of continuity, energy, and entropy, and is the principal equation of a generalised duct flow model. In order to solve it, it is necessary to have separate sub-models with which to calculate values of the discharge flow area, the relative flow angle, and the entropy gain in the duct. Once this has been done the equation can be solved iteratively for the discharge relative Mach number.

The computation of the other flow properties, relative to the duct, is then straight forward. For a stationary duct the blade velocities, U, are zero and eqn [3] gives the absolute Mach number. The computation of other fluid properties can be performed in a single computer subroutine irrespective of whether the component under consideration is rotating or not, see Whitfield and Baines (4,8).

Clearly the main problem for the solution of eqn [3] lies in the empirical determination of the duct discharge flow area, relative flow angle and entropy gain. The cited literature provides numerous procedures to determine these parameters and they will not be repeated here. The empirical models selected, whether from the literature or direct experience, can be described in suitable computer subroutines and readily incorporated into the computation procedure.

3 EMPIRICAL FLOW MODELS AND LOSS CORRELATIONS

The empirical flow models and loss correlations used to calculate the flow area, relative flow angle, and flow entropy gain are essential to any one-dimensional performance prediction procedure. The strengths and weaknesses of any procedure lie in the empirical flow models used to calculate these parameters. The procedures used to quantify the losses extend from direct empirical equations, such as those used for uniform pipe flows, to extremely detailed models of the flow physics involved. In particular detailed flow models have been developed for

(a) the irreversibilities associated with the incidence on to both moving and stationary blade rows, and

(b) the flow process at compressor impeller discharge in order to calculate both the discharge flow angle (slip factor correlations) and the irreversibilities associated with the separated flow pattern.

This review will concentrate on the models commonly adopted to describe these flow process, as the empirical loss equations, such as that for friction loss, are available in the literature.

3.1 Incidence models at inlet to bladed components

Only at one operating point will the fluid move smoothly into the passages of bladed components, at other operating conditions an angle of incidence will exist between the relative velocity vector of the incoming air and the vane blade angle. The operating point at which the incidence losses are a minimum does not usually coincide with the zero incidence condition, and the objectives of the incidence models are to derive both the entropy gain due to incidence and the incidence angle for which minimum loss occurs.

In order to utilise the dimensionless mass flow equation, eqn [3], an imaginary duct, which can be assumed to have a small finite length in the direction of flow, is considered to exist such that the regions immediately upstream and downstream of the blade leading edge are included; the pre-incidence condition being designated x and the post-incidence condition y. The fluid properties at the inlet to this imaginary duct are known from those calculated as the discharge conditions of the previous duct.

The main requirement of the fluid dynamic model is to calculate the entropy gain due to the incidence process, prior to applying eqn.[3] to calculate the post incidence relative Mach number and then establishing all fluid properties through the basic gas dynamic equations. Of the incidence models available in the open literature those due to Wallace (9) and those published by NASA (3,13) are most often employed. The constant pressure model, Wallace(9), was initially developed for application to a radially bladed turbine rotor and proved to be satisfactory if blade thickness was ignored. The basic assumption was that the incidence process occurred over an infinitely small space and the static pressure was therefore constant. However, later development to compressor impellers and blades of finite thickness made it necessary to relax the constant pressure assumption in order to force the model, through arbitrary adjustments, to yield positive magnitudes of entropy gain, Whitfield and Wallace(10). Consequently the model does not address itself fully to the flow physics involved, and in this respect the models described by the NASA publications are to be prefered.

The approach used by NASA to model the incidence process has been developed from techniques used for incompressible flow machines such as fluid couplings and pumps. The main contribution has been to apply these techniques to compressible flow in radial turbines and compressors, Galvas(3)

The general approach to this incidence model is to assume that the kinetic energy associated with the change in relative tangential velocity is converted into internal energy of the working fluid, which manifests itself as an increase in entropy. If the optimum approach flow angle $\beta_{x,opt}$ is defined as that at which there is no change in the tangential component of velocity, the incidence loss is considered to be, in terms of an enthalpy change

$$\Delta h_{oi} = W_x^2 \sin^2(|\beta_x - \beta_{x,opt}|)/2 \qquad [5]$$

The choice of a static enthalpy, stagnation enthalpy or relative stagnation enthalpy change appears to be quite arbitrary amoungst different authors, Fig.2. It is, however, more consistent to use the relative stagnation enthalpy as a basis for the loss calculation. The main problem then lies in the computation of the optimum flow angle.

For impeller inducers Galvas(3) developed a technique given by Stanitz(11) to calculate the optimum incidence angle. The original work by Stanitz was aimed at calculating the rotor blade angle for zero angle of attack (or zero incidence loss), and not directed to the calculation of energy dissipation due to incidence onto a fixed blade. This work by Stanitz can be used to find the optimum approach relative flow angle for any given blade angle.

Stanitz defined an angle ε as the difference between the optimum upstream relative flow direction $\beta_{x,opt}$ and the downstream relative flow direction β_y (the blade angle), i.e.

$$\varepsilon = \beta_{x,opt} - \beta_y$$

This could equally be described as the optimum incidence angle. The objective of the Stanitz analysis was to calculate the optimum magnitude of ε from which the correct blade angle β_y could be found for a given angle of approach. In this case the desire is to

calculate the optimum approach relative flow angle for a known blade angle. Stanitz defines optimum operating conditions as those which lead to zero blade loading at the leading edge, i.e those which produce no change in whirl (product of absolute tangential velocity and radius) as the flow enters the impeller. For the cases considered by Stanitz no pre-whirl existed and optimum conditions were achieved when zero whirl was preserved across the incidence process. Under these conditions the velocity triangles of the incidence process will be as shown in Fig.3. Then

$$\tan \beta_{x,opt} = U_x/C_{mx}$$

and

$$\tan \beta_y = U_y/C_{my}$$

From the continuity condition and assuming no change in density (following Stanitz and Galvas)

$$C_{mx}A_x = C_{my}A_y$$

and it follows that

$$\tan \beta_{x,opt} = \frac{A_x}{A_y} \tan \beta_y$$

The optimum inlet relative flow angle can therefore be derived directly from this expression.

The relative velocity component normal to the optimum flow direction, see Fig.4, is then given by

$$W_L = W_x \sin(|\beta_x - \beta_{x,opt}|)$$

and the relative stagnation enthalpy loss is, see eqn [5]

$$\Delta h_{oi} = W_L^2/2$$

Some authors, for example Conrad et al(6), consider the loss to be a proportion of the change in kinetic energy associated with the tangential component of velocity, then

$$\Delta h_{oi} = kW_L^2/2$$

where k is considered to be between 0.5 and 0.7.
A further modification is to reduce the predicted loss at positive incidence relative to that at negative incidence.

In order to utilise these expressions the loss must be expressed as an entropy gain. The given expression for incidence loss is usually equated to an enthalpy change across the incidence process. Jansen and Qvale (12) used the difference between the static enthalpies, whereas Futral and Wasserbauer (13) used the relative stagnation enthalpies. Using the relative stagnation conditions as illustrated in Fig.2 the incidence loss is given by

$$\Delta h_{oi} = h'_{0x} - h'_{0ys} = C_p(T'_{0x} - T'_{0ys})$$

and the entropy gain then follows from

$$\frac{\Delta S}{R} = \frac{\gamma}{\gamma - 1} \ln(T'_{0x}/T'_{0ys}) \qquad [6]$$

With this model the entropy gain can be calculated from the known pre-incidence conditions and used directly in the Mach number equation, [3], to complete the full solution for the incidence process.

4 SEPARATED IMPELLER FLOWS

Central to any prediction procedure is the modelling of the impeller flow, consequently substantial efforts have been made over a period of almost 40 years to develop a suitable flow model. The generally accepted model of the flow through the impeller, now substantiated by laser anemometry measurements, is one of a separated flow with a high velocity jet and a low velocity wake issuing from the impeller tip, Johnston and Dean(14), Dean(15),

Japikse(7). The relative velocity at the point of separation can be found by specifying the impeller relative velocity ratio which can be sustained prior to separation. The flow model, Dean(15), then assumes that the flow splits into an isentropic jet, in which the relative Mach number remains constant, and a quiescent wake. Equation [3] can then be applied to calculate the flow area of the jet as the relative Mach number is specified through the relative velocity ratio. The calculated jet width, rather than the geometric passage width, can then be used to calculate the effective slip factor, Whitfield (16). More recently Japikse(7) has refined this basic model to allow for two distinct zones within the impeller. The main difference between the two zone model and the single zone jet flow model is that a proportion of the flow is assumed to pass through the wake instead of the wake being treated as a stagnant zone. The proportion of the total mass flow carried by the wake must be specified. Dean(15) considered the mass fraction passing through the wake region, $\dot{m}_w/\dot{m}$, to be 20%.

4.1 Jet flow model with stagnant wake

A simple specification of a gross blockage factor due to the wake does not prove to be satisfactory for the separated flows which are frequently encountered in highly loaded impellers. An alternative procedure, suggested by Dean(15), is to specify the rate of diffusion which can be sustained by the impeller, and then predict the discharge flow area which this implies. This can be done through the specification of a relative velocity ratio or a relative Mach number ratio, i.e.

$$DR = W_x/W_y \qquad [7]$$

or

$$M'_R = M'_x/M'_y \qquad [8]$$

The relative velocity at inlet to the impeller, W_x, was considered by Whitfield and Wallace(17) to be that at the inducer shroud diameter (where relative velocities are highest) either before the incidence process or after, whichever value is larger. Typical magnitudes for D_R are given by Dean(15), and Japikse(18, 19) provides graphical data for M'_R, see Fig.5, as a function of the ideal relative Mach number ratio, i.e. based on the discharge Mach number assuming isentropic fully guided, full passage flow.

Through the application of equations [7] and [8] the impeller discharge relative Mach number can be readily found. If equation [7] is employed the relative Mach number can be derived from

$$M'_y = \frac{W_y}{[\gamma R(T'_{0y} - \frac{\gamma - 1}{2\gamma R} W_y^2)]^{1/2}}$$

where T'_{0y} can be obtained through eqn [2].

The discharge relative Mach number is therefore readily available and the basic Mach number equation, eqn [3], can be used to calculate the discharge flow area, A_y. Before this can be done it is necessary to determine the discharge flow angle, β_y, and the entropy gain of the flow process. The flow angle, β_y, can be obtained from a suitable slip factor correlation, and the entropy gain from appropriate loss correlations. As the assumption of this model is that the total flow is carried by a jet narrower than the passage itself, Whitfield(16) modified the Stanitz slip factor correlation to accommodate the width of the actual jet flow rather than the geometric width of the blade passage, see Fig.6. This led to the slip factor correlation

$$\mu = 1 - 0.63\theta/2 \qquad [9]$$

where

$$\theta = A_y/(r_y b_y Z_B)$$

Whitfield(16) further modified this correlation by the introduction of an empirical parameter K to allow for a non-uniform velocity profile in both the hub-shroud and blade to blade planes of the through flow jet, giving

$$\mu = 1 - K\frac{0.63}{2}\left(\frac{A_y}{r_y b_y Z_B}\right) \qquad [10]$$

This correlation for slip factor is a function of the flow area A_y and must be applied simultaneously with the Mach number equation, eqn [3]. By combining the equations an iteration process can be avoided. Equation [3] can be rearranged to give

$$A_y \cos \beta_y = X \qquad [11]$$

where X is made up of the known parameters of eqn [3]. As an initial estimate the entropy gain can be assumed to be zero and later calculated through the empirical correlations. Equations [10] and [11] can be combined and developed to yield

$$\frac{U_y}{W_y}\left(K \frac{0.63X}{2r_y b_y Z_B \cos \beta_y}\right) = \cos \beta_y \tan \beta_{By} - \sin \beta_y \qquad [12]$$

This expression can be expanded into a quadratic equation in $\sin \beta_y$ and the flow angle found.

With β_y established the discharge flow area follows from eqn [11] and the impeller discharge fluid properties can be calculated. Empirical loss correlations can then be applied to derive the flow entropy gain and the computation repeated until converged. By specifying an impeller diffusion rate it is possible to calculate the discharge flow area, and a slip factor based upon this flow area. The procedure predicts a flow area which increases with increasing flow rate, and a slip factor which decreases with increasing flow rate in accordance with experimental observations, Japikse and Goebel(18), Whitfield(8,16). To calculate the entropy gain and corresponding efficiency loss correlations can be applied either from experience or from the literature as appropriate. With a predicted discharge flow area less than the geometric area it is possible to then calculate a mixing loss at impeller discharge. This procedure is described as part of the two zone model in the next section.

5 TWO ZONE MODEL

The two zone model was described in detail by Japikse(7). The main difference between the two zone model and the single zone jet flow model of the previous section is that a proportion of the flow is assumed to pass through the wake instead of the wake being treated as a stagnant zone. The proportion of the total mass flow carried by the wake must be specified. Dean(15) considered the mass fraction passing through the wake region, $\dot{m}_w/\dot{m}$, to be 20%. He also pointed out that design optimization and performance prediction was not particularly sensitive to the assumed magnitude for the wake flow fraction. This observation was substantiated through experimental studies by Japikse and Goebel(18).

The jet and wake flows were considered as two separate stream tubes, carrying flow rates $\dot{m}_J$ and $\dot{m}_w$ respectively, extending completely through the impeller and no attempt was made to predict the actual point of separation. Whitfield and Baines(8) showed that the basic equations described above can be applied directly to this model if the inlet prewhirl is either zero or of the free vortex type.

5.1 Jet stream tube

With the wake flow fraction specified the mass flow rate through the jet, $\dot{m}_J$, is known. The computation of the jet discharge conditions then proceeds through eqn [3]. In this case the flow is considered to be isentropic and it is not necessary to apply the empirical loss correlations.

A difference which exists between the procedure suggested here and that given by Japikse(7) concerns the calculation of the jet slip factor. The procedure suggested here calculates the jet slip factor by applying the Stanitz correlation to the jet width. Japikse on the other hand assumed a value for the jet slip factor which must be corrected later in order to yield a mixed out slip factor specified through an appropriate correlation such as that given by Wiesner(20). This difference, which will be described further when the jet-wake mixing is considered, does not change the fundamental approach from that originally given by Japikse(7).

5.2 Wake flow analysis

The main assumptions applied to the wake flow are

(i) the fluid is perfectly guided by the blades

$$\beta_w = \beta_{Bx}$$

(ii) the wake and jet static pressures are equal

$$P_w = P_J$$

The relative stagnation enthalpy of the wake can be calculated through eqn [1]. Japikse, however, also included a term for the work done due to shroud cover friction, but did not give an empirical procedure to quantify this additional work. The disc friction correlation of Daily and Nece(21), could be adapted but it is difficulty to derive a magnitude with any degree of certainty. With the relative stagnation enthalpy established through eqn [1] the only unknowns in the basic Mach number equation are the entropy gain $\Delta S/R$, and the wake relative Mach number M'_w. Since the static pressures in the wake and jet are assumed equal the entropy difference between the jet and wake is given by

$$\Delta S/R = \frac{\gamma}{\gamma - 1}\ln(T_{yw}/T_{yJ})$$

As the jet flow was considered to be isentropic this difference in entropy level is also the entropy increase which occurs in the wake flow. Substituting for the wake temperature through the relationship

$$\frac{T'_{0yw}}{T_{yw}} = 1 + \frac{\gamma - 1}{2}M'^2_{yw}$$

the entropy gain is given by

$$e^{-\Delta S/R} = \left[\frac{T_{yJ}}{T'_{0yw}}\left(1 + \frac{\gamma - 1}{2}M'^2_{yw}\right)\right]^{\frac{\gamma}{\gamma - 1}}$$

This equation can be solved simultaneously with equation [3] and all the wake discharge fluid properties established.

The computation of the irreversibilities in the impeller without the recourse to empirical loss correlations is a consequence of the model. The assumptions of the wake mass flow fraction, isentropic flow in the jet, and equality of the jet and wake static pressures leads to the direct computation of the entropy gain across the impeller. Japikse applies this procedure from upstream of the impeller and consequently he does not include an incidence loss model, the whole of the impeller entropy gain being derived from the two zone model. An alternative approach would be to apply the model from the post incidence loss condition. The computational procedure suggested by Whitfield and Baines(4,8) will make it relatively easy to apply either approach by including a duct to describe the incidence process or not, as preferred. The uncertainties associated with the specification and computation of the energy loss mechanisms has effectively been replaced by the specification of the wake mass flow fraction. Dean (15) and Japikse and Goebel (18) considered that design optimization and performance prediction was not sensitive to the assumed wake flow fraction. This is tantamount to saying that predicted performance is insensitive to impeller flow entropy gain, and is a little surprising. The entropy gain attributable to skin friction, clearance and blade loading are not directly accounted for, however the major loss processes at impeller inlet and the jet-wake mixing at discharge are accounted for separately. Frigne and Van den Braembussche (5) dispense with the assumption of an isentropic jet and include skin friction and clearance losses in the jet flow model.

5.3 Mixing process at impeller discharge

The main historical contributions to the development of the jet-wake flow model and the consequent mixing loss are those of Dean and Senoo(22) and Johnston and Dean(14). More recently Japikse(7) developed the mixing process as an integral part of his two zone model. In the original jet-wake model it was assumed that the jet and wake mixed very rapidly after leaving the impeller. However, later experimental investigations, often employing laser anemometry, Eckardt(23), have shown that the mixing process requires several passage heights past the impeller tip before it can be considered complete. Japikse, therefore, considered an effective mixed-out state where the thermodynamic properties can be established on a mass average basis. A static pressure rise and stagnation pressure drop is, therefore, calculated at the impeller discharge due to the mixing of the two zones which in practice is only completed at some unknown point downstream of the impeller.

The energy dissipation due to the mixing process is computed in a very similar manner to the classical sudden enlargement loss, see Massey(24). The energy dissipated as the fluid flows through a sudden enlargement in a duct can be accurately calculated through the application of the one-dimensional energy, momentum and continuity equations. The basic Mach number equation, eqn [3], is a combination of the energy and continuity equations, so that the momentum equations remain to be applied in order to complete the solution. Essentially the tangential momentum equation can be applied to calculate the flow direction, and the radial momentum equation applied to calculate the entropy gain. The basic Mach number equation is then available to calculate the mixed out Mach number. In practice this normally leads to an iterative solution, but this can be avoided if the equations are combined algebraically. In order to accommodate the mixing zone an imaginary duct will be placed across the mixing region with the inlet station designated x and the discharge station designated y, see Fig.7.

Energy equation

At discharge from the impeller the effects of the impeller rear face disc friction and of recirculation are considered. These were described as external losses by Coppage(2) and he gave typical expressions for their derivation. Alternative relationships are given by Daily and Nece(21) and Japikse(7). With the inclusion of these

external losses leading to an increase in stagnation enthalpy the energy equation can be written as

$$\dot{m}_J h_{0xJ} + \dot{m}_w h_{0xw} + \dot{W}_{df} + \dot{W}_{rc} = \dot{m} h_{0y}$$

and rearranged to give the mixed out stagnation temperature T_{oy} as

$$T_{0y} = (1-\delta)T_{0xJ} + \delta T_{0xw} + \frac{\gamma-1}{\gamma R}\dot{m}(\dot{W}_{df} + \dot{W}_{rc})$$

where $\delta = \dot{m}_w/\dot{m}$

Tangential momentum equation

With the imaginary duct or control volume encompassing the mixing process assumed to have an infinitesimal radial extent, the shear forces due to the side walls are neglected and the tangential momentum equation written as

$$\dot{m}_J C_{\theta xJ} + \dot{m}_w C_{\theta xw} = \dot{m} C_{\theta y}$$

The tangential component of velocity follows as

$$C_{\theta y} = (1-\delta)C_{\theta xJ} + \delta C_{\theta xw}$$

Japikse(7) provides a thorough derivation of this equation.

Radial momentum equation

The radial momentum equation can be written as

$$(P_{xJ}A_{xJ} + P_{xw}A_{xw}) - P_y A_y = \dot{m} C_{my} - \dot{m}_J C_{mxJ} - \dot{m}_w C_{mxw}$$

and rearranged to give the mixed out static pressure P_y as

$$P_y = \frac{P_{xJ}}{A_y}(A_J + A_w) + \frac{\dot{m}}{A_y}[(1-\delta)C_{mxJ} + \delta C_{mxw} - C_{my}] \quad [13]$$

Continuity equation

The static pressure P_y cannot be calculated directly from eqn [13] because the radial component of velocity C_{my} is also unknown. Application of the continuity equation yields

$$\frac{\dot{m}}{A_y} = \frac{P_y C_{my}}{R[T_{0y} - \frac{\gamma-1}{2\gamma R}(C_{my}^2 + C_{\theta y}^2)]}$$

Substituting from eqn [13] for pressure P_y and rearranging leads to a quadratic equation in C_{my}

$$C_{my}^2\left(\frac{\dot{m}}{A_y}\left(1-\frac{\gamma-1}{2\gamma}\right)\right) - C_{my}\left[\frac{P_{xJ}}{A_y}(A_{xJ} + A_{xw}) + \frac{\dot{m}}{A_y}(C_{mxJ}(1-\delta) + \delta C_{mxw})\right]$$
$$+ \frac{\dot{m}}{A_y}\left[RT_{oy} - \frac{\gamma-1}{2\gamma}C_{\theta y}^2\right] = 0$$

which can be solved for velocity C_{my}. All other fluid properties can then be readily calculated. The entropy gain associated with the mixing process follows from

$$\frac{\Delta S}{R} = \frac{\gamma}{\gamma-1}\ln(T_y/T_w) - \ln(P_y/P_w)$$

For the two zone model the mixing process completes the calculation to the inlet of the diffuser system. For the procedure described by Japikse(7) a further iteration is necessary in order to converge to the required mixed out slip factor. If the mixed out slip factor, given by

$$\mu = (C_{\theta y} - C_{my}\tan\beta_{By})/U_y$$

does not agree with that given by the selected correlation, the estimated jet slip factor must be modified and the calculation repeated.

6 IMPELLER MODELLING INCLUDING BOUNDARY LAYER GROWTH AND SEPARATION

As the extent of the discharge wake is an important parameter in the determination of the impeller losses an advance from the models described above must include a more thorough technique for its prediction. To allow for variations in the impeller passage shape Herbert(25), and Frigne and Van den Braembussche(5) defined the impeller contours by means of prescribed functions, circular arcs and/or ellipses. This preliminary description of the internal passage enables a more detailed analysis to be carried out in order to predict boundary layer growth, separation and the associated flow blockage and energy dissipation with due allowance for variation in Reynolds number, flow curvature, influence of rotation and compressibility. By the

very nature of these detailed procedures they cease to be a one-dimensional analysis and become pseudo two-dimensional, and are a natural extension of the basic one-dimensional procedures.

Herbert (25) used circular arc profiles to describe both the hub and shroud surfaces, and treated the impeller as if it had an integral shroud. All four walls of each impeller passage were considered to develop boundary layers appropriate to the local relative flow conditions. The boundary layer displacement and momentum thickness on all surfaces were calculated to yield the required boundary layer blockage at impeller discharge by summation of the displacement thicknesses. Herbert (25) acknowledged that the approach used is open to criticism, but considered the need to calculate the discharge blockage to be sufficiently important to justify the simplified model adopted.

Frigne and Van den Braembussche (5) described the hub and shroud contours with elliptical profiles. In addition the impeller passage was divided into 5 equal annular stream surfaces. The flow model considered the impeller in two parts, from the inlet to the point of separation, and from the point of separation, where the flow was considered to split into a jet and wake, to the impeller discharge. The primary objective of the procedure was to predict the point of separation and the consequent development of the jet and wake. The location of the point of separation is important; if the impeller design is such that separation can be delayed until well into the impeller passage the discharge wake width and the associated losses will be small. Conversely a design which leads to early separation will develop a relatively large discharge wake.

Separation was considered to occur when the relative velocity had decreased by a prescribed amount, i.e.

$$W_{sep} = W_{1s}/DR$$

As in the two zone model described above the diffusion ratio, DR, must be specified. The position on the impeller shroud where the relative velocity becomes W_{sep} was calculated using a steamline curvature technique, across the specified stream tubes.

In order to link the flow model from the separation point to the impeller discharge the assumption was made that the mean relative Mach number remains constant along the jet from separation to the impeller discharge, see Dean(15). However, rather than consider the jet to be isentropic, losses due to friction and clearance were included. Instead of specifying the wake flow fraction the relative velocity in the wake was calculated through $W_w = k\,W_J$, where, k = 0.2 was considered satisfactory. The wake mass flow rate was then calculated through the wake density, which in turn was derived from the wake pressure. The wake pressure was calculated from the tangential pressure gradient in the jet through the known streamline curvature.

These attempts to calculate the extent of the discharge wake extends the calculation procedure from a one-dimensional one to a pseudo two-dimensional procedure. Whether the additional complexity is justified or not can only be judge by the quality of the ensuing predictions over a wide range of compressor designs.

7 CONCLUSIONS

To predict the performance characteristics of a proposed compressor design it is necessary to apply suitable flow models to describe both the incidence process at the impeller and vaned diffuser inlet and the separated impeller flows. By considering the fundamental gas dynamic relationships relative to each component it is possible to develop the procedure so that alternative empirical flow models and loss correlations can be readily incorporated. For the separated jet and wake flow of the impeller three alternative flow models have been briefly described. By incorporating the alternative loss models into the prediction procedure the relative

merits of each can be judged against experimental results of existing designs.

8 REFERENCES

(1) Balje O E
A contribution to the problem of designing radial turbomachines
Trans ASME V 741 p 451 1952

(2) Coppage J E   Dallenbach F et al
Study of supersonic radial compressors for refrigeration and pressurization systems
WADC Tech Rept 55-257 1956

(3) Galvas M R
FORTRAN program for predicting off-design performance of centrifugal compressors
NASA TN D 7487 1973

(4) Whitfield A and Baines N C
A general computer solution for radial and mixed flow turbomachine performance prediction
Int. J Mech. Sci. V 18 p 179 1976

(5) Fringe P and Van den Braembussche R
One dimensional design of centrifugal compressors taking into account flow separation in the impeller
Von Karman Institute TN 129 June 1978

(6) Conrad O   Raif K and Wessels M
The calculation of performance maps for centrifugal compressors with vane-island diffusers
ASME 22nd Fluids Eng conf. New Orleans 1980

(7) Japiske D
Assessment of single and two zone modelling of centrifugal compressors; studies in component performance: part 3
ASME Paper No 85-GT-73 1985

(8) Whitfield A and Baines N C
The design of radial turbomachines
Longman to be published 1990

(9) Wallace F J
Theoretical assessment of the performance characteristics of inward radial flow turbines
Proc. Instn. Mech. Engs. V 172 p 931 1958

(10) Whitfield A and Wallace F J
Study of incidence loss models in radial and mixed flow turbomachinery
Instn. Mech. Engs. Conf. Pub.3 Paper C55/73 1973

(11) Stanitz J D
Effect of blade thickness taper on axial velocity distribution at the leading edge of an entrance rotor blade row with axial inlet and the influence of this distribution on alinement of the rotor blade for zero angle of attack
NACA TN 2986 1953

(12) Jansen W and Qvale E B
A rapid method for predicting the off-design performance of radial-inflow turbines
ASME Paper No 67-WA/GT-3 1967

(13) Futral S M and Wasserbauer C A
off-design performance prediction with
experimental verification for a radial-inflow turbine
NASA TN D 2621 1965

(14) Johnston J P and Dean R C
Losses in vaneless diffusers of
centrifugal compressors and pumps
Trans ASME J eng. Pwr. p.49 1966

(15) Dean R C
The fluid dynamic design of advanced
centrifugal compressors
Creare Tech. Note No 153 1972

(16) Whitfield A
Slip factor of a centrifugal compressor and its variation with flow rate
Proc. Instn. Mech. Engs. v 188 32/74
1974

(17) Whitfield A and Wallace F J
Performance prediction for automotive
turbocharger compressors
Proc. Instn. Mech. Engns. v 189 12/75
1975

(18) Japikse D and Goebel J
Turbocharger compressor performance
evaluation and critical flow field
measurements
SAE Paper No 790315 SP-442 1979

(19) Japikse D
Advanced diffusion levels in turbocharger compressors and component
matching
I.Mech.E Conf Turbocharging and Turbochargers paper No C45/82 1982

(20) Weisner F J
A review of slip factors for centrifu-
gal impellers
Trans ASME J Eng.Pwr V.89 p.558 1967

(21) Daily J W and Nece R E
Chamber dimension effects on induced
flow and frictional resistance of
enclosed rotating discs
Trans ASME J Basic Eng. V 82 p 217
1960

(22) Dean R C and Senoo Y
Rotating wakes in vaneless diffusers
Trans ASME J Basic Engn 1960

(23) Eckardt D
Detailed flow investigations within a
high speed centrifugal compressor
impeller
Trans ASME J fluids engn p 390 Sept
1976

(24) Massey B S
Mechanics of fluids
Van Nostrand Reinhold 1985

(25) Herbert M V
Method of performance prediction for
centrifugal compressors
NGTE Mem 78029 Pyestock Hants U.K.
1978

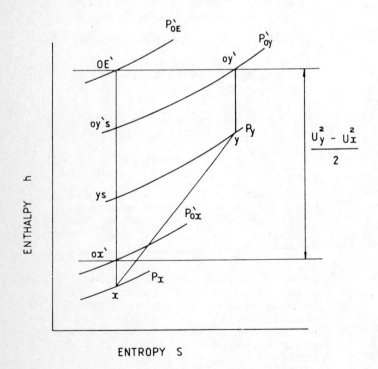

Fig 1   Enthalpy — entropy process for a rotating duct

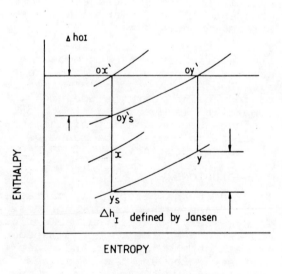

Fig 2   Rotor incidence loss

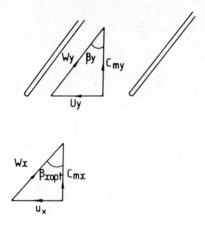

Fig 3   Optimum inlet velocity vectors

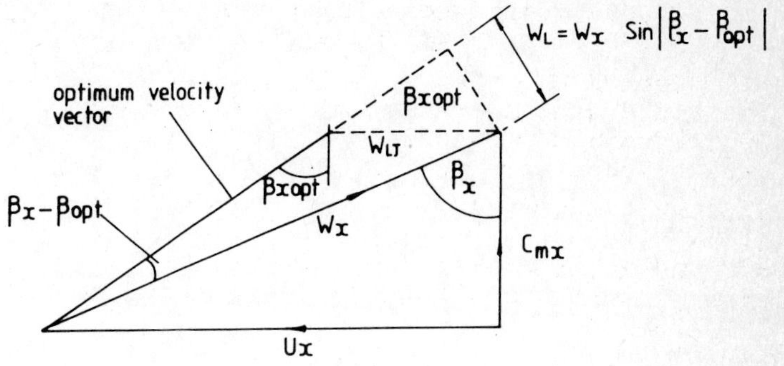

Fig 4   Adjustment of relative velocity vector to optimum direction

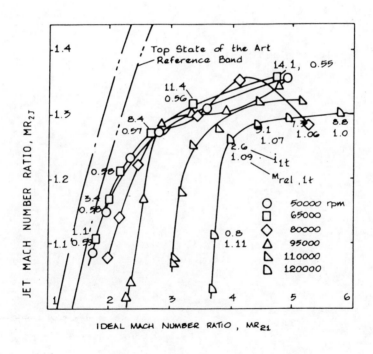

Fig 5   Impeller diffusion characteristic

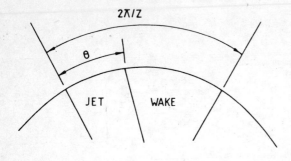

Fig 6   Jet flow for slip factor calculation

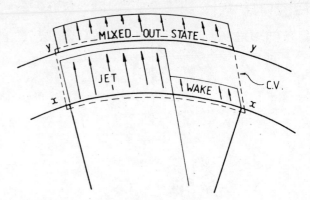

Fig 7   Jet wake mixing stations

A full load test, using a mixture of hydrocarbons, performed on an indoor test stand

F W RIP, Ing, A J F WESSELINK, Ing, and F M de JONGH, Ing
Delaval—Stork VOF, Hengelo, The Netherlands

SYNOPSIS. Under stringent safety precautions an ASME PTC 10 class I test was carried out on a 6-stage high pressure gas lift compressor on an indoor test stand at Delaval-Stork. The test gas used was a mixture of hydrocarbons and carbon dioxide. A detailed description of the preparations and the execution of the test is given.

1 INTRODUCTION

It is common practice nowadays on the off-shore contracts that turbomachinery is very extensively works-tested before it is shipped to site and installed in situ.

The reason for this is obvious, once installed in their modules on the platform, the accessibility is limited, the weather conditions play their role and once the platform is "live" very stringent safety rules are imposed so that even simple fitters work may take weeks to execute.

For centrifugal compressors the works-tests are mostly extended with a full load, full speed, full pressure test, apart from the already customary tests such as a works mechanical-test according to the appropriate code and/or a no-load string test.

For the application which is subject to this paper, the specified gas was natural gas with a molecular weight of about 24. In order to fulfil the requirements of the contract which asked for a full load, full speed full pressure test (a PTC 10 class I test [1]) on the high-pressure compressor, a customary test gas cocktail was not readily available and therefore a special gas mixture of hydrocarbons and carbon dioxide had to be made. Thus, a flammable and explosive gas.

Our company has a licence from the local authorities to run gas turbines in the shop for which activity a gas terminal had been installed which is connected to the natural gas grid. Over the years, a number of gas turbine driven centrifugal compressors were no-load tested. So a number of test engineers were familiar with the basic safety rules involved in working with natural gas.

Together with the Dutch Gas Corporation "Gasunie", we explored the possibility of executing the full load compressor test in our shop on one of the regular test beds, making use of as much of the existing test stand equipment as possible, inclusive of the test stand electric motor. Because the test gas for the compressor test loop was not taken from the main natural gas grid, the Gasunie was not officially involved but agreed to assist us in a consulting capacity. Together with the municipal authorities, the client, the assurance company, Gasunie and the works safety department a number of safety rules were set up which had to be adhered to if the test was to be executed indoors.

On that basis it was decided to go ahead with the indoor test.

2 THE COMPRESSOR AND THE SITE/TEST CONDITIONS

The high-pressure compressor in question is of a 6-stage design with two tilting pad journal bearings, a double thrust bearing and two floating ring seals. At site the compressor train, which consists of a high-pressure and a low-pressure compressor is driven through a gear by a 1780 rpm asynchronous electric motor of rated power 9235 kW.

At the test the high-pressure compressor was driven by a shop asynchronous speed controlled electric motor through a shop gear in series with the contract gear.

The specified gas has the following average composition (volume percents): CH_4 20%; C_2H_6 10%; C_3H_8 12%; N_2 2%; CO_2 2%, rest C_iH_i.

The test gas composition is shown in table 1.

Table 1 Test gas composition

CH_4	53.5%	± 5%	(relative)
C_2H_6	35%	± 5%	(relative)
C_3H_8	7%	± 10%	(relative)
CO_2	4.5%	± 10%	(relative)

For the test conditions versus design conditions see Table 2 on page 5.

3 TEST LOCATION/SET UP

The test location was situated inside a hall with a volume of 90000 m³ (height 27 x width 33 x length 100 m). About 2/3 of the floor space is available for tests, 1/3 for machining operations. The hall itself is in the middle of the site complex of buildings.

The high-pressure compressor is driven through the contract gear 1780/13147 and a test stand gear 1480/2200 by a 1480 rpm test stand asynchronous 6000 kW speed controlled electric motor.

The test loop includes the following components: gas cooler (medium water), flow measuring section, throttle valve, emergency blow-off. The water capacity of the test loop inclusive of the compressor is approximately 2 m³.

The contract oil system has been installed as well as the main control panel and the contract seal oil drain system. A container with 12 bottles filled with test gas was placed on a platform next to the loop. The container was filled with water levelled up to the top of the bottles and kept at 40°C.

Also close-by a control cabin was placed in which the automatic data acquisition system for the aerodynamic performance test was installed, as well as instruments for recording and analysing vibration signals and a control unit for the gas detectors. The cabin was pressurized.

Two air blowers (cap. 7700 m³/hr each) were installed, blowing air over the test site.

The emergency blow-off was capable of evacuating the loop in less than 20 seconds, discharging the gas well above the roof top of the building.

4 SAFETY RULES/MEASURES

- a project manager was appointed with full responsibility for the coordination of all activities involved and the proper execution thereof.

- The test loop with all its components and auxiliary equipment was designed according to the rules of the Dutch Boiler and Pressure Vessel Code.

- The contract oil system with the seal oil and lube oil overhead tank was installed ensuring approx. 10 minutes supply of seal oil after a trip of the seal oil pumps. This oil system had been functionally tested completely prior to the full load test.

- The sour seal oil from the compressor was led through the contract seal oil drain traps and from there to the sour seal oil tank cushioned with nitrogen.

- The contract control panel was installed after being fully functionally tested prior to the full load test.

- Prior to the full load test, the test loop was pressurized with N_2 to 1.2 times full operating pressure at stand-still. After that a test run was done with CO_2 gas in the test loop up to 9300 rpm and full temperature and pressure. All pressure connections were soap bubble tested. This CO_2 test was also used as a last rehearsal on all safety rules.

- During the full load test, the large entrance doors of the hall were opened as well as a large number of windows high up in the side walls of the building.

- Five gas detectors were installed in the test bay above and around the test loop. The detectors were connected to a read-out control unit in the control cabin. Acoustic alarm at 0.5 volume per cent methane. Trip of the main motor and opening the blow-off valve at 1.25 volume per cent methane.

- Two air blowers were installed and directed primarily to keep the air moving in possible air pockets near the test set-up.

- Around the flanges which are under compressor discharge pressure or gas bottle pressure shrouds were installed to control the gas flow if a packing should be blown out.

- The complete test bay was fenced-in one hour before the test loop was charged with gas.

- The admittance to the hall was restricted to authorized persons only. Only one entrance could be used for going into or out of the building. There, everybody received a personal badge and was registered each time when checking in or out.

- The one entrance and the other open emergency exits were guarded by members of works fire brigade. Other members being on duty inside the building made sure everybody kept to the rules.

- The main rules for personal behaviour were put on a big notice board at the entrance:
  - No smoking or open fire.
  - Everybody must wear a safety helmet and safety spectacles.
  - Everybody to turn in lighters or matches at the guards.
  - In case of gas alarm, a specially toned audio signal is given whereupon everybody apart from the works fire brigade, has to leave the building immediately and go to the prearranged meeting place.

- Outside but nearby the building, heavy material of the fire brigade was stationed and ready for instant action.

- Inside, a fair number of fire extinguishers was placed as well as blankets of non-inflammable material.
  Escape routes were clearly marked on the floor.

- Battery powered emergency lights were placed inside, ready for use. Also high power loud speakers were placed inside the building operated from a microphone inside the control cabin.

- Anti-spark tools were available should fitters work be necessary when the test loop was "live".

- The full load tests were run on Saturdays only.

- The commutator space of the electric motor was purged with nitrogen.

- Pressure transducers were boxed-in and purged with nitrogen.

- The works medical department was in attendance.

- The emergency blow-off valve evacuated the loop within 20 seconds.

5 TEST GAS

The test gas was ordered from an outside supplier of industrial gases capable of supplying the gas mixture within the required tolerances.

The mixture was delivered in bottles of 50 l water capacity. The purity of the gas components was 99.5 per cent Because the components are fractions of natural gas, the impurities are N_2, CO_2.

The accuracy of the components in relative volume percentages is 10 per cent for propane and carbon dioxide and 5 per cent for methane and ethane. The bottles were filled at the suppliers works by weighing the components. Bottle pressure 146 bar at ambient temperature.

The critital temperature of the gas mixture was 273 K. The phase envelope of the gas mixture is shown on Figure 1.

At a test on a pilot bottle no liquid was found under the condition 273 K and 70 bar. After delivery to the works, the bottles were stored at an ambient temperature of approximately 290 K. The storing period was three months. Not long enough for the mixture to become inhomogeneous. Thus rolling the bottles was not necessary.

One day before the test, twelve bottles were placed up to the top in water in a container next to the test set-up. The bottles were needed to fill the test loop up to 42 bar suction pressure.

Each bottle was connected to a circle pipeline installed around the top of the container. The circle pipe was connected to the loop with a pipe running downwards. The water in the container was kept at 40°C, raising the bottle pressure from 146 to 170 bar. This made it possible to use more gas from the bottle and the higher temperature enlarged the margin when the gas in the bottle cooled in expansion when charging the test loop.

It was important that in the process of filling the test loop, propane and ethane did not liquidize in the bottle, thus changing the gas mixture in the loop.

Throttling of the gas while filling the loop took place in the valve at the test loop and not at the bottle valve. The temperature in the filling pipe was measured and care was taken to keep the temperature above 280 K by controlling the gas flow.

A second container with 12 bottles at 40°C was kept stand-by in case some empty bottles from the first batch had to be replaced.

Prior to filling the test loop, the system was evacuated (99.9% vacuum) up to the check valves of the gas bottles. One bottle at the time was used to let gas into the loop. In case a bottle had to be replaced with the compressor in operation, the bottle in question was isolated from the circle line by closing the valves at the bottle and at the circle pipe. After the switch, with the bottle valve still closed, the circle line was evacuated to 99.9% vacuum and then filled again with gas from a bottle.

The loop filling process took about 10 minutes to reach atmospheric pressure.

6 TEST

Five test points of the capacity-head curve and the efficiency curve have been measured, see Figure 2. The gas properties of the test gas were calculated with the aid of the equations of state of Lee-Kessler-Plöcker and the equation of Peng Robinson for K-values.

The program used was Process^{TM} of Simulation Sciences Inc.
Prior to the class I test with hydrocarbons a PTC 10 Class III test was performed at equivalent speed on Freon 22 in the same test set-up using the same instrumentation. A number of trim corrections on the stationary parts of the aero assembly was carried out as a result of that test.

6.1 Gas samples from the loop

Together with the bottles with test gas, also calibration gas mixtures were ordered from the same supplier. These mixtures were composed out of gases with the highest obtainable purity 99.95 per cent.

3 bottles of 20 l each, contained the following composition in volume per cents:

	CO_2	C_3H_8	C_2H_6	CH_4
1 (normal mixture)	4.5	7	35	53.5
2 (upper limit)	5	7.7	36.8	51.5
3 (lower limit)	4	6.3	33.2	55.5

These percentages were established at the suppliers by means of analysis of samples from each bottle in the gas chromatograph.

The fabrication accuracy of the mixture was approximately 1%. The deviation from the stated concentration was not greater than 0.5 per cent relative.

These values were accepted by all parties as the correct values.

At each test point of the compressor, a gas sample was taken from the loop. A 2 liter sample bottle was first evacuated to 99.9 per cent and then filled with gas from the loop at suction pressure after the cooler. During this operation a portable gas detector was placed next to the sample bottle.

At the nearby University Laboratory, the quantitative analysis of the components in the test gas mixture from the sample bottle was carried out by means of gas chromatography.

All measurements have been performed by two persons on two different gas chromatographs.

The calibration was performed as follows: Two of the calibration gas mixtures were used to calibrate the gas chromatographs for four components. The third calibration gas was used to check the established calibration factors.

Gas from the sample bottles was led through the two gas chromatographs and the concentrations determined using the calibration factors.
Of all values, standard deviations were calculated. Values deviating more than 2 sigma were rejected.

For the sampling results see Table 3 on page 5.

6.2 Data acquisition system

During the test an automatic data acquisition system was used. This system consists of the following instruments:
- scanner
- digital voltmeter
- frequency counter
- computer work station

Measuring sensors, like thermocouples (type J: Fe/Co), pressure transducers and differential pressure transducers were connected to different channels of the scanner. These channels can be closed manually or by the computer work station.
By closing one channel of the scanner the voltage signal from the corresponding sensor will be measured by the voltmeter. When the instruments are controlled by the computer work station (IEE-488), all measured voltage values from the corresponding sensors are transferred to the computer and then stored on a mass storage medium. With the calibration of each sensor the voltage values were converted to the real temperatures and pressures and could either be printed on the computer screen or on paper.
35 channels were measured every 10 seconds with a typical slow rate of 50 channels per second, the latter to obtain high accuracy for the temperature measurements. Thermocouple voltages were software compensated for cold junction temperature.

Shaft speed was measured with the aid of a frequency counter. Per revolution of the shaft one electrical pulse was generated. With the measured parameters the flow, polytropic head and efficiency were calculated on line, using the gas properties like molecular weight and compressibility for test conditions. The final calculation was done taking into account the gas analysis of every measuring point.
Warnings could be given by the computer when a certain parameter reached an upper or lower limit. Graphics of each parameter could be generated instantaneously against time.

6.3 Calibration

All measuring sensors were calibrated against Measurement Standards which are traceable to the Dutch Calibration Service. For interpolation between the calibrated points the best third order polynomial was drawn through these points with the aid of a curve fit computer program. The polynomial values were stored on a mass storage medium and loaded into the computer.

7 CONCLUSIONS AND RECOMMENDATIONS

The way both the pre-test and the final test
went off confirmed our view that compressor
performance tests up to approximately 10 Mega
Watt using hydrocarbon test gas can be
handled on the existing in-door test stands,
provided stringent safety measures and rules
of conduct for the personnel involved, are
observed. This means that a tight quality
check must be maintained on every aspect of
the test.

The safety measures and the rules of conduct
for the personnel must be discussed well in
advance of the test with all parties concerned
who must fully accept the prescribed measures
and rules.

The members of the test crew must be trained
to deal with emergencies.

A test rehearsal, on the basis of a beforehand
drafted checklist, including the simulation
of a number of possible emergencies, is
strongly recommended.
As an example for this statement it may be
mentioned that during the pre-test on hydrocarbon test gas, while the compressor was in
full operation, the electric power supply to
the test bay was cut off by accident for
three minutes, during which time the overhead
tanks supplied the seal- and lubricating oil.
On the return of the electric power the test
was resumed without the test gas having been
blown off. This same situation had uninten-
tionally occurred during an earlier pre-test
on carbon dioxide test gas, so for the test
crew it was a recognizable situation and
knowing that the overhead tanks and the
related piping system functioned properly
they had a span of ten minutes to deal with
this emergency.

The tests that were carried out allow a
direct comparison between the [1] ASME PTC10
class I test at design conditions and a class
III test at reduced speed using Freon 22
testgas, carried out in the same test loop
using the same instruments. We expect that
a paper on this subject will be published
before long.

ACKNOWLEDGEMENT

The authors are indebted to the managing
director of Delaval-Stork for permission to
publish this paper.

REFERENCE

[1] ASME Power Test Code No. 10-1965.

Table 2 Test conditions versus design conditions

	Test cond.	Design cond.	
volume flow	806.4	805	m³/hr
mass flow	39927	39265	kg/hr
polytropic head	112.89	111.71	kJ/kg
polytropic efficiency	–	.572	–
inlet pressure	42.5	41.97	bar
inlet temperature	30.0	26.7	°C
density inlet	49.52	48.68	kg/m³
discharge pressure	124.14	122.4	bar
density discharge	99.85	98.63	kg/m³
molecular weight	24.175	24.17	–
isentropic coefficient (ns)	1.2385	1.2349	kg/kmol
compressibility factor (inlet)	0.8233	0.833	–
compressibility factor (discharge)	0.8788	0.8881	–
speed	11947	11947	rpm
gas power	2147	2131	kW
load at compressor coupling	2215	2179	kW
balance flow	–	.011	m³/s

Table 3 Sampling results in volume per cents

	Sample 1	Sample 2	Sample 3	Sample 4	Sample 5
CH_4	55.54	55.63	55.80	55.99	56.11
C_2H_6	33.62	33.55	33.46	33.41	33.32
C_3H_8	6.33	6.28	6.21	6.06	6.03
CO_2	4.52	4.54	4.54	4.54	4.54

PHASE ENVELOPE GAS MIXTURE

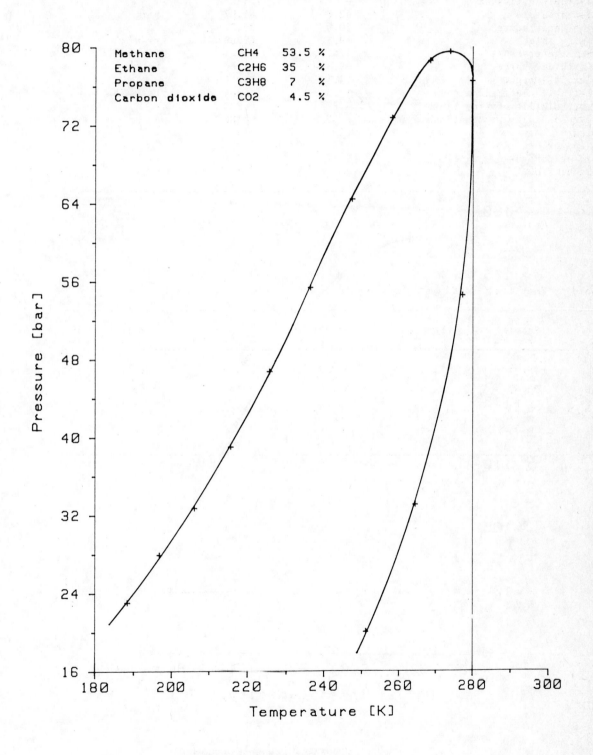

Fig 1   Phase envelope gas mixture

CHARACTERISTIC COMPRESSOR CURVES

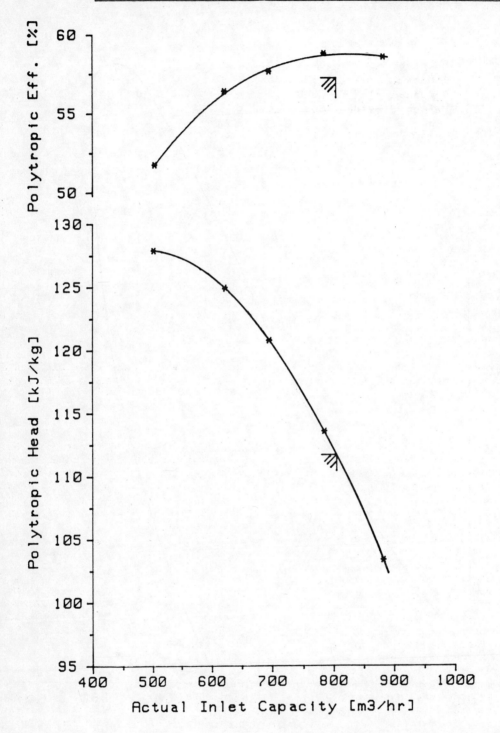

Fig 2   Characteristic compressor curves

C390/016

An examination of the methods used to vary the output of centrifugal compressors with particular reference to part-load efficiency

R P WILLIAMS, FIDiagE
Compair Reavell Limited, Ipswich, Suffolk

ABSTRACT

Most industrial centrifugal compressors are required to operate over a wide range of flows and pressure ratios and although the design point (at which the efficiency is optimised) is usually in the region of maximum power demand, the performance at lower flows often has a considerable effect on overall plant operating costs.

There are several ways of achieving off-design operation and they fall into three categories:-

        Suction Throttling.
        Variable Speed.
        Variable Geometry.

The latter category includes variable inlet guide vanes - (VIGV's).

All three methods are compared in the paper and examples are taken from a range of industrial operating environments. Variable IGV's are shown to be capable of enabling large turndowns in flow to be achieved whilst preserving a good level of efficiency.

The paper concludes that large operating flow ranges are possible for multistage machines and good efficiencies at part load conditions can be achieved by the right combination of impeller design and inlet guide vanes.

INTRODUCTION

Over the last few years there has been a steady advance in aspects of the various technologies incorporated into a centrifugal compressor. Bearing design has been improved, the dynamical behaviour of the shafts can be calculated with a greater degree of confidence and quite respectable aerodynamic efficiencies are being achieved. With these improvements in mind it is of interest to re-examine some of the ideas underlying compressor operation in order to take full advantage of them.

For many processes which use centrifugal compressors to move air or gas around a system, it is common for the end user to lay great emphasis on the efficiency of the machine at some particular combination of flow and pressure. A manufacturer will then optimise the performance of his compressor to meet this duty but in order to cater for variations in demand and chemical composition of the gas or feedstock, some means of controlling the flow must be found. There are three main methods to use:-

    - Variable Speed.
    - Inlet Throttling.
    - Variable Geometry.

This paper reviews all three methods with particular reference to the amount of flow variation which can be accommodated and the

levels of efficiency which can be achieved. Comments are also made regarding the manner in which these parameters influence plant operation and cost. The effect the chosen method of control has on the fundamental design of the compressor stage is also touched upon.

DESIGN CONSIDERATIONS

Before any real analysis can be made it is necessary to define the meaning of the term operating range. We will consider a machine required to operate at a constant delivery pressure (or nearly so) and define the following terms:-

The contract design point CDP is the combination of flow, pressure and speed which best meets the duty required by the customer.

Turndown is the percentage change in flow required to meet another operating condition, ie. if a second duty point required a flow of 40% of the CDP flow then the turndown is 60%.

Unless otherwise stated the surge line will be the locus of the surge points obtained from characteristics run at different speeds.

To further fix our ideas we will first consider cases where the machine is required to operate at a fixed delivery pressure.

It is obvious from an inspection of the overall characteristics – e.g. Fig 1 – that the achievable turndown depends on how far the CDP is from surge at the contract speed. However to keep the discussion within sensible limits we will assume that this is chosen to be within 1% of the peak efficiency. This at once highlights the importance of a key parameter in the impeller design – the outlet angle of the blade (beta). For a radial blade the peak efficiency point will be close to the surge point, moving further away as the degree of sweepback increases (see ref. 1 for example) – Fig 1 illustrates this point. There are of course other factors which affect the choice of blade angle many of them bound up with the actual mechanics of driving the impeller.

A high sweepback on the blade angle necessitates an increase in rotational speed in order to achieve a given pressure ratio. These higher speeds give cause for concern in two areas – impeller stresses and bearing losses/shaft vibration. Leaving aside the stress question, high speeds place a greater emphasis on the bearing design – mainly from the point of view of losses. There is little point in gaining 2% of efficiency on the aerodynamic design if this is offset by losses in the bearings. Tilting pad journal bearings are often used to ensure the stability of high speed shafts but traditionally they have always been thought of as having a high power consumption. Consequently some designers prefer the fixed profile type because of their supposed lower loss. Recent advances in tilting pad design have indicated that they can now be made with losses as low as the fixed profile type (ref. 2) consequently increases in shaft speeds can be accepted. Improvements in techniques for predicting the dynamic behaviour of the bearing/shaft arrangement have also lead – in some instances at least – to a reduction in bearing diameters.

All these factors combine to enable higher shaft speeds to be achieved with excellent mechanical integrity and reasonable power losses.

TYPES OF FLOW CONTROL

Variable Speed Control

The ideal case for variable speed control is when the head requirement falls with speed squared. In such a case the matching of the impeller(s) and diffuser(s) is near the optimum over a wide speed range and the flow change can be accomplished at near optimum efficiency. However, many industrial processes are concerned with the case of near constant delivery pressure and it can be seen (Fig 2a), that for the stages illustrated in Fig 1, the achievable turndown is strongly dependent on the vane angle of the impeller. The limiting turndown is of course determined by the surge line of the stage whilst the efficiency variation is influenced by the shape of the characteristic near surge.

Operation beyond the surge line is not possible unless some form of blow-off or bypass control is used, which are inefficient in energy terms.

Suction Throttle Control

Suction throttling is a very cheap form of control consisting usually of a butterfly valve just upstream of the compressor. As the valve is closed, providing an inlet loss, the pressure ratio across the compressor stage is increased (to meet the constant outlet pressure criterion) and the operating point moves along the constant speed characteristic until the surge point is reached. The stage will surge at the same Va/U throttled or unthrottled, however since the effect of the loss is to increase the axial velocity downstream of the throttle the volume flow upstream of the valve is reduced. Since most users regard the valve as part of the compressor the flow is apparently reduced below that of the surge flow, however th resulting surge line is very little different from the variable speed line.

Variable Geometry

There are two main forms of variable geometry, viz:-

- Variable Inlet Guide Vanes (VIGV).
- Variable Diffusers.

Because of their suitability for both single stage and multistage machines, this paper will concentrate on Variable Inlet Guide Vanes (VIGV's).

Variable inlet guide vanes have three effects – they reduce the Euler work in the stage, they unload the leading edge or inducer portion of the impeller permitting operation to the left of the surge line and they introduce a loss upstream of the impeller. On many machines this loss can be quite difficult to establish since the vanes may be followed immediately by strong curvatures in the flow path making the interpretation of the static pressures difficult and the positioning of traverse probes very awkward.

The range and efficienty achievable with VIGV's is compared with variable speed and suction throttling on Fig 3.

DESIGN OF A TYPICAL STAGE

The results presented here are derived from the stage illustrated in Fig 4a, in which the impeller was designed to have a high flow coefficient (volume flow/rpm x D^3 = 240) and to be suitable for building into a multistage machine such as that illustrated in Fig 4b. In order to ensure that large turndowns were achieved the blade was swept back to an angle of 45°. The use of such a large sweepback ensures that the velocities into the diffuser are not too high – of the order of Mn = .5 consequently a vaneless diffuser was employed which tends to make the incidence at the impeller leading edge the most important factor in triggering surge. The inlet guide vane profile approximates to a lenticular form and is of constant space/chord ratio. Because of the considerations discussed earlier the loss was approximated to by data contained in Ref. 3 and shown in Fig 6a.

SINGLE STAGE TESTING AND ANALYSIS

A two pole induction motor driving through a fluid coupling provided a variable speed drive - the VIGV's being controlled by a standard electric actuator incorporating a 4-20 ma positioner. The motor was rated at 750 kW and the impeller diameter was 500 mm. Being more of a commercial machne than a research machne the tests had the advantage that the Reynolds numbers were more typical of the industrial environment - although the working fluid was of course air.

Static pressures were measured at several radii in the diffuser and these combined with the outlet temperature measurement (after allowing for radiation losses from the casing but not heating due to windage) enabled an estimate of the outlet velocity triangle to be made via an iterative process. From the total temperature rise across the impeller the tangential velocity can be calculated. Assuming a static temperature and knowing the static pressure the radial velocity can be calculated from which the absolute velocity and total temperature are determined. Successive estimates of the static temperature are made until the calculated temperature agrees with the measured temperature.

For IGV angles other than zero, the deviation is taken from the data appropriate to DCA vanes (vanes having their profile defined by two circular arcs) in reference 2 and the resulting tangential momentum is taken into account in assessing the outlet tangential velocity.

The outlet plane was taken to be after the scroll and following a diffuser - fitted to bring pipe line velocities down to around 40 metres/sec.

For all other aspects of the performance the date was analysed in accordance with the methods in Ref 4 which is a much used test code for commercial machines.

From the overall results shown in Figure 5a, it can be seen that the peak efficiency line is well away from the surge line indicating that the objective of a turndown of 60% should be achievable for this single stage. The effects of the inlet guide vanes are shown in Fig 5b whence it can be seen that turndowns of greater than 60% are easily achievable. For clarity only the effect of IGV's at 100% speed is shown - the speed range covered varying from 103% down to 72%.

Results from a three stage machine built with geometrically similar stages to the type tested here and tested with inlet guide vanes are shown in Fig 2b from whence it can be seen that IGV's are as effective on

multistage machines as thay are on the single stage version.

It is apparent from 6b that the effect of the inlet guide vane is to reduce the Euler work at a given Va/U, but since the surge is delayed to a lower Va/U the head at surge is slightly greater than the levels with zero IGV angle.

Breaking down the results into the separate components (Fig 6), it can be seen that the efficiency of the impeller itself is not greatly reduced, (Fig 6d) a result which can also be seen in Ref 5. As far as the diffuser is concerned (Fig 6c) the loss does not rise dramatically at the higher entry angles caused by the IGV's but rather continues the trend established by the variable speed tests.

PERFORMANCE PREDICTION

The results from these single stage tests with a simple inlet and outlet system were used to validate a model based on the loss coefficients of the IGV, impeller and diffuser together with the impeller head coefficients. It was found neccessary to fit the data for a speed separately thus forming a family of predictions for a set of discrete speeds and IGV angles. This set of curves could then be used to derive other speeds and angles by interpolation.

This method was extended to encompass the prediction of the performance of multi-stage machines by incorporating losses for the return flow passages derived from measurements on a test rig which incorporated a return flow passage before the final measuring plane. Again these measurements were made using impeller of 600 mm dia in order to ensure that the measurements were taken at typical Reynolds numbers.

The prediction was modified by including Reynolds number effects derived from testing a variety of multi-stage machines built to suit specific contracts. These machines incorporate impellers of a geometrically similar design built in various combinations of numbers of stages and size of impeller. Normally in multi-stage machines based on the stage described earlier, the impeller diameter is kept constant and the reduced volume flow through the machine is catered for by reducing the width of the impeller. Experience gained on a large number of stages so modified indicates that this factor needs to be modelled in two ways. Firstly there is a small reduction in efficiency for the reduced height and secondly the peak efficiency of the stage occurs at a lower flow coefficient. This latter effect is probably more important contractually since it is essential to ensure that the power consumption at the required flow and pressure is within a very small percentage of that promised - better efficiencies elsewhere do not avoid penalty payments.

One source of error is caused by the fact that the machines use shrouded impellers which are made from a single piece casting. Whereas this avoids problems associated with variations in blade clearance and surface roughness of the casing, it does not mean that the blade passages are not precisely controlled and most of the deviations from the predictions can be attributed to this factor.

THE ACHIEVEMENT OF LARGE TURNDOWNS

The large turndowns achieved by the use of variable inlet guide vanes, over and above those achievable by variable speed, demonstrated on the single stage compressors are carried over to the multi-stage compressors Fig 2b. Furthermore it can be seen that the penalties on efficiency are not greatly different. The loss of efficiency on the variable speed case stems mainly from the fundamental fall off in efficiency on any characteristic between the peak efficiency point and the surge point as was pointed out earlier. However, as far as the IGV'S are concerned the loss of efficiency is due in part to the loss through the IGV's themselves. If this can be reduced, say over the incidence range between 0° and 40°, then some efficiency improvement would occur (halving the loss of Fig 6a at 40° would improve the efficiency by about 4 percentage points). The efficiency loss associated with VIGV's may be reduced by further development, whereas that associated with variable speed is more fundamental and can only be offset by much more research work since it involves evolving blade forms with a flatter efficiency characteristic.

THE ADVANTAGES

There are three main arguments in favour of achieving large turndowns with IGV's.

1) For the simpler processes - waste water treatment, fermentation etc. a wide range of flows can be accommodated simply, efficiently and cost effectively.

2) In the case of the more complex petrochemical processes the composition of the gas can vary with time and in some cases may not be known with great precision. Also future requirements are often difficult to foresee. Inlet guide vanes can allow for a potential for future growth of around 15-20% in flow terms whilst still maintaining a substantial turndown for operational use.

3) Operation with two casings in series.

If the two casings are independently driven then the choice between the alternative methods would depend on the duty, the variations in flow required and the matching between the compressors.

However, the situation with installations which involve two casings in series, both driven from the same prime mover is a little more complex. If no sidestreams are involved then either suction throttles or variable geometry can be used, with advantage, to trim the flow of one or other of the compressors to ensure optimum matching. With sidestreams, especially those which stem from condensate streams the flows can be unpredictable and large turndowns may be required. To accommodate these situations with variable speed would be very expensive since both upstream and downstream compressors would require their own prime movers, even though the costly variable speed drives would only be required on the downstream compressor.

COMPRESSORS IN PARALLEL

In some processes, especially waste water treatment and fermentation the flows required over a period time can vary by an amount greater than the output of a single machine. In such cases it is necessary to run several machines in parallel and it is interesting to examine the effect of turndown capability on this operation. To provide a framework for discussion, consider the case of a requirement to achieve a maximum flow of 150 000 m^3/hr. down to a minimum of 20 000 m^3/hr. Further suppose that a manufacturer has machines capable of delivering 50 000 m^3/hr. with a turndown of 60%. The required duty can be met with the following system:-

1 machine operating between 20-50 000 m^3/hr.

2 machines operating between 25-50 000 m^3/hr.

3 machines operating between 33-50 000 m^3/hr.

Note that if the turndown capability is less than 60% more machines of a smaller capacity would be required involving a higher capital cost - especially if the machines are electrically driven. Even with a relaxed low flow requirement it is apparent that if the turndown capability is reduced to less than 50%, say 45%, for example then there would be a gap in the flow range between 50 000 m^3/hr.and 55 000 m^3/hr. (two machines operating at minimum flows of 27 500 m^3/hr). This gap can only be covered by blowing off some of the already compressed gas - a very wasteful process in energy terms alone. If the turndown capability is reduced to 35% then another gap opens up between 100 000 and 105 000 m^3/hr. whilst the first gap becomes 50 000-70 000 m^3/hr.

The scheme shown above is apparently simple in control terms, each operating machine being given the same signal. There would be a discontinuous change in the signal as machines are switched in or out. Even this simple scheme would not find favour with some operators who maintain that automatic systems cannot cope with the discontinuous changes without going unstable and who therefore prefer to run all the machines together, treating the installation as one giant machine.

It is not the purpose of this paper to discuss control techniques but it is interesting to note that for parallel operation based on the equivalent single machine, it is the control system which limits the minimum flow rather than the compressors.

CONCLUSIONS

It has been established that two factors influence the achievable turndowns for centrifugal compressors:-

1) The ability to alter the surge line.

2) The distance of the peak efficiency from the surge point on the design speed characteristic.

For installations in which the required outlet pressure falls rapidly as the flow falls then variable speed is an excellent method of control - if expensive. The main use of variable geometry or suction throttling is in the cases where the delivery pressure is maintained at a near constant value. In such cases the use of variable geometry - in particular variable IGV's coupled with impellers employing large sweepbacks (made viable by improved rotordynamic design) can produce turndowns of 60%.

Large turndowns can be utilised with advantage in a variety of situations and in some cases it is the control technology which is the limiting factor.

SYMBOLS USED

ALPH2   :   Angle between radial direction and air direction at impeller outlet.

Beta   :   Angle between the impeller vane at outlet and the radial direction.

CFM   :   Cubic feet/minute.

D   :   Impeller diameter.

ETAP   :   Polytropic efficiency.

ma   :   milli amps.

Mn   :   Mach number.

P_1 :   Inlet total pressure.

P_2 :   Outlet total pressure.

RPM   :   Rotational speed.

Va   :   Axial Velocity of air at impeller inlet.

VIGV   :   Variable Inlet Guide Vane.

U   :   Impeller tip speed.

CDP   :   Contract Design Point. ie. flow, pressure speed required to satisfy a contractual obligation.

Flow coefficient   :   Inlet Volume flow/ (rpm x D^3).

Note to achieve values quoted the flow is in cfm, with the diameter in ft.

$\dfrac{M\sqrt{T}}{P}$:   Flow parameter, M - lb/sec., T - K, P - psi

Work coefficient   :   Enthalpy rise/U^2.

Loss coefficient   :   Loss/Dynamic head.

REFERENCES

Ref 1 -   High performance turbochargers for marine diesel engines.

           P.Came, Connor, Fyles and Swain. Trans 1 Mar E(TM) vol 96, 1984, paper 64.

Ref 2 -   Design problems in turbo machinery bearing selection.

           R. Gozdawa. CME Journal Sept 1986.

Ref 3 -   Aerodynamic design of Axial Compressors NASA SP-36.

Ref 4 -   Performance test code PTC 10. ASME.

Ref 5 -   Impeller stalling as Influenced by Diffuser Limitations.

           C. Rodgers ASME Journal of Fluid Engineering March 1977.

CURVES ATTACHED

Fig 1 -   Influence of sweepback on efficiency.

Fig 2 -   Effect of sweepback on turndown.

           Effect of IGV on multi-stage machine.

Fig 3 -   Comparison of Efficiencies at part flows.

Fig 4 -   Single and Multi-stage machines.

Fig 5 -   Component losses from single stage tests.

Fig 6 -   Impeller/Diffuser Performance.

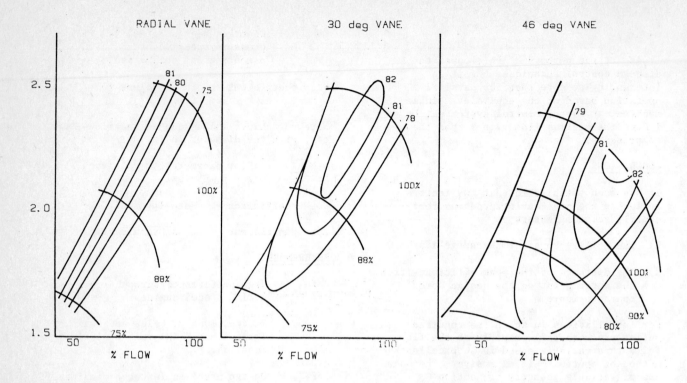

Fig 1   Influence of sweepback on efficiency

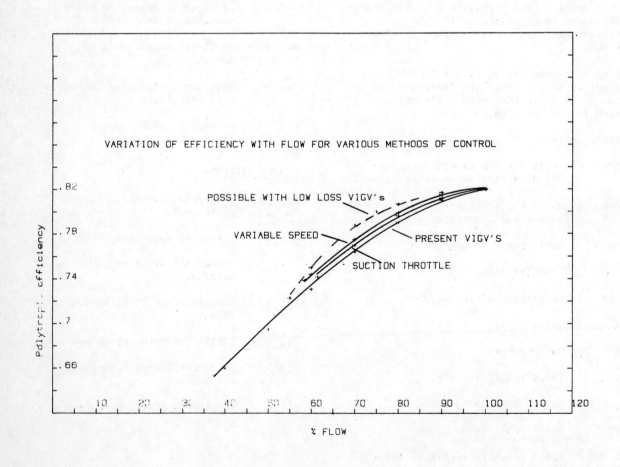

Fig 3   Comparison of efficiencies at part flows

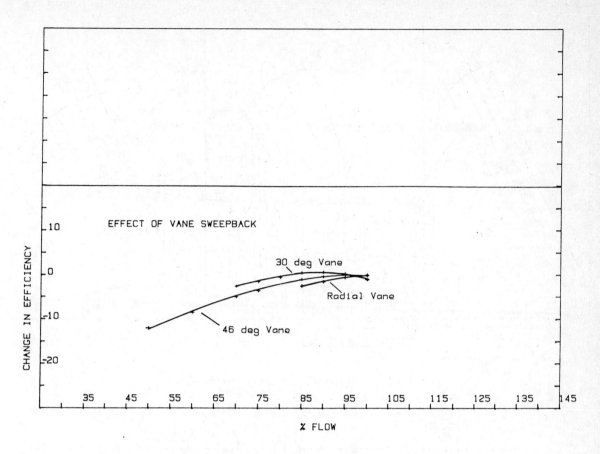

Fig 2a   Effect of sweepback on turndown

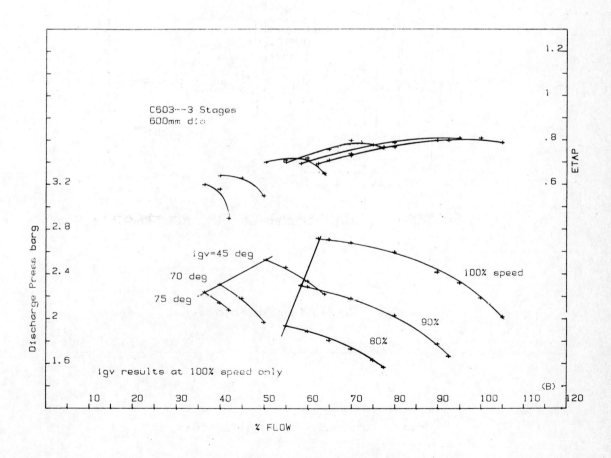

Fig 2b   Effect of IGV on multi-stage machine

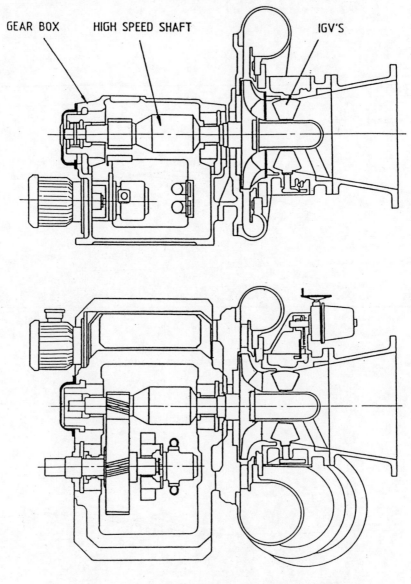

GEAR BOX   HIGH SPEED SHAFT   IGV'S

SECTIONAL ARRANGEMENT OF COMPRESSOR

(a)

Fig 4   Single and multi-stage machines

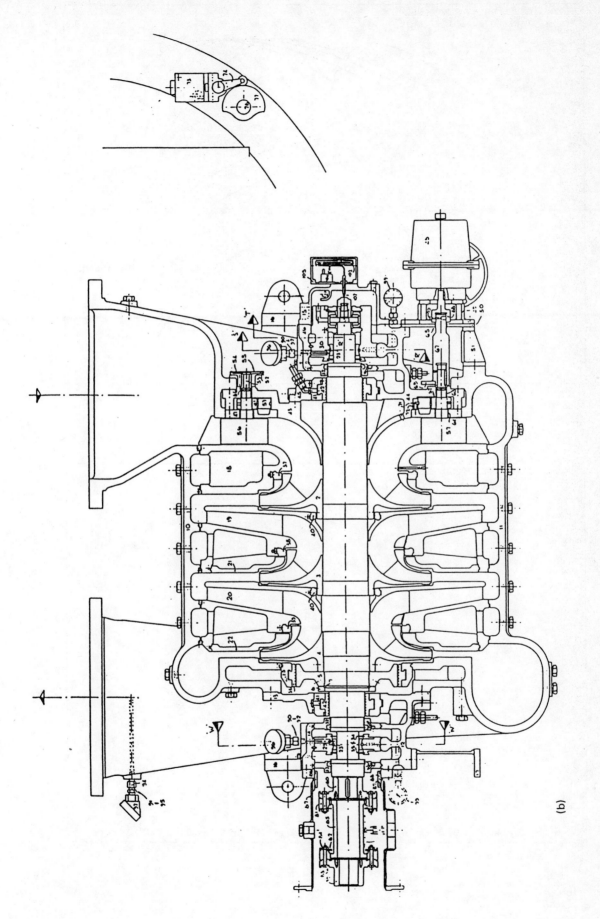

Fig 4 contd

(b)

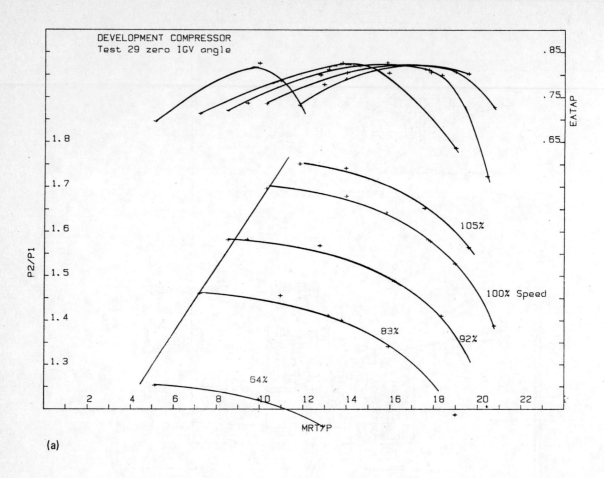

(a)

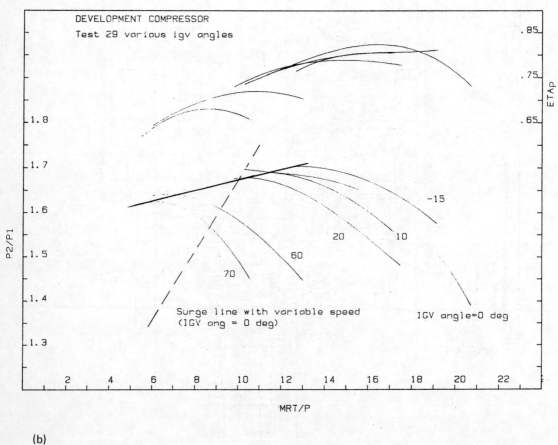

(b)

Fig 5   Component losses from single stage tests

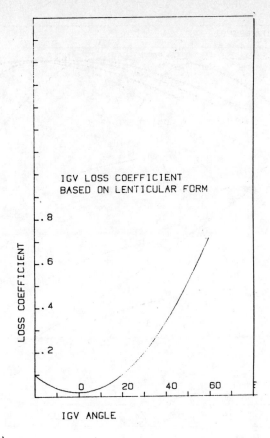

(a)

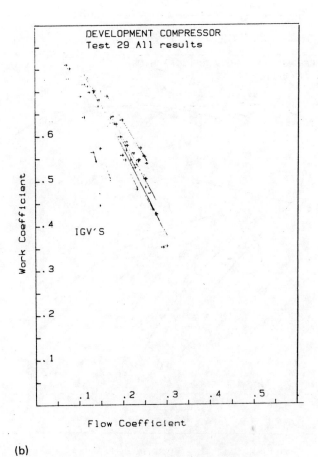

(b)

Fig 6   Impeller/diffuser performance

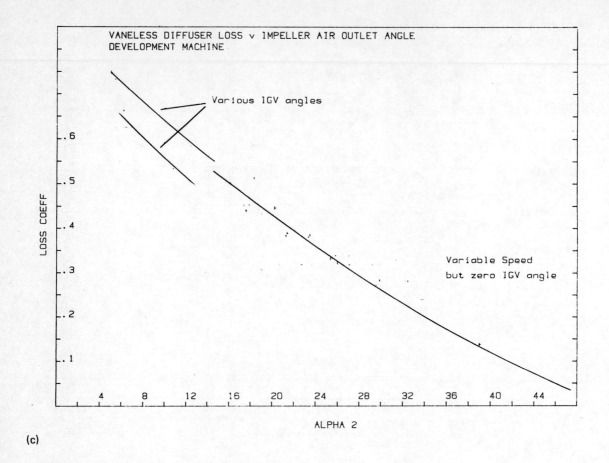

(c)

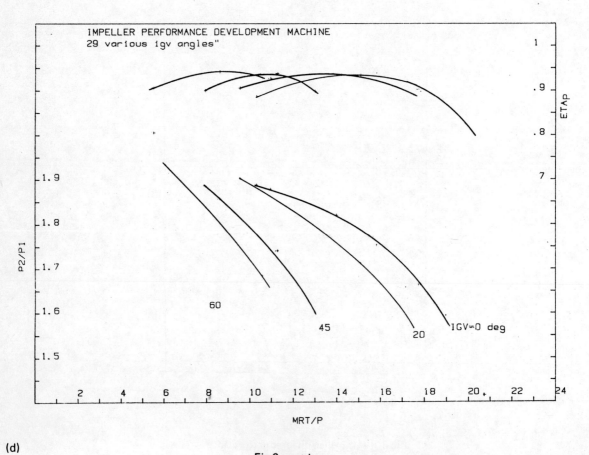

(d)

Fig 6 contd

C390/022

Active magnetic bearings and centrifugal compressors—a revolution and an industrial reality

H ZLOTYKAMIEN
Société de Mécanique Magnétique, Saint-Marcel, France

ABSTRACT

The idea of a magnetic suspension is very old : Professor Earnshaw demonstrated in 1842 that a totally passive magnetic suspension is unstable.

The active magnetic bearings (AMB) technology has been developed in S2M (Société de Mécanique Magnétique) since 1969 for numerous applications and the bearings manufactured range from 25 mm (1 in) to 1,250 mm (50 in) in diameter.

This paper recalls the principle, technology basic data and typical advantages of the AMB and then, focuses on their application to centrifugal compressors in the field of gas distribution and chemical industry.

1. MAGNETIC BEARINGS TECHNOLOGY

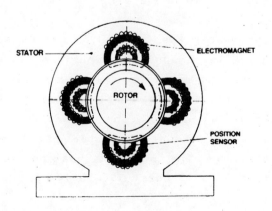

Fig 1   Bearing schematic diagram

1.1 Principle of operation

As in any bearing, the active magnetic bearing is essentially composed of two parts: the rotor and the stator.

The rotor which may be internal or external, consists of a stack of ferromagnetic laminations without any slots or windings, force-fitted onto the shaft.

The stator, also made of stacked laminations, slotted and including windings, includes the electromagnet section of the bearing itself and the position sensor section.

The rotor is located in the magnetic field of the electromagnets which have to provide attractive forces which equal the load applied on the rotor.

The system is basically unstable, so as soon as a small motion appears, the currents in the electromagnets must be adequately modified to maintain the equilibrium.

This is the reason why position sensors are required to provide information of actual rotor location.

For a complete rotor, where five degrees of freedom must be controlled, ten electromagnets are required.

It must be emphasized that, on the contrary of all other types of bearings, this bearing operates by attraction rather than repulsion.

Moreover, control is effective upon bearing activation and does not require any speed taking off.

1.2 Control loop and feedback system

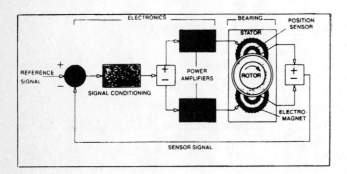

Fig 2   Control loop schematic diagram

The position sensor, which uses a high frequency carrier, provides a linear signal versus the rotor location.
This signal is compared with the reference set point (generally zero when a centered rotor is desired).

Then it is treated in a PID network (Proportional, Integral, Differential) and amplified in power amplifiers which feed the electromagnets according to the error signal sign.

1.3 Radial bearing technology

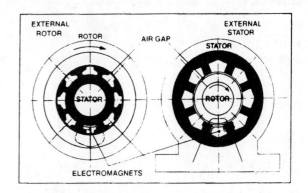

Fig 3   Radial bearing technology

The technology of a magnetic bearing is very close to that of the asynchronous induction motor.

The rotor which can be either internal or external, is composed of ferromagnetic laminations without slots.

The thickness of these laminations varies from 0.05 mm(2 mils) to 0.35 mm (14 mils), according to the application, and are generally made of 3% Fe-Si, non-oriented material, thereby allowing linear rotation speeds up to 200 m/s (40,000 sfm).

The stator also uses 0,35 mm (14 mils) thick ferromagneticlaminations. In most cases, the material used consists of non-oriented 3% Fe-Si material. With this material, the specific load capacity (load acceptable per bearing area) of the magnetic bearing varies from 8 to 10 bars (110 to 140 psi).

For a few applications where the load density of the machine is critical, Fe-Co laminations are used (51% Fe, 49% Co), enabling a higher specific load up to 14 bars (200 psi).

The air gap of the magnetic bearings varies from 0.3 mm (12 mils) to 1 mm (40 mils) or more, according to the diameter of the bearing.

These air gap values, very high with respect to those encountered in other bearings, allow less accurate machining (generally a turning process is good enough).

The windings of the electromagnets, simpler than those of electric motors, use, however, the same technology and the same insulation classes.

1.4 Axial thrust technology

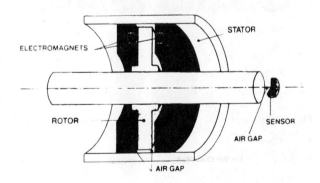

Fig 4   Double axial thrust bearing

Axial control of the machines is generally performed by means of a double axial thrust.

In the case of magnetic bearings, the stator of the bearing is of the annular type as well as the winding.
The lamination of the bearing is performed by sawing and filling the slots with ferromagnetic laminations.
The gap values are similar to those of the radial bearings.
The rotor generally consists of solid steel material allowing linear speeds up to 400 m/s (80,000 sfm). There is no necessity for the wheel to be laminated, because the bearing is not subject to any magnetization change during rotation, and therefore to any eddy current losses.
The specific load is the same as for the radial bearings, with, in addition, the fact that the whole surface is used in projection.
The axial sensor is not always located close to the thrust bearing. It is often at the shaft end as presently, especially in machine tool applications.

1.5 Typical bearing arrangement

Fig 5   Typical bearing

Fig 5 summarizes the magnetic bearings technology :

- it depicted a 500 kg radial load capacity for a Transamerica Delaval compressor,
- the radial bearing rotor with the bearing and sensor laminations, and a thrust bearing flywheel,
- the stator of the radial bearing and associated sensor are split for assembly purposes,
- the axial bearing stator can be seen at the back, on the left. This axial bearing is in two sections with semi-circular windings.

1.6 Auxiliary bearings

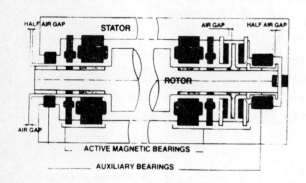

Fig 6   Auxiliary bearings

In order to protect the electromechanical parts in case of bearing overload or electronics failure, a set of auxiliary bearings is used for both radial and axial motions.

These bearings are usually ball bearings or carbon sleeves. They are located on the stator and therefore are at standstill in normal operation. The clearance between the inner race and the rotor is generally half the magnetic bearing clearance: 0.2 mm (8 mills) to 0.5 mm (20 mils).

This mechanical redundancy is not used in case of mains failure, the control electronics being protected by batteries.

1.7 Electronic cabinet

Fig 7   Electronic cabinets

The purpose of the electronic cabinet is to accomodate:
- the printed circuit boards for the signal conditioning,
- the power amplifiers providing the current to the electromagnets.

There are different standardized cabinets giving various powers for the bearings.

The cabinet size is basically related to the power amplifier performance which is determined by two factors:

- the load applied on the bearing which defines the maximum current needed,
- the frequency of the disturbance which defines the minimum voltage required on all coils.

For very disturbed and heavy loaded machines like milling spindles, the standard cabinet produces 80 Volts/ 25 Amps. per power amplifier with a water-cooling system.

These water cooled electronics cabinet are today replaced by a new generation of air-cooled cabinets, size having been divided by a factor of 2, weight by 3, and price by 2.

2 ADVANTAGES OF THE ACTIVE MAGNETIC BEARING TECHNOLOGY

There are two main areas of advantages.

2.1 Fluidless and contactless bearings

The first area of advantages is due to the fact that there is no contact between the rotor and the stator.

This feature brings several advantages and their related consequences such as:

NO WEAR
- eliminates mechanical maintenance
- very high reliability

NO LUBRICATION
- together with dry gas seals, eliminates totally oil, pumps, filters, tanks, pipings,
- eliminates bearing oil seals,
- eliminates process fluid contamination,
- eliminates fire hazard

VERY HIGH PERIPHERAL SPEED: 200m/s (40,000 sfm)
- very high rotation speed
- large shaft diameters at the bearings

VERY LOW LOSSES
- negligible heat input to process fluid.
- very low power consumption either for the bearings themselves as for the control cabinet. The energy consumption is 10 to 100 times less important compared to conventional bearings one (N°8)
- can operate in environments such as: vacuum, steam, hydrocarbons and other hostile environments

WIDE OPERATING TEMPERATURE RANGE
- from cryogenic to elevated temperatures: 20 K to 450°C (840°F).

2.2 Controlled bearing

The second area of advantages is due to the fact that the magnetic bearing is permanently controlled with adaptive parameters. This allows :

CONTROL OF ROTOR INSTANTANEOUS POSITION
- capability of rotor axial and radial position adjustment
- automatic balancing (rotor rotation about its axis of inertia) eliminating vibrations due to unbalance
- elimination of other vibrations by generation of opposite forces in the bearings

HIGH AND ADJUSTABLE STIFFNESS
- high rotor position accuracy (typical stiffness curves: re. Fig. 9 and 10)

VERY HIGH AND ADJUSTABLE DAMPING
- passing through the critical speeds of the bearings and the shaft

CONTINUOUS MONITORING OF OPERATING CONDITIONS WITHOUT ADDITIONAL EQUIPMENT
- speed
- bearing loads
- rotor position
- rotor run-out (unbalance and eccentricity)

3 APPLICATION OF THE ACTIVE MAGNETIC BEARINGS TO CENTRIFUGAL COMPRESSORS

Among many applications of the AMB Technology to different kinds of turbomachines like steam turbines or turbo expanders, centrifugal compressors represent an important field of experience of these bearings, mostly for the following reasons:

- completely oil-free machines, elimination of the lube oil system,

- capability to operate at speeds higher than the third critical speed first shaft bending mode),

- no process gas pollution by lube oil and elimination of fire hazard,

- vibration free equipment,

- permanent monitoring of the operating conditions,

- reduced operating cost (lower losses, reduced maintenance).

Better than words, the picture 11 will give you a good idea about the results of a retrofit on a centrifugal compressor installed in the KNIGHT power station of the Canadian NOVA gas pipeline (Photograph by the courtesy of NOVA).

The main characteristics of the compressors on pictures 12, 13 are the followings:

.Operating speed range (rpm)	0-13,000	0-5,250
.Driving power (kW/HP)	4,000/ 5,500	11,000 15,000
.Process gas	air/ nitrogen	natural gas
.Rotor weight (daN / lbs)	375/830	1,500/ 3,000
.Thrust load (daN / lbs)	1,400/ 3,100	5,500/ 12,400
.Bearings environment	process gas	air
.Third critical speed (rpm)	9,000	5,500
.Journal bearing diameter (mm/in)	190 / 7	270/10.6
.Bearings manufacturer	S2M	S2M/MBI
.Compresseur manufacturer.........	INGERSOLL RAND	INGERSOLL RAND
.User	INGERSOLL RAND	NOVA CORP.
.Date of delivery	1980	1985

Many other centrifugal compressors are now operating, a large part of them in Canada for NOVA, gas distributor in Canada (cf. annex n° 1).
AMB have now been installed on centrifugal compressors, (either new machines or retrofits) by INGERSOLL RAND, TRANSAMERICA DELAVAL, COOPER BESSEMER, DRESSER RAND, SOLAR, DELAVAL, FRAMATOME.

Test rigs are operating in different facilities: MAN GHH in Germany, NUOVO PIGNONE in Italy, KOBELCO and HITACHI in Japan.

These compressors are mainly used in the gas distribution industry and the petrochemical industry:
- 25 of them are operating actually, accumulating about 121.000* hours altogether (up to 30/09/1988), as these ones for SHELL in Montreal (Fig 14) and ELF AQUITAINE in Lacq (Fig 15),
- the first one, installed in Hussar power station in Alberton has accumulated 10,200* (up to 30/08/1988) hours without any bearing failure,
- 52* of them have been ordered up to now and 10* will be delivered in 1989.

More details are indicated on picture 16.

A new era is on the way to be opened: the oil-free shaft line is about to operate in the U.S.A. for TRANSCO, utilising a SULZER gas compressor driven by an ACEC variable high speed electrical motor.

We can guess from this point that this concept (dry compressor and electrical drive) will be very soon in operation on offshore platforms.

*Figures available today ; will be updated during the presentation.

REFERENCES

(1) S. EARNSHAW, "On the nature of the molecular forces", Trans. Cambridge Phil. Soc. 7, 97-112, 1842.

(2) M. TOURNIER and P. LAURENCEAU, "Suspension magnétique d'une maquette en soufflerie", La Recherche aéronautique 7-8, 1957.

(3) J. M. BEAMS, "Magnetic bearings", Society of automative engineers, automative engineering congress, Detroit, Michigan, Paper 810A, 13-17, January 1964.

(4) J. LYMAN, "Magnetic bearings - Pivot and Journal", paper given at 22nd ASLE Annual meeting in Toronto, May 1-4, 1967.

(5) Cambridge Thermionic Corporation, "A survey of magnetic bearings", 1972.

(6) H. HABERMANN, "Das aktive Magnetlager - ein neues Lagerungsprinzip", Haus der Technik, VortragsveröffentlichungenEssen, 21.09.77.

(7) H. HABERMANN, "Le palier magnétique actif ACTIDYNE", AGARD Conference proceedings N°323, 1982.

(8) H. HABERMANN - M. BRUNET, "The active magnetic bearing enables optimum damping of flexible rotors", ASME International Gas Turbine Conference N° 84 - GT 117 - 1984.

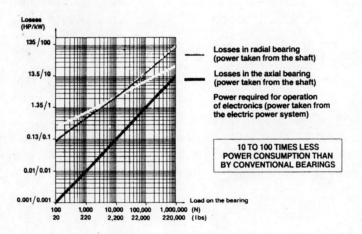

Fig 8   Power consumption of active magnetic bearings

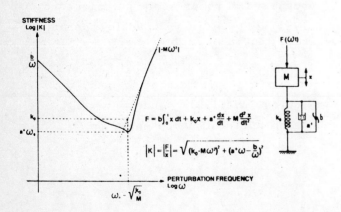

Fig 9   Active magnetic bearings — general stiffness characteristics

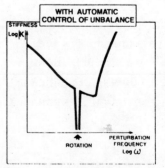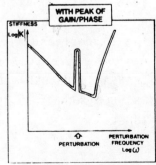

Fig 10   Active magnetic bearings — particular stiffness characteristics

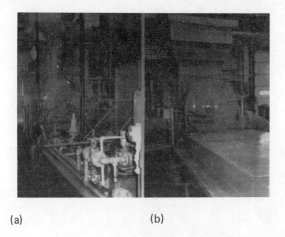

(a)   (b)

Fig 11   Nova Knight; (a) before retrofit; (b) after retrofit
          with active magnetic bearings

Fig 13   Nova Hussar centrifugal compressor — the world's
          first oil-free compressor

Fig 12   Ingersoll centrifugal compressor

Fig 14   Shell compressor in Montreal

Fig 15   Elf Aquitaine compressor in Lacq

MACHINE TYPE	QUANTITY	POWER RANGE kW/HP	NOMINAL SPEED RANGE	APPLICATION
TEST COMPRESSORS	6	20 to 4,000 kW 30 to 5,400 HP	10,000 rpm to 16,000 rpm	- TEST STAND
INDUSTRIAL COMPRESSORS	24	3,100 kW to 26,100 kW 4,200 to 35,500 HP	3,000 rpm to 15,700 rpm	- PIPELINE - REFINING - CHEMISTRY
HERMETIC MOTOCOMPRESSORS	1	6,000 kW 8,100 HP	10,000 rpm	- PIPELINE
MOTORIZED BLOWERS	4	5 to 200 kW 7 to 270 HP	3,600 rpm to 12,000 rpm	- TEST STAND - HOT HELIUM LOOP
GAS TURBINES	1	12,000 kW 16,300 HP	5,250 rpm	- COMPRESSOR DRIVE
STEAM TURBINES	1	3,000 kW 4,100 HP	15,000 rpm	- COMPRESSOR DRIVE
TURBOGENERATORS	1	5,000 kW 6,800 HP	3,000 rpm	- ENERGY RECOVERY (BLAST FURNACE GAS)
TURBO EXPANDERS	14	200 kW to 900 kW 275 to 1,200 kW	30,000 rpm to 47,000 rpm	- AIR LIQUEFACTION

Fig 16   Main turbomachines fitted with active magnetic bearings

Compressor rational efficiencies

J A McGOVERN, BE, MEngSc, MA, PhD, CEng(Irl), EurIng, MIMechE, FIEI, MASHRAE, AMIIR
Department of Mechanical and Manufacturing Engineering, University of Dublin, Ireland

SYNOPSIS Conventional figures of merit for the quantification of compressor power
utilisation, i.e. isothermal and isentropic efficiencies, are shown to be deficient as
objective functions for the purposes of compressor design optimisation. A general
rational efficiency and purpose related rational efficiencies, founded on the Second Law
of Thermodynamics and derived from exergy analysis, are proposed instead. These
efficiencies are applied to heat pump, refrigeration and gas compressors. Actual values
are presented for an open reciprocating refrigerant compressor. An indication is given
of how this approach is consistent with the attribution of losses in shaft power
utilisation to specific causes and is also consistent with overall plant optimisation
where the compressor is one of the components.

NOTATION

b specific flow exergy function
$(b = h - T_o s)$

b_{so} specific flow exergy function of saturated refrigerant at T_o
$(b_{so} = h_{fo} - T_o s_{fo} = h_{go} - T_o s_{go})$

c_p specific heat capacity at constant pressure

E_s isentropic efficiency

E_t isothermal efficiency

h specific enthalpy

h_{2s} specific enthalpy evaluated after an assumed isentropic compression process to the discharge pressure

h_{2t} specific enthalpy evaluated at the discharge pressure and the suction temperature

h_{fo} specific enthalpy of saturated liquid refrigerant at the temperature of the environment

h_{go} specific enthalpy of dry saturated vapour refrigerant at T_o

$\dot{m}$ mass flow rate of fluid being compressed

n number of secondary fluid streams

P input power

p pressure

Q quantity of heat transfer

$\dot{Q}$ rate of heat transfer

q_c net heat transfer per unit mass (from the fluid) between the suction and discharge states

q_t heat transfer per unit mass from the fluid during an assumed constant temperature compression process

R specific gas constant

s specific entropy

s_{2t} specific entropy evaluated at the discharge pressure and the suction temperature

s_{fo} specific entropy of saturated liquid refrigerant at T_o

s_{go} specific entropy of dry saturated vapour refrigerant at T_o

T absolute temperature

T_o absolute temperature of the environment

v specific volume

w_c net work of compression per unit mass (done on the fluid) between the suction and discharge states

γ ratio of specific heat capacities of an ideal gas

η compressor rational efficiency

η_{cr} rational efficiency for compression and heat rejection

η_o rational efficiency for the production of compressed fluid at environmental temperature

ρ density

Ξ quantity of exergy transfer

$\dot{\Xi}_c$ exergy transfer rate to a fluid being compressed between specified states

$\dot{\Xi}_{co}$ exergy transfer rate to a fluid being compressed between specified states, both at environmental temperature

$\dot{\Xi}^Q$ exergy rate outwards though the compressor analysis boundary, corresponding to the rate of useful heat transfer provided by the compressor

ξ quantity of exergy transfer per unit mass

ξ_c specific exergy transfer to a fluid being compressed between specified states

general subscripts

1   refers to the compressor suction condition, or, the entry state of a secondary fluid stream

2   refers to the actual compressor discharge condition, or, the exit state of a secondary fluid stream

i refers to secondary fluid stream i

o refers to the environment

1 INTRODUCTION

For the purposes of this paper, a compressor is defined as a machine within an imaginary boundary, which accepts a steady mass flow rate of a gas or vapour at a specified thermodynamic state and, due to a mechanical or electrical power input, discharges the same steady mass flow rate of the same fluid at a pressure which is higher than the intake pressure. The imaginary boundary which is used for the overall power utilisation analysis of this machine is shown in Fig 1.

Interaction with the environment may take place in the form of heat transfer in either direction across the boundary. Interaction with other systems may also take place as heat transfer, but, there are restrictions on the direction of any such heat transfer: any heat transfer at temperatures above the environmental temperature, T_o, must be outwards through the compressor analysis boundary, while any heat transfer at temperatures below T_o must be inwards through the boundary. One or more steady flow fluid streams, in addition to the principal fluid stream, may cross the analysis boundary and may receive or reject heat within the compressor. The same restrictions apply to any such heat transfer as apply to heat transfer across the analysis boundary. Furthermore, no secondary fluid stream may do work within the analysis boundary. The fluids within any secondary steady flow streams are, for simplicity, assumed to have constant specific heat capacities.

The compressor model outlined above is not the most general possible, but, is sufficient to encompass many actual compressor types such as the following:

(a) A two stage shaft driven air compressor with inter cooling.
(b) An air compressor, including its driving motor.
(c) An air compressor with inter and after coolers.
(d) A shaft driven refrigeration compressor with fins for heat rejection to the environment.
(e) An electrically driven hermetic refrigeration compressor.
(f) A refrigeration compressor, including a de-super-heater, which provides useful heating to a secondary steady flow fluid stream.
(g) An electrically driven hermetic heat pump compressor, which also provides useful heating to a secondary steady flow fluid stream.
(h) A shaft driven compressor which forms part of a diesel engine turbo charger.
(i) A shaft driven axial flow air compressor which forms part of a gas turbine engine.

The isothermal efficiency has traditionally been used to quantify the power utilisation of air compressors which supply pneumatic systems, e.g. examples (a), (b) and (c). The reversible isothermal compression process has, thus, been regarded as the ideal model for this application. In the field of refrigerant compressor engineering and for compressors which form part of cyclic plant, e.g. examples (d) to

(i), a reversible adiabatic compression process has been regarded as the ideal model and the isentropic efficiency has traditionally been used for the purposes of quantifying power utilisation.

The isothermal efficiency is only a suitable figure of merit for a very restricted subset of compressors in two classes:

1. those which increase the pressure of a fluid which is taken in at the temperature of the environment and discharged at the same temperature.
2. those whose sole purpose is to increase the pressure of a fluid which is taken in at the temperature of the environment.

In fact, for these two cases it is a rational efficiency - this statement will be elaborated (see section 5).

The isentropic efficiency, too, is a suitable figure of merit only for a very small subset of compressors: those which increase the pressure of a fluid, while causing no net change in its specific entropy. Compressors used in cyclic plant, e.g. engines, heat pumps or refrigeration plant, need not belong to this subset and, if not, the use of the isentropic efficiency leads to difficulties in the attribution of compressor power utilisation deficiencies to the true causes.

While recognising that a heat pump cycle and a refrigeration cycle are fundamentally the same, it is sometimes necessary to make a distinction on the basis of purpose or function between refrigerant compressors used for refrigeration, i.e. to provide a cooling effect, and those used for heat pump applications, i.e. to provide a heating effect. This distinction can become blurred, e.g. example (f), and in such cases a precise definition of the function of the plant is necessary if optimisation is to be attempted. In fact, a definition of function is always necessary when the effectiveness of power utilisation is to be considered together with the question of suitability for purpose. A compressor which provides compressed air in a factory has a different function to the compressor of a gas turbine engine and, here too, this difference may require the use of different figures of merit for the quantification of power utilisation, taking purpose into account.

In this paper compressor efficiencies are described and discussed and a case is made for quantifying power utilisation in a way which recognises the thermodynamic worth of the discharge state produced by a compressor (and of intermediate states in more detailed analyses), using the principles of exergy analysis (1)(2)(3). The technique which is described, and applied to the analysis of the overall power utilisation, has scope for the detailed attribution of deficiencies in input power utilisation, i.e. exergy destruction and losses, to discrete causes, such as heat transfer with finite temperature differences, throttling, and perhaps even effects such as cyclic solubility of the fluid being compressed in the lubricating oil. (Cyclic solubility effects are discussed in (4).)

2 ISENTROPIC EFFICIENCY

Isentropic efficiency (sometimes called the adiabatic efficiency) is defined by equation (1) and may be calculated according to equation (2).

$$E_s = \frac{\begin{pmatrix} \text{ideal power for reversible} \\ \text{adiabatic compression} \end{pmatrix}}{P} \quad (1)$$

$$E_s = \frac{\dot{m}(h_{2s} - h_1)}{P} \quad (2)$$

Note: the kinetic energy of the fluid at compressor suction and discharge is assumed to be negligible.

The isentropic efficiency, as stated in equation (2), includes the externally measured compressor mass flow rate. It incorporates three fundamentally different types of effect. The numerator in the fraction, the ideal power for isentropic compression, is not equal to the denominator, the input power, because:

1. The actual compression process is not reversible. The following description applies to reciprocating compressors, but, various irreversibilities occur in other types as well. In addition to a non flow compression process which is somewhat irreversible, mainly due to temperature gradients, the fluid undergoes two flow throttling processes, which are highly irreversible, in passing through the suction and discharge valves. The irreversibilities of the valve flow processes cause an increase in the area of the indicator diagram and, thus, in the indicated power. A small proportion of the mass which passes through the compressor also undergoes the irreversible processes of back flow or leakage through the valves or leakage past the piston. These and other irreversible effects always tend to reduce the isentropic efficiency.

2. There is generally heat transfer from the fluid as it passes through the compressor. In many cases, e.g. refrigerant compressors, heat transfer occurs first to the fluid and then from the fluid during the process. Equation (3), the steady flow energy equation, illustrates the relationship between the net heat rejection and the net work of compression.

$$w_c = (h_2 - h_1) + q_c \quad (3)$$

An analysis of a reversible polytropic compression process for an ideal gas, e.g. that presented by Rogers and Mayhew (5) leads to the finding that, compared with the ideal adiabatic compression process, heat rejection during compression leads to a reduction in the work of compression. A polytropic index of γ corresponds with adiabatic compression, while an index of unity corresponds with isothermal compression. Heat transfer from the fluid during compression, thus, increases the isentropic efficiency by reducing the work of compression. Similarly, any heat transfer to the fluid during compression reduces the isentropic efficiency.

If isentropic efficiency, expression (2), were to be used as the objective function for compressor design optimisation, the compression process would need to approach the isothermal model in order to maximise the calculated 'isentropic' efficiency. An ideal isothermal compressor would have a lower work input than an ideal isentropic compressor operating between the same pressures. This could, in theory, result in the isentropic efficiency being greater than unity.

3. There are leakage effects no matter what the compressor type. These are described here for a reciprocating compressor. Some of the fluid, on which work has been done by the piston, leaks back into the suction plenum or back into the cylinder from the discharge plenum. This causes a decrease in the isentropic efficiency due to a reduction in the external mass flow term in equation (2) which is proportionally greater than any reduction in the input power.

Isentropic efficiency is discredited as an efficiency measure of compressor performance since its value can conceivably be greater than unity, as explained in point 2. Furthermore, this parameter does not distinguish between different discharge temperatures. For example, of two heat pump compressors which have the same isentropic efficiency, the one with the highest discharge temperature may be the best for overall system performance.

3 ISOTHERMAL EFFICIENCY

Isothermal efficiency is defined in equation (4) and may be calculated according to equation (5) or (6).

$$E_t = \frac{\begin{pmatrix} \text{ideal power for reversible} \\ \text{isothermal compression} \end{pmatrix}}{P} \quad (4)$$

$$E_t = \frac{\dot{m}(h_{2t} - h_1 + q_t)}{P} \quad (5)$$

$$E_t = \frac{\dot{m}[h_{2t} - h_1 - T_1(s_{2t} - s_1)]}{P} \quad (6)$$

Note: h_{2t} and s_{2t} are only valid if the fluid is in a vapour or gaseous state at the discharge pressure and the suction temperature.

For an ideal gas, specific enthalpy is a function of temperature only. The isothermal compression work is therefore equal to the isothermal heat rejection. The expression for isothermal efficiency can be written as follows:

$$E_t = \frac{\dot{m}\, p_1\, v_1\, \ln(p_2/p_1)}{P} \quad (7)$$

$$E_t = \frac{\dot{m} R T_1 \ln(p_2/p_1)}{P} \qquad (8)$$

Within an actual cycle, reversible isothermal compression can be approached (e.g. using inter coolers), much as an ideal reversible adiabatic compression process can be approached. From the thermodynamic point of view any process which can be realised with little irreversibility is intrinsically good. Whether that process is well suited to the overall purpose of the plant or complements other plant processes is a separate issue. Since the reversible isothermal process is just one of a family of reversible compression processes, a compressor efficiency such as the isothermal efficiency which is based on that process alone is inappropriate as an objective function for the design optimisation of compressors in general within cyclic plant. For example, in a conventional refrigeration plant, the compressor must raise the temperature of the refrigerant to at least the temperature of the environment so that heat rejection can occur from the refrigerant.

4 SECOND LAW RATIONAL EFFICIENCY

The concept of exergy analysis, also known as thermodynamic availability analysis, has been described in the literature, e.g. by Aherne (1), Moran (2) and by Kotas (3). An excellent review of the fundamentals, with special reference to refrigeration and to refrigerant compressors is included in (6). At the Fourth International Symposium on Second Law Analysis of Thermal Systems (7) it was agreed that the term 'exergy' should be encouraged, rather than 'availability' or any of numerous other synonyms which have been used in the literature.

4.1 Exergy transfer to the primary fluid stream

For specified entry and exit states of a fluid passing through a steady flow system, and for a specified temperature of the surroundings, the minimum work which must be done on the fluid per unit mass is given by the increase in the specific flow exergy function between the entry and exit states. This can also be regarded as the specific exergy transfer to the fluid stream, equation (9), and will be termed the specific exergy transfer of compression.

$$\xi_c = b_2 - b_1$$
$$= h_2 - T_o s_2 - (h_1 - T_o s_1) \qquad (9)$$

The rate of exergy transfer to the fluid being compressed is given by expression (10).

$$\dot{E}_c = \dot{m} \, \xi_c \qquad (10)$$

The value of the flow exergy function, b, depends on the temperature of the surroundings as well as on the thermodynamic state properties of the fluid. The minimum specific work quantity for compression can be achieved only if the flow process between the states is

reversible (internally and externally). For an actual process between measured entry and exit states, the power input, P, which is also an exergy input rate, will always be greater than the rate of exergy transfer to the fluid being compresssed, $\dot{E}_c$.

4.2 Exergy transfer associated with heat

The exergy transfer associated with heat transfer across a boundary is given by expression(11).

$$\Xi^Q = \int \left(1 - \frac{T_o}{T} \right) dQ \qquad (11)$$

In this expression, T is the temperature at which an infinitesimal amount of heat transfer, dQ, occurs across the boundary. For a finite quantity of heat transfer, the integral must be evaluated over a region of the boundary surface. It is pointed out in (6) and implied in expression (11) that heat and exergy have the same direction if $T > T_o$ and have opposite directions if $T < T_o$. The exergy transfer associated with any heat transfer which occurs at the temperature of the environment is zero.

4.3 Exergy transfer to a secondary fluid stream

The exergy transfer rate to steady flow fluid stream i is given by expression (12).

$$\dot{E}_i = \dot{m}_i (b_{i2} - b_{i1}) \qquad (12)$$

It is shown by O'Toole in (8) that if the fluid has a constant density, ρ_i, and a constant specific heat capacity, c_{pi}, the exergy transfer rate can be written as follows:

$$\dot{E}_i = \dot{m}_i \left\{ c_{pi} [(T_{i2} - T_{i1}) - T_o \ln(T_{i2}/T_{i1})] \right.$$
$$\left. - (p_{i1} - p_{i2})/\rho_i \right\} \qquad (13)$$

4.4 Application to compressors

In applying the technique of exergy analysis, a clear definition of the system boundary and any constraints on the processes of the system is necessary. The description of the compressor given in the introduction, together with Fig 1, serves this purpose. Four types of exergy transfer across the analysis boundary of the steady flow system are involved.

(1) The exergy transfer rate, P, corresponding to the mechanical or electrical power input. This is constrained to be inwards through the analysis boundary.
(2) The exergy transfer rate to the fluid being compressed, $\dot{E}_c$. This is outwards through the analysis boundary.
(3) The exergy transfer rate, Ξ^Q, corresponding to the rate of heat transfer directly across the boundary. The direction of such heat transfer may be inwards or outwards, but,

the corresponding exergy transfer is constrained to be outwards.

(4) The exergy transfer rate, $\dot{E}_i$, corresponding to the change, normally an increase, in the flow exergy function of a secondary fluid stream, is evaluated at the positions on the analysis boundary where the secondary fluid stream enters and leaves the system. The change is due to two effects: firstly, heat transfer to the secondary fluid stream within the system boundary. The direction of such heat transfer may be to or from the secondary fluid and may, thus, represent either a heating or a cooling effect. However, the direction of the corresponding exergy transfer is constrained to be to the secondary fluid. The second effect which contributes to the change in the flow exergy function of the secondary fluid is exergy destruction within the secondary fluid while it is within the analysis boundary, due to irreversibilities such as fluid friction and heat transfer with finite temperature differences. It is conceivable that the exergy destruction within the secondary fluid stream, within the analysis boundary, could be greater than the exergy transferred to it in association with heat transfer. In this case the net exergy transfer corresponding to the change in the flow exergy function of the secondary stream, and evaluated at the entry and exit positions on the analysis boundary, would be inwards across the analysis boundary, but, this would be exceptional.

The four rates of exergy transfer across the system analysis boundary are shown in Fig 2. The compressor rational efficiency is defined in equations (14) and (15).

$$\eta = \frac{\text{rate of exergy transfer outwards through the analysis boundary}}{\text{rate of exergy transfer inwards through the analysis boundary}} \quad (14)$$

$$\eta = \frac{\dot{E}_c + \dot{E}^Q + \Sigma_1^n \dot{E}_i}{P} \quad (15)$$

Note: in exceptional cases a rate of exergy transfer, $\dot{E}_i$, could be inwards through the analysis boundary. It would then appear in the denominator of expression (15).

It is proposed that this rational efficiency be used to quantify the power utilisation of all compressors which correspond with the definition given in the introduction and illustrated in Fig 1. In determining the rational efficiency of an actual compressor the measured suction and discharge states and the temperature of the surroundings would be used in equation (9) to calculate the specific exergy transfer of compression and hence, using equation (10), to calculate the rate of exergy transfer to the fluid being compressed. Equations (11) and (13) would be used to calculate the exergy transfer associated with direct heat transfer across the analysis boundary and the exergy transfers to any secondary fluid streams. Equation (15) would then be used to calculate η. It should be noted

that the rational efficiency depends on the temperature of the surroundings. It is important, therefore, that this temperature is stated whenever a rational efficiency is quoted.

In cases where no useful heating or cooling effects are provided directly at the analysis boundary, or, indirectly via secondary fluid streams, expression (15) for the rational efficiency reduces to

$$\eta = \frac{\dot{E}_c}{P} \quad (16)$$

5 RATIONAL EFFICIENCY FOR THE PRODUCTION OF COMPRESSED FLUID AT ENVIRONMENTAL TEMPERATURE

For a compressor whose sole purpose is the production of compressed fluid (typically air), irrespective of the discharge temperature, with the minimum power input, it remains valid to calculate a rational efficiency, η, according to expression (16), based on an analysis boundary which contains the compressor, and intersects the input power cable or shaft and the suction and discharge pipes. This general rational efficiency quantifies the effectiveness of input power utilisation in producing the actual discharge state from the specified suction state. It contains no information on the suitability of the actual discharge temperature to the purpose of the plant, i.e. the production of compressed fluid at any temperature with the minimum power input. No matter what the actual discharge temperature, the fluid can be brought to the environmental temperature by heat exchange with the surroundings. However, if the discharge temperature differs from the environmental value it will be found that the exergy of compression is greater than it would be if the discharge temperature were equal to the environmental value. The environmental temperature is, thus, the most suitable discharge temperature.

The rate of exergy transfer to a fluid being compressed between two equilibrium states is given by expression (10), which can be re-written as follows.

$$\dot{E} = \dot{m} [b(p_2, T_2, T_o) - b(p_1, T_1, T_o)] \quad (17)$$

If $T_1 = T_2 = T_o$ then

$$\dot{E}_{co} = \dot{m} [b(p_2, T_o, T_o) - b(p_1, T_o, T_o)]$$

$$= h_{2t} - h_1 - T_o(s_{2t} - s_1) \quad (18)$$

The rational efficiency, η_o, for compression between two states at the environmental temperature may be defined according to expression (19).

$$\eta_o = \frac{\dot{E}_{co}}{P} \quad (19)$$

Where $T_1 = T_2 = T_o$, expression (19) for η_o is identical to expression (6) for the conventional isothermal efficiency. Thus, with a suction temperature of T_o, the isothermal efficiency is a purpose based rational efficiency: the rational efficiency for the production of compressed fluid at environmental temperature.

6 RATIONAL EFFICIENCY APPLIED TO CONVENTIONAL REFRIGERATION COMPRESSORS

The rational efficiency defined in equation (16) quantifies the effectiveness of shaft power utilisation in transforming the thermodynamic state of the refrigerant from the suction to the discharge condition. For a specified suction state and discharge pressure, the parameter does not incorporate any information on the appropriateness of the discharge temperature to the overall purpose of the plant, i.e. the production of a cooling effect in the evaporator with minimum power input.

In a refrigeration plant the discharge pressure must be higher than the saturation pressure corresponding to the temperature of the surroundings and depends on the interaction of the characteristics of the compressor and the condenser. For a given condenser a lower condensing temperature and pressure will result if a significant part of the heat rejection occurs in the compressor. For this reason, and because the work of compression is less when there is heat rejection, compressors which involve a high degree of heat rejection are to be preferred for refrigeration applications. In an extreme case an ideal reversible compressor could involve isentropic compression to the temperature of the surroundings followed by isothermal compression and condensation at that same temperature. In fact, whether condensation takes place within the compressor, or within the condenser, or partly within each, does not affect the ideal compression work, once the discharge vapour is saturated and at the temperature of the surroundings. This is because the flow exergy function has a single value for saturated refrigerant at the temperature of the surroundings, no matter what the dryness fraction. If the compressor discharge vapour is at a temperature above that of the surroundings, then, unnecessary work has been expended in the compression process. The extent of the unnecessary work depends on the characteristics of the compressor and on the characteristics of the condenser. With a condenser of finite heat transfer area, the condensing pressure and the discharge pressure of the compressor will be higher than the saturation pressure corresponding to the temperature of the surroundings. However, even with an ideal condenser of infinite heat transfer area and zero pressure drop, the discharge temperature of the compressor at the saturation pressure corresponding to the temperature of the surroundings, T_o, might be higher than T_o. This would invariably be the case for current technology reciprocating refrigeration compressors.

On the basis of the above discussion a new type of rational efficiency, which depends on the characteristics of a refrigeration compressor combined with a condenser, can be defined by assuming the purpose of the compressor is to produce saturated refrigerant in thermal equilibrium with the environment.

$$\eta_{cr} = \frac{\dot{m}(b_{so} - b_1)}{P} \qquad (20)$$

Given the compressor suction condition, the input power and the temperature of the surroundings, the rational efficiency for compression and heat rejection, η_{cr}, can be evaluated for a specified suction pressure, suction temperature and discharge pressure. This parameter represents the performance of the compressor, combined with a condenser which operates at the specified pressure and de-super-heats, condenses and sub cools the refrigerant to the temperature of the surroundings. Strictly speaking, it must also expand the sub cooled liquid to the saturation pressure corresponding to T_o, but, this expansion work can normally be considered negligible.

Where the compressor is to be used to provide cooling only, the value of η_{cr} can be quoted to quantify its performance in conjunction with a condenser which will cause it to operate at the specified discharge pressure. This parameter incorporates information on the suitability of the discharge state to the purpose of the plant.

η_{cr} could also be evaluated experimentally for the special case where the discharge pressure is the saturation value corresponding to the temperature of the surroundings. This would represent the rational efficiency of the compressor combined with an ideal condenser - this figure could be of interest where the highest possible rational efficiency for the entire plant was to be achieved by using a highly oversized condenser.

Situations sometimes arise where, in addition to the cooling effect, some useful heating is provided. In these cases the rational efficiency, η, expression (15), and the discharge temperature should be quoted in order to describe the merit of the refrigeration compressor in utilising its shaft power input, when operating between a specified suction state and discharge pressure with a specified ambient temperature. An exergy analysis of the entire plant would be necessary to evaluate the suitability of the compressor for its purpose.

7 RATIONAL EFFICIENCY APPLIED TO HEAT PUMP COMPRESSORS

The rational efficiency defined in equation (15) is an appropriate measure of the effectiveness of shaft power utilisation for 'heat pump compressors'. It is appropriate also for compressors within plant which provide simultaneous heating and cooling. A further point is that the expression for rational efficiency takes account of any useful direct heating (or cooling) provided from the compressor. As in the case of refrigeration compressors, the parameter does not include information on the suitability of either the suction or discharge states of the refrigerant to the purposes of the plant. Where the rational efficiency of a compressor is quoted the discharge condition must be specified by means of a second thermodynamic state property, normally temperature, as well as the discharge pressure.

8 RATIONAL EFFICIENCY APPLIED TO GAS TURBINE COMPRESSORS

The rational efficiency of a gas turbine compressor can be calculated, based on test measurements, from expression (16), or from expression (15) if necessary. The result quantifies the degree to which reversibility is approached in converting the power which passes inwards through the analysis boundary into one or more exergy transfer rates outwards. It contains no information on the suitability of the compression process to the overall purpose of the plant.

There is no reason to assume, as is often the case, that the compression process should ideally be isentropic, i.e. reversible and adiabatic. A reversible non-adiabatic compressor could be an ideal component for a gas turbine engine. In fact, for an open cycle gas turbine, if heat recovery from the turbine exhaust gas is to take place right down to the temperature of the environment, a reversible isothermal compressor may be the required ideal component, see Bejan (9).

9 ACTUAL POWER UTILISATION EFFICIENCIES OF A RECIPROCATING REFRIGERANT COMPRESSOR

Fig 3 compares three power utilisation efficiencies of a reciprocating refrigerant compressor over a range of suction temperatures. The compressor was a two cylinder shaft driven type operated at 600 r.p.m. with R-12. The suction saturation temperature was $-10\,^\circ C$ and the discharge saturation temperature was $40\,^\circ C$. Tests were carried out on different dates and ambient temperature was not controlled. The range of the ambient temperatures was from $18.5\,^\circ C$ to $24.5\,^\circ C$, with a mean value of $22.8\,^\circ C$.

The rational efficiency for compression and heat rejection was not sensitive to the suction temperature. It had a value of approximately 44%.

The isentropic efficiency and the rational efficiency both showed an increase with suction temperature and had roughly the same slope, the rational efficiency being higher than the isentropic efficiency. The rational efficiency varied from 55.5% to 61.2% over the suction temperature range.

10 ATTRIBUTION OF POWER UTILISATION DEFICIENCIES TO SPECIFIC CAUSES AND OVERALL PLANT PERFORMANCE

On the basis of the comparison in the previous section between the rational efficiency, η, and the isentropic efficiency it might be argued that the latter parameter is adequate for comparing different compressors. This may well be so for particular types of machines, e.g. reciprocating refrigerant compressors or gas turbine compressors, but, the isentropic efficiency does not have the potential to yield a more detailed breakdown of discrepancies in input power utilisation.

In order to obtain a more detailed breakdown of the rational efficiency it is necessary to partition the system within the analysis boundary into sub regions, e.g. the suction plenum, the cylinder, the electric motor, the discharge plenum. In the case of the reciprocating compressor, the task is further complicated in that fluid flow within the sub regions cannot be regarded as steady. Nonetheless, it is possible to identify the exergy transfers (per cycle, if necessary) across the boundaries of each sub region. The rational efficiency of a sub region can be defined as the ratio of the exergy transfer outwards across its analysis boundary to the exergy transfer inwards. The overall rational efficiency of the compressor is a function of the rational efficiencies of the sub regions and of the characteristic exergy transfer paths between the sub regions.

A compressor is often part of an overall plant, e.g. a refrigeration plant, or a gas turbine plant. The overall plant has a rational efficiency which is a function of the rational efficiencies of its sub regions and of the characteristic exergy transfer paths between the sub regions. In this context, the rational efficiency of a compressor is of considerable use, while the isentropic efficiency is not.

The science of exergy analysis is relatively young and, except for rather simple cases, a general methodology has not been developed for relating overall plant rational efficiency to the rational efficiencies of the sub regions. A methodology described by Valero and Alconchel (10), however, has promise.

11 CONCLUSIONS

Parameters for quantifying the input power utilisation of compressors have been described and discussed. A strong case has been made for the use of a rational efficiency founded on the Second Law of Thermodynamics. It is not felt that the rational efficiency must totally replace the more conventional isentropic or isothermal efficiencies. Rather, it should be used to gain a deeper understanding of the factors which tend to reduce the effectiveness of input power utilisation. It, thus, provides a basis for more detailed examinations in which correct thermodynamic values can be apportioned to various adverse effects. Two purpose based compressor rational efficiencies, one for the production of compressed fluid at environmental temperature and one for the production of saturated refrigerant at environmental temperature have also been described.

ACKNOWLEDGEMENTS

The author is indebted to his colleague, Professor W.G. Scaife, for many helpful discussions and comments over the years. The author is also indebted to Francis O'Toole, for his work as a postgraduate student in the field of Second Law analysis.

REFERENCES

(1) AHERNE, J.E., _The exergy method of thermal plant analysis_, 1980 (John Wiley & Sons Ltd.)

(2) MORAN, Michael J., _Availability analysis_, 1982 (Prentice Hall)

(3) KOTAS, T.J., _The exergy method_, 1985 (Butterworths)

(4) McGOVERN, J.A., _On refrigerant compressors_, PhD thesis, 1988 (University of Dublin, Trinity College)

(5) ROGERS, G.F.C. and MAYHEW, Y.R., _Engineering thermodynamics work and heat transfer_, 3rd ed., pp.383 & 384, 1980 (Longman)

(6) NOWOTNY, S. et al., _Saving of energy in refrigeration_, 1980 (International Institute of Refrigeration, Paris)

(7) WEPFER, W.J., LIOR, N. and BEJAN, A., eds., _Second-law analysis in heat/mass transfer and energy conversion_, AES-vol.6, HTD-vol. 97, 1988, papers presented at the Winter annual meeting of the ASME

(8) O'TOOLE, F., _The application of thermodynamic availability analysis_, MSc thesis, 1988 (University of Dublin, Trinity College)

(9) BEJAN, ADRIAN, _Advanced engineering thermodynamics_, fig. 8.24, p. 448. 1988 (John Wiley & Sons. Inc.)

(10) VALERO, A. and ALCONCHEL, J.A., Toward a universal formula of efficiency, in _Second law analysis of thermal systems_, Moran, M.J. and Sciubba, E. editors, Papers presented at the fourth international symposium on second law analysis of thermal systems, Rome, Italy, May 25-29 1987, pp.193-197. (The American Society of Mechanical Engineers)

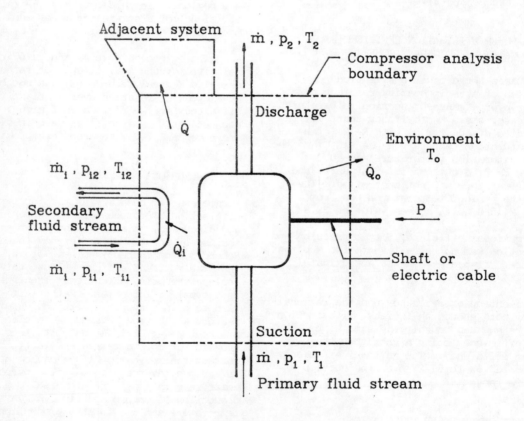

Fig 1   The analysis boundary of a compressor

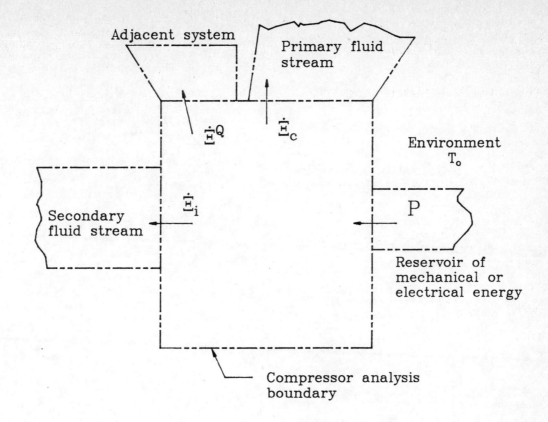

Fig 2   Exergy transfer rates through a compressor analysis boundary

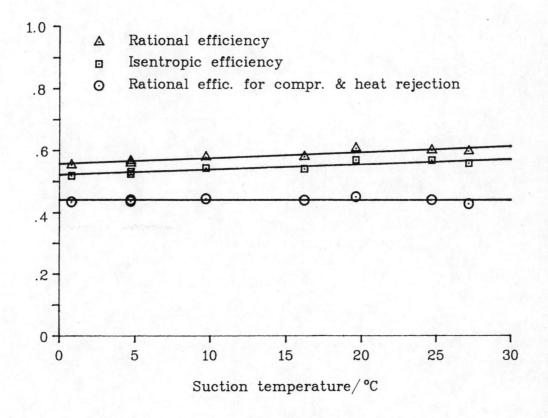

Fig 3   Power utilization efficiencies of a reciprocating refrigerant compressor

C390/015

Improved design and performance of Demag-Wittig oil injection rotary vane compressors

W SANDKÖTTER, Dipl-Ing
Mannesmann Demag, Schopfheim, West Germany

Abstract

Demag Wittig oil injected rotary vane compressors cover a volume flow range from 12 to 4400 m3/h at discharge pressures up to 11 bar.

The single-stage compressor series are employed for the compression of air as well as gases. In addition to some common features with other positive displacement compressor types they all exhibit some characteristic differences which will be discussed here.

In common with other oil injected compressor systems, the "ROL" series have an oil circulation and an oil separation system which is decisive for compressor operation and quality of the compressed air.

The essential differences in comparison with screw compressors, for example, are based both on the slow circumferential speed required and on the movable sealing vanes.

The high specific swept volume of the rotary vane system permits direct coupling to a standard four-pole electric motor at a compact design of the compressor stage. The vanes, which are rotating seals, make the volumetric efficiency practically independent of the rotational speed and permit design of very small compressor stages as well as allocating rotational speed to other criteria.

In addition to the geometric comparison of screw and rotary vane compressors, this paper also contains calculations and test results which are used both in completing and improving the performance of the "ROL" compressor series.

1. Introduction

The rotary vane compressor had already been invented by Karl Wittig in 1908. It was originally his intention to invent a steam engine but this failed. Nevertheless, he founded the basis for a generation of compressors which are in worldwide use today.

The patent document from 1908 is shown in Fig. 1. Decisive for this invention was the introduction of a barrel ring which reduced the relative velocity between the vanes and the ring itself which absorbed the forces instead of the housing wall, and thereby making possible a long-term operation incorporating low wear and high efficiency.

Modern rotary vane compressors, of which I would like to present to you the "ROL" series, no longer require these ancillary means: with practically fully hydrodynamic lubrication between the vanes and housing wall, an excellent method was found of obtaining a machine with a simpler design and improved operating results. Moreover, oil injection made possible an almost isothermal single-stage compression of discharge pressures to 11 bar by means of direct absorption of the compression heat, whilst the previous system required two or three stage compression with intercooling.

With single-stage compression, the "ROL" series covers at present the volume flow range from 400 – 4400 m3/h and the pressure range up to 11 bar. The smaller "ROL" series have volume flows between 12 and 36 m3/h at 11 bar, Fig. 2.

Since Mannesmann Demag also builds screw compressors please permit me to compare some of the aspects of both systems.

2. Compressor design

First of all, let us consider the common features between the oil injection compressor systems: Fig. 3 schematically shows the compressor design.

Please now consider the air channel: the air gets into the compressor stage via an air filter and the suction control valve. Here the air is compressed by clearance volume decrease, whereby about 2 % cooling and lubricating oil, related to the suction volume, is injected into the closed cell. The mixture of oil and air leaves the compressor stage through the pressure connection and arrives at the preliminary oil separator where more than 99 % of the oil is recovered from the pressurised air. From the preliminary separator the air then arrives at the oil storage and separate vessel and then into the oil separation cartridge. The oil content in the air is reduced here to 1-4 ppm. Downstream from the filtration system the air then passes through the "minimum pressure and check valve", then to the after-cooler onto which a cyclone separator may be coupled at the outlet side.

Let us now consider the oil circulation: The oil from the pressurised vessel the first arrives at the oil cooler. Since up to 85 % of the motive energy of the electric motor is accumulated here as heat which has to be eliminated, a heat recovery system for exploitation of the heat can be installed at this point. After leaving the oil cooler and passing the oil filter the oil arrives at the injection nozzles in the compressor stage. Here the oil is intimately mixed with the air to be compressed, after which it is separated from the pressurised air as described above and then recirculated to the oil storage vessel.

In principle, this plant and schematic could also be used for an oil-injected screw compressor if the rotary vane compressor stage were to be exchanged for a screw compressor stage.

However, where are the characteristic differences between screw and rotary vane compressor stages, and what characterises the rotary vane compressor?

3. The compressor stage

Oil-injected rotary vane compressors and screw compressors typically belong to path-controlled positive displacement compressors with fixed built-on pressure ratio.

The rotary vane compressor (Fig. 4) is characterised by:

- the rotor
- several movable rotary vanes
- the housing
- 2 housing covers
- 2 rotor bearings

The slow speed of the bearings and their dimensioning allow for a long service life (more than 100,000 h have been reached). In the event that a bearing defect actually arises it need not result in secondary damage; due to the discharge pressure applied, the rotor is pressed towards the housing centre. This means, that under normal operating conditions one can wait for the accoustic indication before changing the bearings.

Full hydrodynamic motion can be reached between the rotor vane and housing wall and between the vane and rotor: The latter makes possible high running times at extremely low wear rates.

Let me now explain the functional principle of the compressor stage using Fig. 5.

The air enters the compressor through the suction connection and arrives at the compression space via the inlet channel. The suction cell is closed by the lagging vane when the cell is in the top dead centre range where it achieved maximum volume. When the rotor turns the cell volume is decreased and therefore the air compressed. Hence, a special importance must be given to the rotor vane as a sealing element: It is brought into position at the housing circumference by centrifugal force; this function can be compared

to the initial tensioning of a piston ring. Analogeous to the piston ring, the decisive sealing function is achieved by gas forces which can be demonstrated by Fig. 6.

The different radial forces acting on one single vane as function of rotor angle " " are illustrated:

- the frictional force (friction between vane and slot)
- the mass force (centrifugal and coriolis force)
- the gas force
- the total radial force resulting acting on the hydrodynamic oil film

The following can be recognised:

- the mass forces dominating on the suction side of the machine in the range of the vane TDC.
- the gas forces dominant on the pressure side of the machine in the range of the vane BDC.

The gas forces acting on the vane within the slot result in a sealing force which is proportional to the pressure to be sealed. This sealing force must be borne by the hydrodynamic lubricating film.

This means that the sealing effectiveness of oil-injected rotary vane compressors is obtained by means of a well-proportioned force which always is in relationship to the gas force and which can be controlled by the geometry of the machine. This is the fundamental reason for the good volumetric efficiencies which can be achieved with these compressor types.

The almost fully elastohydrodynamic lubrication results in low frictional forces leading to frictional coefficients between 0,01 and 0,02 as shown in Fig. 7. It can be seen that the resulting frictional power is negligibly small compared to the effective power of the compressor stage. This effect is the basis for good mechanical efficiency as well as an almost wear-free operation.

The results of solving Reynolds differential equations for hydrodynamic lubrication of the rotary vanes compare well with test results which will be illustrated later.

By observing the screw compressor it can be seen that when the secondary rotor is driven by the primary rotor that a movable sealing contact is present at the point of meshing, however, not between the rotors and the housing wall.

The gap seal existing here implies that the volumetric efficiencies are dependent on the circumferential speed and thus on the rotational speed and on oil supply. On the one hand this results in the high speeds of standard screw compressors, and on the other hand the comparable lower volumetric efficiencies.

4. Geometric comparison of the rotary vane compressor to the screw compressor

Another reason for the low speed of the rotary vane compressor is implied by the basic geometry: The basic geometry of both compressor principles is given in Fig. 8.

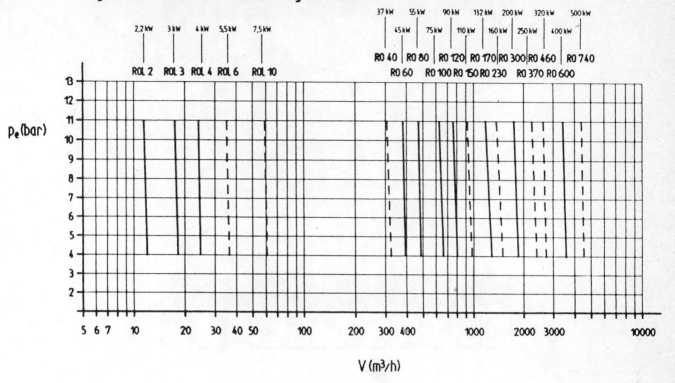

Fig 2   Volume flow and pressure

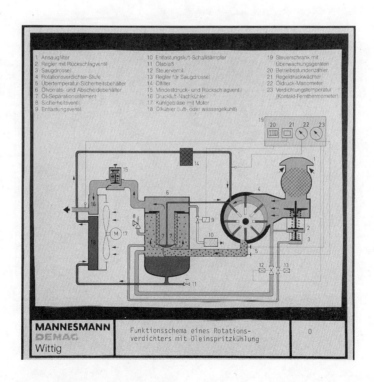

Fig 3   Functional diagram of a rotary vane compressor with oil injection cooling

Fig 4   Section of compressor stage

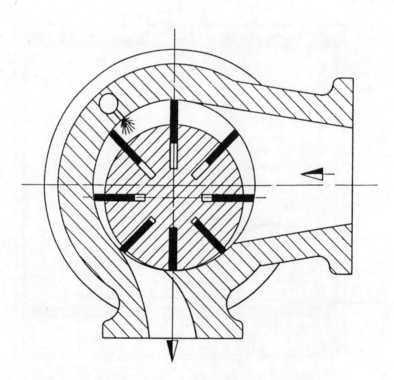

Fig 5   Functional principle of a rotary vane compressor

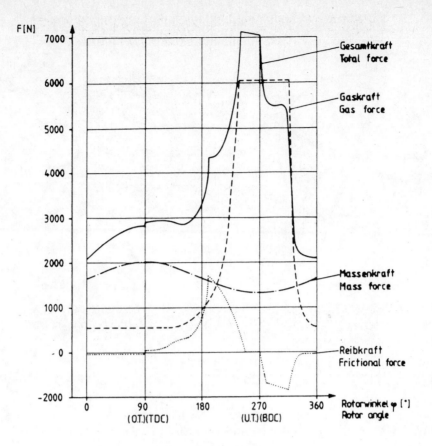

Fig 6   Radial forces on rotor vane

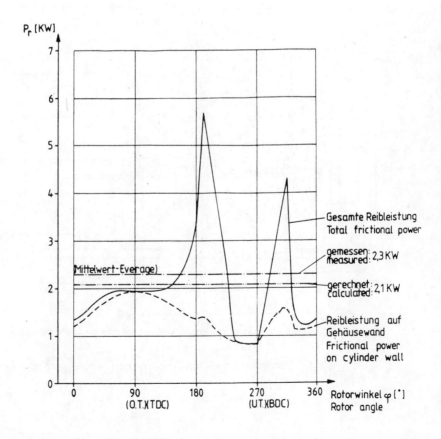

Fig 7   Frictional power on rotor vane

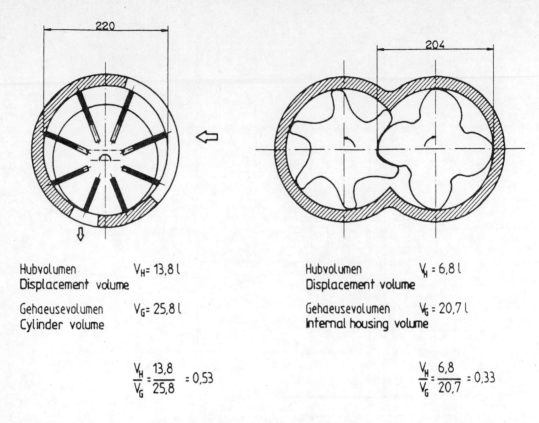

Hubvolumen	V_H= 13,8 l	Hubvolumen	V_H = 6,8 l
Displacement volume		Displacement volume	
Gehaeusevolumen	V_G= 25,8 l	Gehaeusevolumen	V_G = 20,7 l
Cylinder volume		Internal housing volume	

$$\frac{V_H}{V_G} = \frac{13,8}{25,8} = 0,53$$

$$\frac{V_H}{V_G} = \frac{6,8}{20,7} = 0,33$$

Fig 8   Volumetric comparison of rotary vane and screw compressor

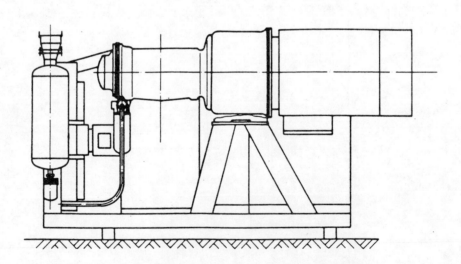

Fig 9   Schematic layout of the compressor stage and standard el. motor

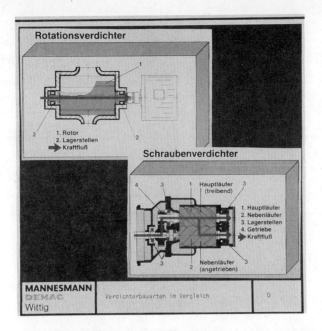

Fig 10   Comparison of force flow in the screw and rotary vane compressor

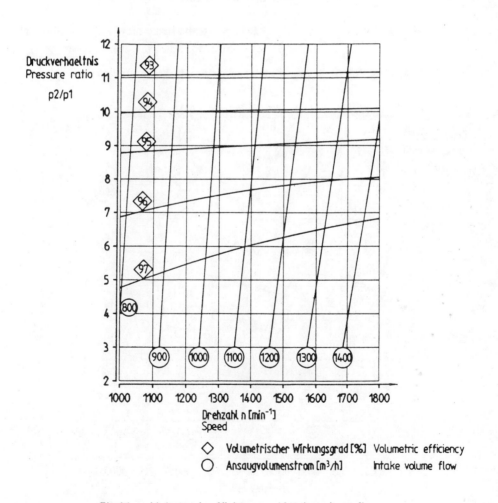

Fig 11   Volumetric efficiency and intake volume flow

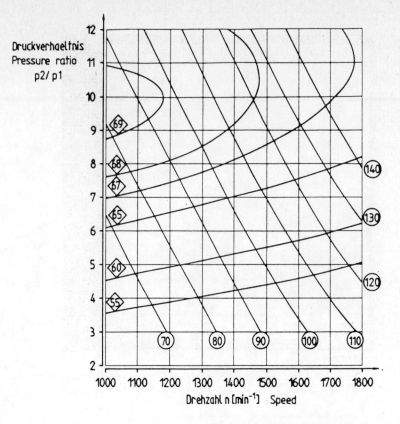

Fig 12   Polytropic overall efficiency and shaft power requirement

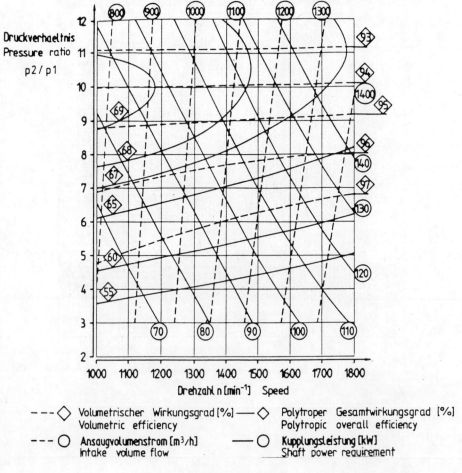

Fig 13   Performance graph

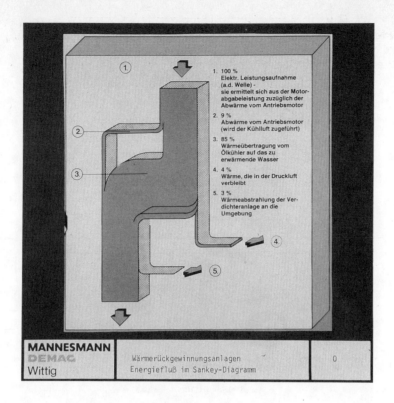

Fig 14   Energy flow in a Sankey diagram

Fig 15   Air-cooled compressor type 0 100 A-1 LL

MANNESMANN DEMAG Wittig | Kompressorenstation mit schallgedämmten Verdichtern | 0

Fig 16   Compressor installation with sound absorbing hood

Fig 17   ROW 300 with electric motor of 200 kW

Fig 18   ROW 300, back side view

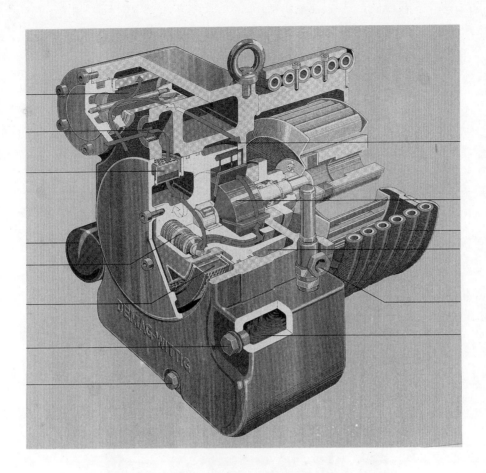

Fig 19   ROL 2 compressor offering a volume flow of 100 l/min

Fig 20   Roller bearing after 81,000 operating hours

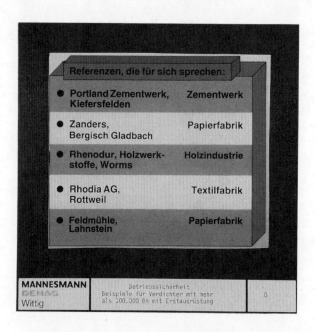

Fig 21   References from five German customers where Wittig compressors
          reached more than 100,000 operating hours with first equipment

C390/019

Quality classes for screw compressor rotors

S E H EDSTROEM, MSc
Svenska Rotor Maskiner AB, Stockholm, Sweden

SYNOPSIS As the quality of the rotors in a screw compressor has a very direct bearing on the performance of the machine, there is a need for quality norms for such rotors. Most widely used today are the oil-flooded screw compressors, which operate without timing gears. In all screw compressors the rotors are pumping and sealing members, but in these machines they also perform the task of timing gears as well as power-transmitting gears. Quality norms for such rotors should consequently account for their sealing ability as well as their gear-related performance. Different aspects on the design of such norms are discussed and some possibilities are indicated.

1 INTRODUCTION

A screw compressor has rotors that look like screws. The most common type has two dissimilar and complementary cylindrical rotors with helical grooves. These compressors are sometimes referred to as being of the "twin-screw" type and the following discussion applies only to such machines.

The screw compressor has some indigenous features that are very desirable in the compressor world: simplicity, ruggedness, compactness, smoothness, endurance. The rapid growth of the number of compressors manufactured provides solid proof that this relatively young type of machine has come to stay.

The advantages that come from a purely rotary motion combined with the absence of valves are, however, to a certain extent off-set by the strong relationship between rotor quality and performance. The key to success in this field is the ability to get "good" rotors at a reasonable cost. Most screw compressor manufacturers make their own rotors, but an increasing number prefer to obtain the rotors from outside. Sometimes they purchase the rotors from several different rotor manufacturers. In that situation a very natural question is: what constitutes a "good" rotor?

It is much easier to ask the question than to come up with an answer. As in many other cases, we could start with: "that depends...", but in order to make this discussion more specific we will in the following discuss rotor sets for oil-flooded screw compressors only. It is for that application that most screw rotors are being used and the need for some sort of quality norm is most pressing.

Naturally, the performance of a screw compressor is not only related to the quality of the rotors. As the inside of the rotor housing also takes part in the sealing and "breathing" process, proper tolerances have to be applied to all components that affect those processes.

In this context we cannot, however, elaborate much further on that theme. With the term "sealing qualities" we will here mean the ability of the rotors to prevent leakage in the mesh, and when running qualities and contact pattern are discussed, we will assume that the rotors are mounted in a "perfect" housing.

2 BASIC CONSIDERATIONS

In all screw compressors the rotors work primarily as pumping members, but in oil-flooded (timing-gear-less) compressors, certain parts of the rotor flanks have to assume the tasks that in dry screw compressor are performed by the timing gears, i.e. maintain the proper relative motion between the rotors.

Thus, when evaluating the quality of a set of non-timed rotors, proper attention should be paid to these two aspects:
- ability to seal, and
- ability to work as gears.

The coupling between rotor quality and performance on one hand, and between quality and cost on the other hand, are the two most important aspects to keep in mind when attempting to design norms for rotor classification. In this general context, "performance" means good efficiency, smooth operation and long life. As long as one is dealing with only one specific compressor, the coupling is normally positive in both respects, in such a way that a higher quality means better performance as well as higher costs.

When comparing compressors that have different geometric proportions, the picture is not so clear. A typical case is when the same basic design appears in models with different rotor length. If the short rotors have the same wrap angle and the same inter-lobe clearances as the long rotors, the short machine will give lower efficiency due to the increased relative leakage between the rotors - and the question is: "Shall we consider these rotors as having the same quality or not?"

Then we have the case (albeit not so common) when for different reasons, fairly large clearances are desired, while at the same time only a small variation in these clearances is acceptable. The rotors would here have to be labelled "high-class" when considering the manufacturing costs involved. (Normally, one specifies tight tolerances only to be able to obtain small clearances.)

We see that two kinds of clearance-related classes could be justified:
- a "clearance class", which would be very useful as a reference value with respect to the sealing qualities of a rotor set with given geometric proportions, and
- a "clearance variation class", which would give the rotor manufacturer useful information.

Another scenario could also be considered: The rotors are made to a certain clearance variation class and the sets classified with respect to the actual clearances measured. This method is often used for prototypes, but in series production the possibilities for this are more limited.

When it comes to deciding how to look upon short versus long rotors, the argument could be brought forward that it would be most fair to let the clearance class as well as the clearance variation class be independent of the rotor length. In this way the manufacturing costs would be more directly related to the class. It would be up to the designer to decide what class to specify in order to obtain the efficiency desired.

The most important gearing aspects on a set of rotors are that the operation should be smooth and quiet and that there should be no wear on the contacting surfaces (and, of course, no seizure). Basically, the smoothness of operation is connected with how well the rotors perform their task as timing gears, while the general mechanical soundness depends on the size and location of the contacting areas. This points to the need for two gearing-related quality classes, which we could call:
- "timing-gear class", and
- "contact pattern class".

The conclusion we can draw from this general discussion is that there should be different norms for different functions. This would mean that the same set of rotors could

belong to different classes in different respects, something that would help in the general striving for "optimum quality". That which is "good enough" can refer to quite different properties in different applications.

3 SEALING

3.1 Sealing line

The ability to seal is a function of the clearance between the flanks, which in its turn is dependent on the whole surface of the basic screw rotor.

The so-called "sealing line" is a curve in space where this sealing takes place. As the rotors rotate, the sealing line moves axially in the direction from inlet to discharge. This sealing line, of fundamental importance in screw rotor technology, can be seen in Figure 1.

3.2 Leakage areas

The clearances along the sealing line form a leakage area and the sealing quality of the rotor pair is to a very large extent given by the size of that area. Thus, for classification purposes it would be appropriate to relate the sealing quality class ("clearance class") to this leakage area. It must, however, be possible to obtain this area in a reasonably simple way and one must be able to compare rotor sets of different sizes and shapes in a reasonably fair way.

Behind the word "reasonable" is the recognition that what actually takes place inside the compressor is a very complex affair. Different areas of the rotors are engaged in the sealing contact as pressures, temperatures and oil content in the gas vary. For instance, in a rotor set where the male rotor has five lobes and the female rotor seven, there will be 35 different lobe-groove combinations possible. If all lobes and grooves are different, if the rotors are tapered and if there is a run-out of the rotor surface as related to the bearing surfaces, then the picture is truly complex.

To complicate things further, the different parts of the sealing line do not have the same "sealing efficiency" and if we would try to account for all this, we would probably not be able to find our way out.

3.3 Checking methods

If a norm shall be of any value, it must be possible to perform the checking in a way which can be universally accepted. Today, there are two basic methods being employed for rotor quality control - feeler gauge measurements in a "pairing stand" and coordinate measuring machine (CMM) checking. Neither one of these methods is very practical for series production on a large scale, which is why there is a need for an efficient and reasonably accurate machine that can ascertain the sealing qualities of a set of rotors in an automatic way. Most likely, such a machine would have to be calibrated against some more "basic" values.

A way to obtain such "more basic values" could be to use a combination of the pairing stand method and the CMM method. Both methods use the fundamental idea that if the interlobe clearances can be obtained at well defined places - identification points (ID-points) - along the sealing line, then the task of finding an average leakage area (corresponding to an average interlobe clearance) is reduced to simple arithmetic. Figure 2 shows how this can be done.

The number of ID-points to use depends on the accuracy desired, but since there are inescapable uncertainties built into both methods, it does not pay to go to any extremes.

3.4 Pairing-stand measuring

In the pairing stand, the rotors should be checked at their nominal center distance and with contact on the actual "drive side". For very small rotors, checking at an increased center distance can be considered, followed by a recalculation of the figures obtained to nominal center distance. In all instances, feeler gauge measuring of screw rotor sets requires skill and good judgement.

Measurements would have to be made for several mesh combinations and at both ends of the rotors. From these data, the average clearance for each ID-point can be calculated.

If the number of check points is sufficiently large and the points well distributed along the sealing line, the arithmetic mean value of the (averaged) individual clearances will give a value that can be useful for classification of the rotor set with respect to sealing quality.

3.5 CMM measuring

When using a CMM for these measurements, the method would have to be somewhat different. A practical way is to first mount the rotor set in the pairing stand and observe where the rotors make contact. When checked in the CMM, these contact areas should be used as datum for the flanks in the rotational direction. The actual x, y, and z coordinates are found for the same ID-points on each rotor as those used for the feeler gauge checking. The distance from each measured point to the surface of an imagined zero-clearance rotor would then represent a clearance in the case when there had been a zero-clearance mating rotor. By adding these kinds of "clearances" for each rotor, the total interlobe clearance for the set at that particular ID-point can be obtained.

Preferably these measurements should be

made in all the grooves at both ends of the rotor. Thereafter the average interlobe clearance can be calculated as before.

4 GEARING

4.1 Angular motion transfer

When one rotor is driven with a constant angular velocity, the other rotor should, through the mesh contact, be given its own specific angular velocity, which also should be constant. If the rotors have dividing errors then, obviously, this cannot be the case. There are also other kinds of errors that will have the same effect.

Ideally, the quality of the rotors working as timing gears should be checked in an apparatus which resembles a machine for checking gears by single flank rolling. (1). Contact should be maintained between the actual contacting surfaces of the flanks for the drive mode in question, and the deviations from true rolling are registered. However, this would require equipment with a degree of sophistication that many rotor manufacturers could not justify. It would be very desirable to find a way to get at least an indication of the timing-gear qualities.

Something that could be used as an indicator is the variation in backlash noted when checking a rotor set. As dividing errors and variation in depth between the different grooves will create a rough-running set of rotors - and the same errors also show up as a variation in backlash - there exists a sufficiently strong coupling so that this backlash variation can be used as a base for a classification with respect to "timing-gear quality".

4.2 Contact pattern

What is normally required of screw rotors is that they shall give long and dependable service. As this is a very important aspect, there should be some norms by which the quality could be checked also in this respect.

The reliability and longevity of the rotors has much to do with what is often referred to as "contact pattern". The rotor profile and the clearance distribution shall be designed in such a way that certain "drive bands" are created, which shall be wide enough to be able to carry the load from the torque transfer. Also, if the contact takes place far outside that design contact area, there can be a definite risk of mechanical problems. Figure 3 shows typical contact areas for male- and female-rotor-driven compressors.

This means that the quality norms should also contain something that has to do with the contact pattern. By contact pattern in this context would be meant the actual location of the contact, radially as well as axially on the flanks. Also the size of the contacting areas and to a certain extent the surface finish in those areas would have to be included in these norms.

This is clearly a case when good judgement must come into the picture. Even if it will be practically impossible to create absolutely "hard" norms for these qualities, the contact pattern aspects are too important to be left out. Something like "contact pattern evaluation guidelines" could be issued which, in the hands of an experienced inspector, could still serve the purpose.

5 CLASSES AND TOLERANCES

5.1 Guiding tolerances and classifying tolerances

There is a direct connection between the complex form of a screw rotor and the complexity of the manufacturing method. A number of operations have to be performed before the final shape of the rotor is obtained.

In the most common case the shape of the cutter blade is copied from a template. Errors in the form of this template are transferred directly to the blade and additional errors are also likely to be introduced in the process. Thereafter, errors in the rigging of the rotor cutting machine, coupled with deficiencies in the accuracy of the machine - inherent or caused by wear and temperature deformations - will further aggravate the situation. Theoretically, every setting of the machines used in the process as well as every machined dimension should be affixed a tolerance.

If all the errors that could be allowed according to these tolerances would go in the same direction, the result would be a rotor which is intolerably out of shape. Fortunately, the statistical outcome looks much better. As there are so many operations involved in the process of making a rotor, many of the errors tend to neutralize each other. To make this more likely, all tolerances should be of the symmetric type and one should really aim at the center of each tolerance field. (2).

Still, when the demands on the final product are as high as in the case of screw rotors, it is common that final adjustments have to be made after test-machining of a set. Unless this check reveals some obvious rigging errors, it is the form of the tool that is touched up.

This points to the fact that it is not possible to create the different quality classes for screw rotors simply by specifying tolerances for all the different steps of the operation. Those tolerances would have to be looked upon as guiding tolerances, while the classifying tolerances are the ones to be considered for the finished product - in this case the rotor set. (It would be possible to design classifying norms for individual rotors also, but that would be even more

difficult - which is why we probably should not burden ourselves with such thoughts at this stage.)

5.2 Tolerances and size

When screw compressors were first being developed in Sweden about fifty years ago, it was natural to apply "normal" tolerances to all components in the machine - and "normal" in Sweden meant ISO- tolerances. According to this, for instance, the root diameters of the rotors were made with a tolerance basically in agreement with the ISO-tolerance h8. (3). (For oil-flooded compressors it was later tightened to h7.)

Most rotors in those days were of medium size (around 200 mm in diameter) and these tolerances appeared to be very appropriate. They corresponded fairly well to what could be achieved with a good machine and careful operation. There were, however, a few early attempts to develop also some very small compressors. That those attempts failed, can to a high degree be traced back to the fact that the ISO-tolerances were not "linear enough". In other words, the relative clearances given by these tolerances turned out to be too large to give the machines an acceptable efficiency. The really large compressors, on the other hand, turned out to be quite good performers - but with growing size, it became increasingly more difficult to make the rotors to the tolerances specified.

The small screw compressor has now come into the picture in a very definite way. (By "small" we normally mean something below 100 mm in diameter.) In many cases the "normal" ISO-tolerance class has to be tightened by a couple of steps for these machines to be viable products in the market place.

It appears to be appropriate that the tolerancing system for screw compressors is revised so that, when a machine is scaled up and down, one does not have to "jump" between the tolerance classes.

5.3 Tolerances tailored for screw compressors

At Svenska Rotor Maskiner (SRM) in Sweden, and at some of SRM's licensees in various parts of the world, a new tolerancing system has been used for some time on a trial basis. This new system incorporates much of what has been discussed above.

The size of the tolerance field is more directly proportional to the dimension in question. Also, in this new system all tolerances applied to the rotors are based on the center distance instead of on the actual dimension. This simplifies the tolerancing and at the same time it is in good agreement with the laws of nature. (Rotor interference due to excessive temperature, for instance, is a function of the center distance.)

5.4 Tolerance classes tailored for screw rotors

When this field was studied at SRM, it was felt that there was a need for more diversification, which is why the tentative screw tolerance classes 1, 2 and 3 were created. Very soon after this system had been launched, however, there appeared to be a need for a class between 1 and 2 - so it was named 1.5. Then, for symmetry, the class 2.5 was also created.

In principle, class 1 should correspond to what is achievable with good equipment and a somewhat extraordinary effort, class 2 would correspond with the old screw tolerances for medium-sized rotors, while the third class could be appropriate in cases where the demand on performance was not so pronounced.

Figure 4 shows how these tentative screw tolerances differ from the old ones and from the ISO-tolerances. It can be noted that when the center distance goes below 100 mm this new system calls for a gradual tightening of the tolerances - in line with the discussion in the foregoing. The tolerance field obtained in this way could be regarded as basic, and different fractions or multiples of it could be used for different dimensions on the rotors.

6. CLASSES AND FUNCTION

If we assume that we had norms so that we could specify the quality of a set of rotors with respect to sealing, angular motion and contact pattern, we could create different "quality profiles" for different applications.

For instance, small, male-rotor-driven compressors running at moderate speeds should have rotors which are rated high for sealing, while the angular motion and contact pattern qualities do not matter so much. On the other hand, a fairly large, female-rotor-driven air compressor for a portable application would require a high rating for angular motion and contact pattern, while the sealing qualities are not quite so important.

This "quality profile" could also be used "backwards" in such a way that weighing factors for the different functions could be derived from it. Something like a combined class could be created, which would provide useful information primarily for the party that is responsible for the performance of the compressors.

In the same manner, the manufacturer would get good guidance from these quality profiles when making up his price lists. In that case, of course, the clearance variation class discussed previously should also be included.

7 SUMMARY

The screw compressor has now reached a high degree of maturity and it appears to be appropriate that norms for the classification of screw rotors are created. Of greatest benefit to the compressor industry would be quality norms for oil-flooded screw compressor rotors.

The following types of classes have been discussed:
- clearance-class, giving information about the sealing qualities of a set of rotors;
- clearance-variation class, giving the manufacturer guidance about cost to produce;
- timing-gear class, having its strongest bearing on the running qualities of a rotor set;
- contact-pattern class, providing a verdict on reliability and longevity.

A new tolerancing system is also suggested, with features that follow more closely the basic characteristics of the screw compressors.

REFERENCES

(1) SMS handbok 515:1987. "Kugg- och snäckväxlar", 1987, 204-209 (Sveriges Mekanstandardisering and Standardiseringskommissionen i Sverige).

(2) MAURITZSON, B.H. "Cost Cutting with Statistical Tolerances". Machine Design, 1971, Nov 25, 78-81.

(3) SMS handbok 504. "Tolerances for linear dimensions", 1983, 60-71 (Sveriges Mekanstandardisering and Standardiseringskommissionen i Sverige).

ACKNOWLEDGEMENTS

The author wishes to thank the management of Svenska Rotor Maskiner AB for their encouragement to prepare this paper. Many persons in the development, manufacturing and quality control departments at SRM have also provided valuable input into this work. Their contributions have been much appreciated.

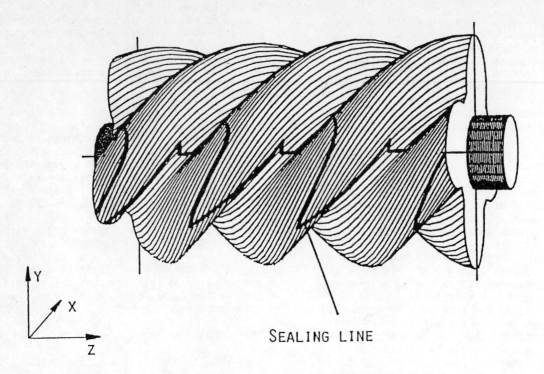

SEALING LINE

Fig 1   Male rotor with sealing line

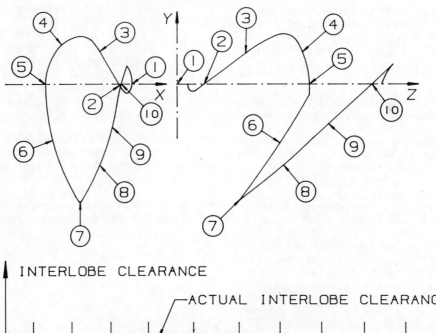

Fig 2   Sealing line with identification points and clearances

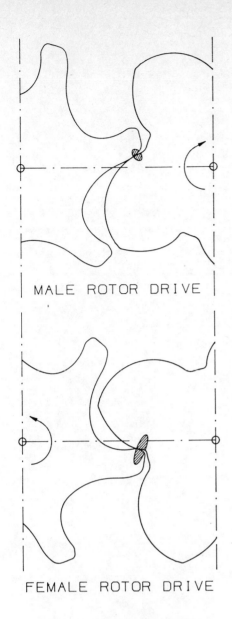

MALE ROTOR DRIVE

FEMALE ROTOR DRIVE

Fig 3   Typical contact areas

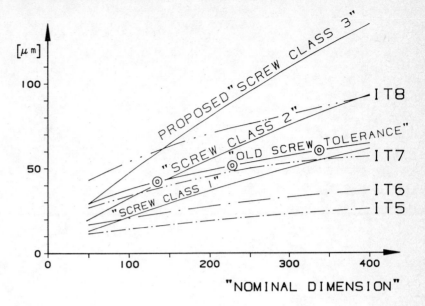

TOLERANCE FIELD

Fig 4   Tolerance field versus size for ISO classes and tentative 'screw-classes'

C390/014

The calculation of flow in regenerative turbomachines by a streamline curvature method

D N ANDREW, MA, PhD
Whittle Laboratory, University of Cambridge

SYNOPSIS The streamline curvature method of calculating the axisymmetric flow through conventional turbomachines is adapted to calculate the non-axisymmetric flow in a thin meridional sector of a regenerative turbomachine. The method provides an important tool for investigating the effects of spanwise variations on machine performance. The incorporation of a mixing model and a model for the friction on the passage walls, in addition to the use of a loss model through the blade row, allows an estimation of the relative importance of these sources of loss for the performance of regenerative machines, and the effect of friction is shown to be significant.

NOTATION

$\frac{D}{Dt}$	substantive derivative
$\frac{dS}{dt}$	entropy generation rate
C_f	skin friction coefficient
F	blade force density
h	spanwise distance
h_0	specific total enthalpy
m	direction tangential to stream-surface in meridional plane
$\dot{m}_c$	circulatory mass flow rate
$\dot{m}_\theta$	tangential mass flow rate
p	static pressure
q	direction along quasi-orthogonal
q_c	circulatory volume flow rate
r	radius from machine axis
r_c	radius of curvature
s	specific entropy
T	thermodynamic temperature
T_x	torque
t	stream-surface thickness
V	velocity
W	relative velocity
W_x	work
α	angle between QO & stream-surface
θ	tangential direction
μ_t	turbulent eddy viscosity
ρ	density
τ	wall shear stress
Φ	dissipation function
ϕ	flow coefficient
Ω	rotational speed

1 INTRODUCTION

Regenerative turbomachines, despite finding a fairly wide range of application in a number of fields, have been much neglected so far as attempts to improve their design and performance are concerned. The basic nature of the recirculating flow pattern in the machines, in which a fluid particle follows an approximately helical-toroidal path through the machine, passing through the same blade row several times as shown in Figure 1, is now firmly established, and a number of authors (e.g. Wilson et al (**1**), Burton (**2**), Abdalla (**3**)) have developed theoretical models to correlate the performance of the machines on the basis of this flow pattern. However, these methods all suffer from two basic defects which severely limit their use as a design tool. The first of these is that they contain empirically derived loss coefficients which are not directly related to design parameters. They therefore give no indication of how the design might be modified to reduce the losses and cannot be used to evaluate designs which differ significantly from those on which the models were based. The second defect is that they are derived from an essentially one-dimensional analysis which considers only a 'mean streamline' and takes no account of spanwise variations. They can consequently offer the designer no guidelines on the choice of a spanwise distribution of blade angle, for instance.

Given this dearth of information it is hardly surprising that most designs of regenerative turbomachine retain a fairly basic geometrical configuration, with simple vanes either machined or cast into the impeller. However, Sixsmith & Altmann (**4**) have shown that significant improvements in performance can be achieved by the addition of a core in the flow channel to direct the circulating flow, together with the provision of aerofoil blades. Yet even with this type of design the efficiency remains on the low side (typically around forty per cent), indicating the continuing presence of large, and largely unexplained, losses associated with the very complex three-dimensional flows encountered in the machines.

In this context, the possibility of calculating the flow in regenerative turbomachines naturally suggests itself, both as a means of predicting the likely effects of design modifications and in the hope of gaining a clearer insight into the origin of some of the losses. The only previous attempt to calculate the flow in regenerative machines was undertaken by Abdalla (**3**), who applied an incompressible version of the Denton (**5**) time-marching scheme to the flow outside the blade row of a regenerative pump with aerofoil blades. However, this took no account of the losses and, because the solution did not include the blade row, suffered from an uncertainty in the correct specification of the boundary conditions. The present method, by contrast, is based on an adaptation of the streamline curvature technique commonly used for axisymmetric throughflow calculations in conventional axial and radial flow turbomachines. Although this does not calculate the details of the blade-to-blade flow there is no difficulty in extending the calculation through a blade row in which the mean flow angles can be specified, and it is also relatively easy to incorporate loss models into the basic scheme.

2 THE BASIC STREAMLINE CURVATURE METHOD

The theory underlying the streamline curvature method has been described by Novak (**6**), and the present method is a modification of that described by Denton (**7**). The principles of the scheme can be summarized as follows.

It is assumed that the flow is reversible and adiabatic, so that entropy and total enthalpy (or rothalpy in a blade row) are constant along streamlines, *i.e.*

$$\frac{Ds}{Dt} = 0 = \frac{Dh_0}{Dt} \tag{1}$$

This means that the energy equation and the streamwise momentum equation are automatically satisfied, and leaves only two momentum equations and the continuity equation to be solved numerically. It is further assumed that the flow is axisymmetric, thus reducing the tangential momentum equation to a statement that, in the absence of any tangential blade forces, the angular momentum is constant along streamlines. Since the flow is axisymmetric, any streamline must be confined to a surface of revolution, and the streamline curvature coordinate system, shown in Figure 1, is defined in terms of the projection of these stream-surfaces in a meridional plane together with a series of quasi-orthogonal lines (QOs) which are roughly perpendicular to them. The position and inclination of each QO is specified at the start of the calculation and at each QO the q-direction (measured along the QO) therefore remains constant throughout the calculation. The flow is solved iteratively, with the position and shape of the stream-surfaces being updated after each iteration, so that the m-direction (the tangent to the stream-surface in the meridional plane) changes as the calculation proceeds. The momentum equation along a QO can be written in the form

$$\frac{\partial}{\partial q}\left(\frac{V_m^2}{2}\right) = \frac{\partial h_0}{\partial q} - T\frac{\partial s}{\partial q} - \frac{1}{2r^2}\frac{\partial}{\partial q}\left(r^2 V_\theta^2\right) - F_q$$
$$\qquad\qquad \text{I} \qquad\quad \text{II} \qquad\quad \text{III} \qquad\qquad \text{IV}$$
$$\qquad + \frac{V_m^2}{r_c}\sin\alpha \;+\; V_m\frac{\partial V_m}{\partial m}\cos\alpha \tag{2}$$
$$\qquad\qquad\qquad \text{V} \qquad\qquad\quad \text{VI}$$

as given by Denton (**7**). The distribution of total enthalpy, entropy and angular momentum along the QO are found by tracing their values along streamlines from the previous QO, allowing terms I – III of equation (2) to be evaluated. Term IV represents the component of blade force in the QO direction, and can usually be neglected if the blades are not leaned, as will be assumed to be the case. The remaining terms V & VI are evaluated from the streamline slope and curvature in the last overall iteration, so that equation (2) can be solved for the variation of meridional velocity along the QO. The absolute value of meridional velocity is then fixed by the continuity condition.

3 ADAPTATION OF THE BASIC EQUATIONS

3.1 Assumptions

As far as the basic streamline curvature equations are concerned, the chief difference between conventional and regenerative turbomachines is the lack of axisymmetry in the latter. However, this difficulty can be overcome by considering only the flow in a small (infinitesimal) sector of the periphery of the machine, and assuming it to be in a region where the tangential pressure gradient is constant and there is no tangential variation of velocity. Such a region may be termed an 'equilibrium' region. In this case, the only tangential variations will be in fluid properties, the tangential derivatives of velocities and flow angles will all be zero, and the flow will still be confined to a series of surfaces of revolution.

Such equilibrium regions take up most of the periphery of regenerative pumps and are also commonly observed to occur in regenerative compressors. However, Andrew (**8**) has shown that they cannot coexist with a tangential variation in density, so that their occurrence in compressors is a reflection of the rather low efficiencies currently achieved. The present method is therefore limited to incompressible flow, and although it could be made compressible to the extent that the density could be calculated from the enthalpy and entropy this would, in general, violate the tangential continuity condition if the tangential derivatives of velocity remained zero. This is not as great a restriction as might at first sight seem to be the case, since the Mach numbers are low and, although the details of the flow are likely to be modified in a non-equilibrium region or where there is a variation in density, the overall picture which emerges (including any insight into the origin of the losses) should not be affected very much.

3.2 Duct Region

The assumption of reversible adiabatic flow is, for the moment, maintained, so that equations (1) still hold. However, this no longer implies that the meridional derivatives of entropy and total enthalpy are zero. The substantive derivative can be expressed as

$$\frac{D}{Dt} \equiv V_m\frac{\partial}{\partial m} + \frac{V_\theta}{r}\frac{\partial}{\partial \theta}$$

Hence

$$\frac{Ds}{Dt} = 0 = V_m\frac{\partial s}{\partial m} + \frac{V_\theta}{r}\frac{\partial s}{\partial \theta} \tag{3}$$

and

$$\frac{Dh_0}{Dt} = 0 = V_m\frac{\partial h_0}{\partial m} + \frac{V_\theta}{r}\frac{\partial h_0}{\partial \theta} \tag{4}$$

For the axisymmetric case with $\partial s/\partial\theta = 0 = \partial h_0/\partial\theta$ it follows that $\partial s/\partial m = 0 = \partial h_0/\partial m$; but in the regenerative case there will, in general, be both a tangential entropy gradient and a tangential enthalpy gradient. Whereas for the conventional scheme entropy and total enthalpy can be found by tracing back along streamlines to find the values on the previous QO, in the present method these values have to be incremented by an amount calculated from the flow velocities and the tangential gradient of the quantity.

This meridional variation in flow properties does not represent a true streamwise variation but is a reflection of a convective process, whereby fluid seen at one QO is convected out of the small sector under consideration by the tangential velocity and replaced by fluid with different properties.

The tangential momentum equation can be expressed as

$$\frac{D}{Dt}\left(rV_\theta\right) = rF_\theta - \frac{1}{\rho}\frac{\partial p}{\partial\theta} \ .$$

When the tangential blade force is zero, as is the case in a duct region, and $\partial V_\theta/\partial\theta = 0$ this reduces to

$$\frac{\partial}{\partial m}\left(rV_\theta\right) = -\frac{1}{\rho V_m}\frac{\partial p}{\partial\theta} \qquad (5)$$

which describes the meridional change in angular momentum due to the effect of the tangential pressure gradient.

3.3 Blade Region

Within a blade region the tangential velocity is fixed by the blade angle and the meridional velocity (as in the conventional scheme), and the meridional change in entropy is found from equation (3) as for a duct region. The entropy may also be incremented to allow for losses.

The evaluation of the total enthalpy needs more care, since the presence of a tangential pressure gradient means that the Euler work equation is not valid in its usual form (relating changes in total enthalpy to those in angular momentum) and rothalpy is not conserved along a streamline. Consider a control volume consisting of a small portion of a stream-surface of thickness t in the computational sector, $d\theta$, with a meridional length dm, as shown in Figure 2. Since the tangential derivatives of velocity are all zero the continuity equation becomes

$$\frac{\partial q_c}{\partial m} = 0$$

where q_c is the 'circulatory volume flow rate' through the control volume, given by

$$q_c = V_m\,tr\,d\theta \qquad (6)$$

The angular momentum equation for the control volume is

$$-T_x = \rho q_c\frac{\partial}{\partial m}\left(rV_\theta\right)dm + r\frac{\partial p}{\partial\theta}d\theta\,(t\,dm) \qquad (7)$$

where T_x is the torque exerted *on* the blades by the fluid in the control volume. The steady flow energy equation for the control volume for adiabatic flow is

$$-W_x = \rho q_c\frac{\partial h_0}{\partial m}dm + \rho V_\theta t\,dm\,.\,\frac{\partial h_0}{\partial\theta}d\theta \qquad (8)$$

where W_x is the work done on the blades by the fluid in the control volume. Clearly,

$$W_x = T_x\Omega \qquad (9)$$

Ω being the rotational speed, so that equations (6) – (9) can be combined to give

$$\frac{\partial h_0}{\partial m} = \Omega\frac{\partial}{\partial m}\left(rV_\theta\right) + \frac{\Omega}{V_m}\frac{1}{\rho}\frac{\partial p}{\partial\theta} - \frac{V_\theta}{rV_m}\frac{\partial h_0}{\partial\theta} \qquad (10)$$

The first term on the right hand side of this equation is the normal 'Euler' work term, while the third term is the convective term which would result from assuming the substantive derivative of rothalpy to be zero (there is no tangential derivative of angular momentum). The middle term is an extra term arising form the torque exerted on the blades due to the tangential pressure gradient. For the machine as a whole this makes no contribution to the net torque on the rotor since there is an equal and opposite torque across the stripper between the exit and inlet ports; but it is significant for the calculation of the flow in a single sector of the machine.

The tangential enthalpy gradient can be related to the pressure and entropy gradients by the thermodynamic relation

$$\frac{\partial h_0}{\partial\theta} = \frac{\partial h}{\partial\theta} = T\frac{\partial s}{\partial\theta} + \frac{1}{\rho}\frac{\partial p}{\partial\theta}$$

since $\partial\,(V^2/2)/\partial\theta = 0$. Equations (4) & (10) for the meridional variation of enthalpy in a duct and a blade region can therefore be expressed as

$$\frac{\partial h_0}{\partial m} = -\frac{V_\theta}{rV_m}\left(T\frac{\partial s}{\partial\theta} + \frac{1}{\rho}\frac{\partial p}{\partial\theta}\right) \qquad (4a)$$

and

$$\frac{\partial h_0}{\partial m} = \Omega\frac{\partial}{\partial m}\left(rV_\theta\right) - \frac{W_\theta}{rV_m}\frac{1}{\rho}\frac{\partial p}{\partial\theta} - \frac{V_\theta}{rV_m}T\frac{\partial s}{\partial\theta} \qquad (10a)$$

4 IMPLEMENTATION

4.1 Computational Domain

Provided that the tangential pressure and entropy gradients and the conditions on the first QO are known, equations (3), (4a), (5), & (10a) together with the blade angles can be used to calculate the values of s, h_0 & rV_θ on each QO, and hence the basic streamline curvature equation (2) (which is unaffected by the tangential gradients of fluid properties) can be solved. However, the net throughflow is in a tangential direction and there is no 'inlet' or 'exit' in the meridional plane. This is illustrated in Figure 3, which shows a meridional section and in which the net throughflow is perpendicular to the plane of the figure. For the purposes of the calculation, therefore, the meridional plane has to be split at some arbitrary QO which then becomes both the first and last QO in the computational domain, as shown in Figure 3. To ensure that the streamline curvature terms are correctly evaluated in the region of the computational boundary they are calculated using a slightly larger domain which includes a small overlap.

At the end of each iteration the meridional velocity on the

first QO is set equal to that on the last QO, and the angular momentum and gradients of total enthalpy and entropy in the QO direction are are also adjusted to match across the boundary of the computational domain, though with some relaxation. The levels of entropy and total enthalpy are not adjusted, however, so that the total amount of entropy and total enthalpy convected into the computational domain at the first QO is the same for each iteration.

The meridional (i.e. circulatory) mass flow rate is set at the start of the calculation and initial guesses are made for the tangential entropy and pressure gradients. These gradients are then adjusted as the calculation proceeds until the levels of enthalpy and entropy on the first and last QOs are equal. Thus it is the meridional mass flow rate and the rotational speed which are set at the start of the calculation, and the overall volume flow rate and pressure gradient for this condition are determined as part of the calculation.

4.2 Mixing

The tangential entropy gradient is related to the tangential mass flow rate, $\dot{m}_\theta$, and the rate of entropy generation by the equation

$$\dot{m}_\theta \frac{\partial s}{\partial \theta} \, d\theta = \frac{dS}{dt}$$

where dS/dt is the rate of entropy generation in the computational sector, which is related to the losses in the flow, being zero where there are no losses. In general, the tangential mass flow rate and entropy generation will be different on each stream-surface, so that, in the absence of any mixing, the tangential entropy gradient will also differ from stream-surface to stream-surface.

This is clearly unrealistic in practice, since the large amount of mixing which does occur in regenerative machines means that spanwise variations in properties will reach an equilibrium (i.e. the tangential derivatives of fluid properties will be uniform) in an equilibrium region. In order to allow a uniform tangential entropy gradient to be applied, therefore, a simple mixing model is incorporated. This has the effect that, between each QO, a specified proportion of the entropy, total enthalpy and angular momentum are exchanged between adjacent stream-surfaces.

Although fairly crude, this model ensures that energy and momentum are conserved across the span. It can be interpreted in terms of turbulent shear forces and heat transfer between adjacent streamlines, and the specified proportion to be exchanged can be related to a mean turbulent eddy viscosity. Since entropy is conserved there is no loss associated with the mixing model itself, and the contribution made to the overall loss by viscous dissipation can therefore be examined independently.

5 LOSS MODELS

At present, three sources of entropy generation can be included in the scheme, as outlined below.

5.1 Blade Losses

As in the original Denton scheme (7), a spanwise distribution of loss coefficients can be specified for each QO within a blade region. In the results to be presented below losses have been specified to be distributed through the blade row so that the spanwise distribution of loss at exit from the row is roughly equivalent to that measured by Andrew (8) in a stationary rig modelling the flow inside a regenerative machine of the same geometry as that used in the calculations. The specification was identical for each of the cases described, and represents the total loss included in the blade row: neither of the other two models were applied to the flow in the blade region.

5.2 Mixing Losses

Any turbulent mixing process must have some dissipation associated with it, and in the present method this is assumed to arise purely from the spanwise velocity gradients in the same way that the mixing itself was assumed to be associated purely with spanwise variations. For such a case, the mean value of the mechanical dissipation function between two streamlines can be estimated to be

$$\Phi = \mu_t \left\{ \left(\frac{\Delta V_m}{\Delta h}\right)^2 + \left(\frac{\Delta V_\theta}{\Delta h}\right)^2 \right\}$$

where μ_t is a turbulent eddy viscosity, Δh is the spanwise distance between the streamlines and ΔV is the velocity difference between the streamlines. The entropy generation is then calculated from

$$\rho T \frac{Ds}{Dt} = \Phi$$

and the value on each streamline altered accordingly relative to the value calculated from conditions on the previous QO. The value of μ_t is specified independently of the amount of mixing actually used in the calculation, but it can be related to the mixing coefficient used and its value is usually set to be consistent with the amount of mixing, or else set to zero.

5.3 Wall Friction

The effect of wall friction is included by specifying a skin friction coefficient based on the velocity on the wall stream-surface, allowing the wall shear stress to be evaluated. This shear stress has two effects: its tangential component has to be included in the tangential momentum equation; and its presence also leads to entropy generation on the wall streamline. The shear stress is given by

$$\tau = C_f \tfrac{1}{2} \rho V^2$$

and its direction is opposite to that of the velocity. The tangential component is therefore given by

$$\tau_\theta = -\frac{C_f}{2} \rho V V_\theta$$

Applying this to a control volume extending from the wall to include half the circulatory mass flow between the wall and the adjacent stream-surface, and assuming the velocities and fluid properties to be uniform at entry and exit to this control volume, the tangential momentum equation becomes

$$\frac{\partial}{\partial m}\left(rV_\theta\right) = \frac{\tau_\theta \, r^2 \, d\theta}{\tfrac{1}{2} \, \dot{m}_c} - \frac{1}{\rho V_m} \frac{\partial p}{\partial \theta}$$

where $\dot{m}_c$ is the circulatory mass flow between the wall stream-surface and the stream-surface adjacent to it.

The entropy generation due to the shear stress is taken to be

$$T \frac{dS}{dt} = \tau V \times \text{wall area}$$

which, when averaged over the same control volume as the tangential shear stress, gives the dissipation function on the wall stream-surface to be

$$\Phi = C_f \, \rho V^3 \, \frac{\rho V_m r \, d\theta}{\dot{m}_c}$$

6 SAMPLE RESULTS

6.1 Performance Coefficient

Because neither the pressure gradient nor the throughflow can be specified independently in the present version of the program, the following results will be compared by means of the performance coefficient defined by Andrew (**8**). This is essentially a non-dimensional pressure gradient which characterizes the effectiveness of a given geometry of regenerative turbomachine independently of the operating point, making use of the fact that, provided that Coriolis and centrifugal effects have a small impact on the overall performance, the equilibrium flow pattern is virtually independent of the blade speed. For a given geometry, the overall performance coefficient of a machine is proportional to

$$\frac{1}{\rho \, \Omega^2 (1 - \phi)^2} \frac{\partial p}{\partial \theta}$$

where ϕ is the flow coefficient (defined as the actual flow rate divided by that which would be achieved if the fluid in the channel rotated with angular velocity Ω). The performance coefficient would be infinite if there were no losses.

6.2 Blade Loss Only Included

Figure 4 shows contours of the meridional velocity and relative yaw angle ($\tan^{-1} (W_\theta/V_m)$) for the case with the wall friction and dissipation losses set to zero. The blade region is marked and the dotted line shows the computational boundary. The meridional flow is anticlockwise, radially outward through the blades. Although there is a clear difference in the mean value of meridional velocity between the upper and lower parts of the figure, due to the difference in radius giving an effectively larger flow area, the spanwise variations are relatively small. Similarly, although there is a certain amount of skewing in the flow due to the specified blade angles, this is nowhere very great. It is worth noting that, as expected, the meridional variation in flow angle is greater where the meridional velocity is less. The performance coefficient for this case was 38.8, which is about twenty per cent larger than that measured in the stationary rig on which the loss specification was based. This difference is thought to be due mainly to Coriolis and centrifugal effects, the wall friction being very low in the experiment. The losses are equivalent to an overall blade loss coefficient of about 0.7, based on exit dynamic head, which is very large by the standards of conventional turbomachines. It is relatively small compared to values assumed in correlations for regenerative machines, however, and since it is based on measurements this calculation can reasonably be used as a datum for comparing the effects of wall friction and mixing losses.

6.3 Effect of Wall Friction and Mixing Losses

There are no measurements of the amount of mixing present in regenerative turbomachines, so the selection of a suitable mixing coefficient has to be somewhat arbitrary. Experience has shown that the level of mixing has little effect on the performance coefficient when dissipation is not included. In this case, although the spanwise entropy and enthalpy gradients show a large dependence on mixing level, the mixing has very little influence on the velocities, and a variation of more than two orders of magnitude in mixing level only changed the performance coefficient by three per cent.

However, if the significance of the mixing loss is to be assessed, a reasonable estimate must be made of the mixing coefficient. Gallimore & Cumpsty (**9**) have measured mixing levels in an axial flow compressor which are similar to those in a two-dimensional wake, and it seems reasonable to suppose that a similar level might be found in regenerative machines. Applying a mixing loss calculated on this basis to a calculation for the same geometry and blade loss as described above gave a performance coefficient of 37.8, a drop of about two and a half per cent on the previous value.

The choice of skin friction coefficient is similarly problematic, and a number of different values have been tried. The results of these, with and without the mixing loss included, are tabulated in Table 1. 0.05 was the highest value of skin friction coefficient for which the program could be made to converge, and examination of the unconverged solutions for higher values suggested that the problem was probably due to an attempt by the flow to separate.

Table 1. Variation of Performance Coefficient with Skin Friction Coefficient

	Performance Coefficient	
C_f	No Mixing Loss	Mixing Loss Included
0.000	38.8	37.8
0.001	36.4	35.4
0.010	24.4	23.4
0.030	15.7	14.4
0.050	12.5	11.0

Figure 5 shows the contours of meridional velocity and relative yaw angle for the case with $C_f = 0.05$ and the mixing loss included. While the influence of the friction in slowing down the flow near the walls is evident right around the channel, there is a very marked spanwise velocity gradient at the inner radii, just before the leading edge of the blade. There is also a very large amount of skewing near the walls, particularly near the trailing edge. It is clear, however, from the performance coefficients, that this has not greatly increased the significance of the mixing loss, as it might have been expected to. Contours of entropy generation rate are shown in Figure 6, and it is apparent from these that, apart from the blades, the most significant regions for loss generation are the walls near to the trailing and leading edges of the blades, where the magnitude of the tangential velocity is high (positive and negative, respectively).

6.4 Comparison with Experiment

A machine with this geometry has been tested as a pump running at low speed in water and the tangential pressure gradient found to be constant over a large part of the periphery, indicating an equilibrium flow, as expected. The largest value of performance coefficient deduced from the pressure gradient was 4.56, which is substantially below the lowest value predicted by the calculations, despite the extremely large values of skin friction coefficient used. The wall surface in the machine was a fairly rough casting, so a high value of skin friction coefficient might be expected, but this is unlikely to exceed 0.007, and although the coefficient is based on the wall velocity (rather than the mean) this is never less than half the mean and cannot really compensate for a difference of nearly an order of magnitude in the coefficient.

It is clear, therefore, that the calculation method is not yet capable of resolving the large losses which occur in regenerative machines. One possible reason for this is that the use of a uniform grid spacing and uniform mixing across the span, together with such a simple friction model, means that friction effects cannot be expected to be resolved with great accuracy. In particular, a tendency for the flow to separate, causing large losses, at lower skin friction coefficients may have been artificially suppressed by the model. Another possibility, which cannot be discounted, is the existence of a significant source of loss which is not modelled in the program. Potential candidates might include tip clearance and leakage losses (which would reduce the experimentally measured flow coefficient).

7 CONCLUSIONS

The streamline curvature method can be adapted with little difficulty to calculate the flow in an equilibrium region of a regenerative turbomachine. Although such a scheme cannot yet produce reliable, quantitative predictions of the performance of a machine, it does allow the designer to assess, for the first time, the likely effects of parameters such as the spanwise variation in blade angle on the overall performance. The poor performance of regenerative machines at present appears to be due, at least in part, to significant friction effects.

ACKNOWLEDGEMENTS

The author would like to express his thanks to the Science and Engineering Research Council for financial support and to CompAir Reavell Ltd for financial support and permission to publish this work.

REFERENCES

1 **Wilson, W.A., Santalo, M.A.** and **Oelrich, J.A.** A Theory of the Fluid Dynamic Mechanism of Regenerative Pumps. *Trans. ASME*, November 1955, vol. 77, pp. 1303-1311.

2 **Burton, J.D.** The Prediction and Improvement of Regenerative Turbo-Machine Performance. BHRA Members Conference, Cranfield, 1967 (in *Rotodynamic Pump Research, Vol. II*. Cranfield: BHRA, 1974).

3 **Abdalla, H.M.M.** A Theoretical and Experimental Investigation of the Regenerative Pump with Aerofoil Blades. Ph.D. thesis, Applied Mechanics Branch, Royal Military College of Science, Shrivenham, September 1981.

4 **Sixsmith, H.** and **Altmann, H.** A Regenerative Compressor. *Trans. ASME*, Series B, J. Eng. Ind., August 1977, vol. 99, pp. 637-647.

5 **Denton, J.D.** A Time Marching Method for Two and Three Dimensional Blade to Blade Flows. ARC R & M No. 3775, 1975

6 **Novak, R.A.** Streamline Curvature Computing Procedures for Fluid-Flow Problems. *Trans. ASME*, Series A, J. Eng. Power, October 1967, vol. 89, pp. 478-490.

7 **Denton, J.D.** Throughflow Calculations for Transonic Axial Flow Turbines. *Trans. ASME*, J. Eng. Power, April 1978, vol. 100, pp. 212-218.

8 **Andrew, D.N.** Flow in Regenerative Compressors with Aerofoil Blading. Ph.D. dissertation, Cambridge University, 1987.

9 **Gallimore, S.J.** and **Cumpsty, N.A.** Spanwise Mixing in Multistage Axial Flow Compressors: Part I— Experimental Investigation. *Trans. ASME*, J. Turbomachinery, July 1986, vol. 108, pp. 2-9.

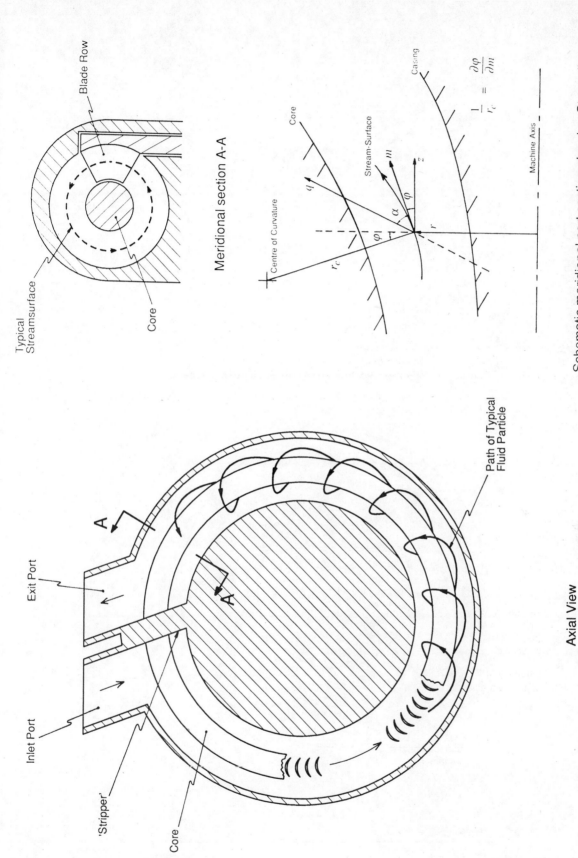

Blade Row

Typical
Streamsurface

Core

Meridional section A-A

Core

Stream-Surface

Centre of Curvature

Casing

$$\frac{1}{r_c} = \frac{\partial \varphi}{\partial m}$$

Machine Axis

Schematic meridional part section showing Streamline
Curvature Coordinate System

Exit Port

Inlet Port

'Stripper'

Core

Path of Typical
Fluid Particle

Axial View

Fig 1   Geometry and operation of a typical regenerative compressor,
showing the streamline curvature coordinate system (not to scale)

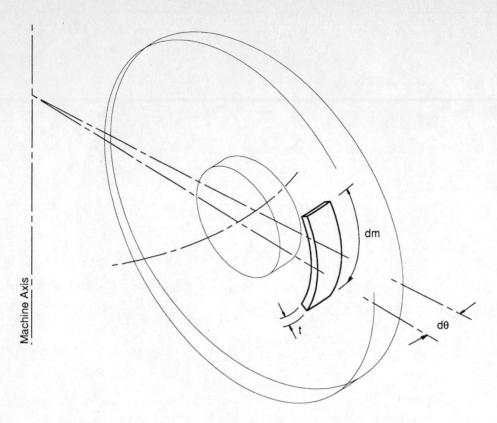

Fig 2   Control volume for considering changes in enthalpy in a blade row

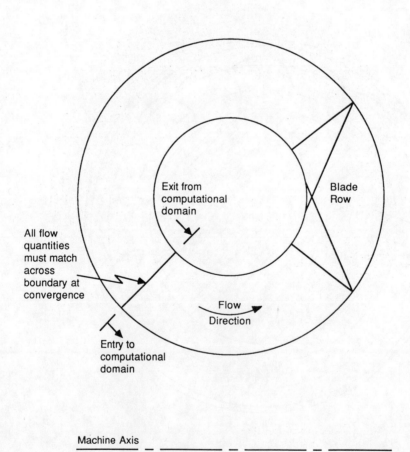

Fig 3   Meridional view of the computational domain, showing the
computational boundary which forms the first QO (at entry to
domain) and the last QO (at exit)

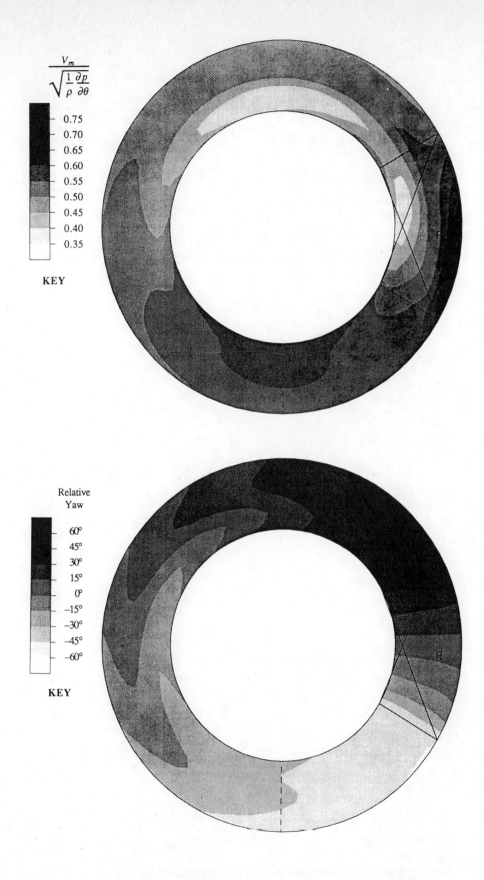

Fig 4   Contours of meridional velocity and relative yaw angle —
         C_f = 0.000; no mixing losses

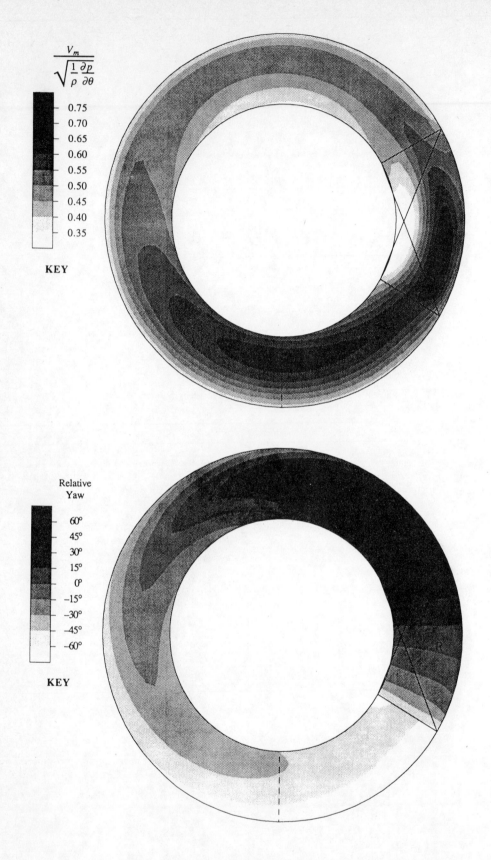

$$\frac{V_m}{\sqrt{\frac{1}{\rho}\frac{\partial p}{\partial \theta}}}$$

0.75
0.70
0.65
0.60
0.55
0.50
0.45
0.40
0.35

KEY

Relative
Yaw

60°
45°
30°
15°
0°
−15°
−30°
−45°
−60°

KEY

Fig 5   Contours of meridional velocity and relative yaw angle —
C_f = 0.050; mixing loss included

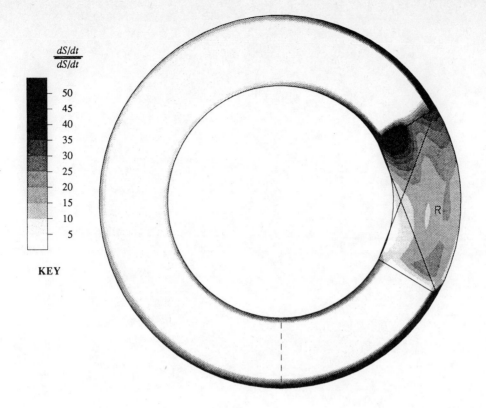

Fig 6   Contours of entropy generation per unit volume (non-dimensionalized with respect to mean over whole sector) — C_f = 0.050; mixing loss included

Geometrical optimization of sliding vane compressors

A B TRAMSCHEK, BSc, PhD, CEng, MIMechE, FInstR and **K T OOI**, BEng
Department of Mechanical and Process Engineering, University of Strathclyde, Glasgow

SYNOPSIS This paper presents results of analytical studies intended to assist in the production of sliding vane air compressors. By linking a mathematical model with an optimization algorithm it was possible to predict which combination of 11 geometrical variables would produce for a given machine capacity the maximum air throughput per unit of power input. A constrained multi-variable direct search technique was used in which the 11 geometric variables and a mixture of 27 explicit and implicit constraints were accommodated. Theoretical studies on an 8 radially disposed vane compressor indicated that an 8% improvement in specific capacity could be achieved.

NOTATION

Cs	mm	Sealing arc clearance
Ws	mm	Width of the slot
F_1		Fraction of frictional energy transfer to air phase
F_2		Fraction of frictional energy transfer to oil liquid phase
FAD	l/s	Free air delivery under the atmospheric condition
FLOWL	l/s	Difference between induced air and the discharged air
FOPT	l/kWs	Objective function
h	kJ/kg	Enthalpy
Hv	mm	Height of the vane
L, H		Lower and upper of constraints
Ld, Ls	mm	Axial length of the discharge and suctoin ports
Lr	mm	Length of the rotor–stator unit
Lv	mm	Length of the vanes
m	kg	mass flow
Nv		Number of vanes
P	N/m²	Pressure
Pfr	kW	Frictional dissipation of the sliding vane
Pi	kW	Indicated power
Pt	kW	Total Power ie the sum of the Pi and Pfr
Q	J	Heat transfer
Rr	mm	Rotor radius
Rs	mm	Stator radius
Rt	mm	Radius of Vane tip
Sd	mm	Rotor shaft diameter
T	K	Temperature
TDC		Top dead centre
tv		Vane thickness
v	m³/kg	specific volume
ε	mm	Offset between the centres of rotor and stator
β1	°	Suction port opening angle, w.r.t. TDC
β2	°	Suction port closing angle, w.r.t. TDC
β3	°	Discharge port opening angle, w.r.t. TDC
β4	°	Discharge port closing angle, w.r.t TDC
Θ	°	Angular position

Subscripts

a	air
c	cell
d	down stream
i	in
o	out
E	explicit
G	geometrical
I	implicit
u	up stream
ov	oil vapour
ol	oil liquid
or	orifice
fr	friction
c	cell
evp	evaporation

Second subscripts

c	convective heat transfer
e	entering
l	leaving

1 INTRODUCTION

Rotary sliding vane compressors are compact, geometrically simple machines which are widely used in the air compression and refrigeration industries. In their simplest form, see figure 1, they comprise a cylindrical rotor mounted between end plates and positioned eccentrically within a circular stator. The rotor has a number of radial slots machined along its length into which closely fitting vanes may be introduced.

When the rotor is spun about its longitudinal axis centrifugal forces cause the vanes to move radially outwards in the slots until the vane tips touch the stator surface. The combined rotary and sliding motions result in the formation of a number of variable volume cavities (cells) whose size depends on the angular positions of a pair of adjacent vanes and the dimensions of the mechanism. Provision of appropriately placed suction and discharge ports allows the device to function as a positive displacement compressor with a built-in volume compression ratio. The overall performance of a given machine depends on a balance of frictional effects (vane tip/stator surface, vane/slot wall, end plates and bearings), compression and cell to cell leakage effects (at both vane tips and flanks), suction and discharge port effects.

Over the years that have elapsed since the basic form of the machine was conceived many experimental and theoretical considerations have contributed to its development. Significant performance improvements were secured by the advent of oil or liquid injection (1) during the compression process. This feature not only reduced frictional effects but also promoted better sealing of the cells formed by the rotor, the stator and the sliding vanes. Oil injection did however necessitate the provision of oil injection and oil separation facilities. Much work has also been done on the identification of compatible materials for use as rotor, stator and sliding vane elements.

This paper illustrates how a theoretical study may be used to predict performance characteristics thus pointing the way to the selection of the most effective combination of design variables and thereby avoiding the need for extensive ad hoc testing. Analysis may also be used to assess what design modifications may be made in the interest of more cost effective manufacture without undue sacrifice of hard won performance improvements.

2 OVERALL STRATEGY

In order to implement the type of study referred to above it was necessary that:-

(a)   A mathematical model of the compressor be developed.

(b)   The model be shown to be capable of predicting the behaviour and performance trends of existing machines.

(c)   A set of size, performance, reliability, economic, manufacturing criteria be defined to which a possible design should conform.

(d)   A specific functional relationship be agreed by which an optimum or 'best' design might be selected.

(e)   A suitable optimization algorithm be chosen and used to identify the optimum design.

(f)   A prototype of the optimum design be manufactured and tested to verify that the predicted performance characteristics are achieved.

Provided that the outcome of steps (a) to (f) is judged to be satisfactory then a manufacturer can decide if he wishes to bring a new product to the market place.

3 MATHEMATICAL MODELLING

The modelling of sliding vane compressors can be seen as part of an overall compressor modelling development. All forms of positive displacement compression machinery were targets for would be modellers, see MacLaren (2), and reciprocating, screw, vane (see references (3,4,5,6,7,8)), rolling piston, scroll and other novel geometrical forms have been studied.

Manufacturers have used modelling to assist them in the production of machines which operate efficiently, reliably and perhaps at higher rotational speeds than may have initially been contemplated. Modelling has benefitted from more than three decades of computer and computational development so that today geometrical, dynamic, stress and both heat transfer and fluid flow effects may be studied with comparative ease.

It should be stated that models should be as simple as possible yet be able to identify significant aspects of any design. This is particularly true as will be demonstrated later when optimization matters are considered.

In the case of the sliding vane compressor a model must relate geometric, dynamic, fluid mechanic and heat transfer effects.

3.1   Geometric considerations

The cell volume V may be expressed as a function of some 12 variables, i.e.

$$V = f(Rs, Rr, \epsilon, Lr, Hv, Ds, tv, Ws, Rt, Nv, Cs, \theta)$$

(1)

A detailed description of the relationship is given by Chang (9) and the meaning of the various terms is illustrated in figure 2.

For the purposes of optimization the vanes are assumed to have semi-circular profile tips where

$$2Rt = tv = Ws \qquad (2)$$

and by implication the vane thickness and slot width are equal.

3.2   Vane dynamics

In a vane dynamic analysis the assumption is made that centrifugal forces cause the vane tip surface to remain in contact with the stator surface. By postulating the existence of a number of vane position modes (9) see figure 3 it is possible to determine the normal contact and friction forces acting upon the vanes, the rotor and the stator and hence determine the friction energy component of the compressor driving power. An optimization analysis is simplified if a Coulomb frictional model is employed but the coefficient of friction used has to be consistent with an equivalent value deducible from hydrodynamic lubrication theory. The vane dynamic analysis depends on the pressure distributions acting on the vane surfaces and must therefore be coupled to the thermodynamic and fluid flow analyses which are needed to calculate the pressure, temperature and phase distributions of the working fluids which occupy a cell volume.

3.3 Thermodynamic processes

In the case of an oil injected air compressor the cells will contain air, oil liquid and oil vapour. The air and oil vapour are considered to behave as a homogeneous mixture and occupy that part of the cell volume not occupied by oil liquid. Thus

$$V_a = V_{ov} = V_c - V_{ol} \qquad (3)$$

The cell pressure P_c is the sum of the partial pressure of the air and the saturation vapour pressure of the oil at a given temperature

$$P_c = P_{ol} = P_a + P_{ov} \qquad (4)$$

Assuming that thermodynamic equilibrium exists between the air and the oil vapour then

$$T_a = T_{ov} \qquad (5)$$

Applying the Law of the Conservation of Energy, the thermodynamic properties of each phases may be expressed by the following differential equations:

for the Air phase :-

$$\frac{dQ_{a.c}}{d\theta} + F_1 \cdot \frac{dQ_{fr}}{d\theta} - \frac{dQ_{evp}}{d\theta}$$

$$- P_a \left(\frac{dV_c}{d\theta} - \frac{dm_{ol}}{d\theta} \cdot v_{ol} + \frac{dm_{evp}}{d\theta} \cdot v_{ol} \right)$$

$$= - \frac{dm_{a.e}}{d\theta} \cdot (h)_{a.e} + \frac{dm_{a.l}}{d\theta} \cdot (h)_{a.l} + \frac{d(mu)_a}{d\theta} \qquad (6)$$

for the liquid oil phase :-

$$\frac{dQ_{ol.c}}{d\theta} + F_2 \cdot \frac{dQ_{fr}}{d\theta} - \left(P_a + P_{ov} \right) \left(\frac{dm_{ol}}{d\theta} \cdot v_{ol} - \frac{dm_{evp}}{d\theta} \cdot v_{ol} \right)$$

$$= - \frac{dm_{ol.e}}{d\theta} \cdot (h)_{ol.e} + \frac{dm_{ol.l}}{d\theta} \cdot (h)_{ol.l} + \frac{d(mu)_{ol}}{d\theta} \qquad (7)$$

for the oil vapour phase :-

$$\frac{dQ_{ov.c}}{d\theta} + \left(1 - F_1 - F_2 \right) \frac{dQ_{fr}}{d\theta} + \frac{dQ_{ovp}}{d\theta} - P_{ov} \left(\frac{dV_c}{d\theta} - \frac{dm_{ol}}{d\theta} \cdot v_{ol} + \frac{dm_{ovp}}{d\theta} \cdot v_{ol} \right)$$

$$= - \frac{dm_{ov.e}}{d\theta} \cdot (h)_{ov.e} + \frac{dm_{ov.l}}{d\theta} \cdot (h)_{ov.l} + \frac{d(mu)_{ov}}{d\theta} \qquad (8)$$

Peterson (10), Smith (11), showed that the presence of oil in this type of machine did not contribute significant internal heat transfer effects. Smith mentioned that the difference between the discharge air temperature and the predicted adiabatic air temperature was caused by after-cooling effects which occurred at the outlet of the discharge port where a highly turbulent air-oil mixture existed.

Comprehensive simulation studies must account for the effects caused by the presence of lubrication oil in the machine. However, in any optimization study, compromise between the necessity for a realistic model and minimal computing time is needed. Some loss of the completeness of the model in representing the real physical system is unavoidable but may be acceptable providing that the adequacy of the model to represent the real system within practical tolerance bounds is maintained.

For the optimization study, a simplified dry model embodying perfect sealing and adiabatic processes was employed and the above equations were reduced to the equation of the air phase alone. Rearranging the temperature and the pressure terms and assuming ideal gas behaviour gives:

$$\frac{dT_c}{dt} = T_c \left(\frac{1}{V_c} \frac{dV_c}{dt} + \frac{1}{P_c} \frac{dP_c}{dt} - \frac{1}{m_c} \frac{dm_c}{dt} \right) \qquad (9)$$

$$\frac{dP_c}{dt} = \frac{1}{V_c} \left(- \gamma P_c \frac{dV_c}{dt} + \gamma R \left(\sum T_i \frac{dm_i}{dt} - T_c \frac{dm_o}{dt} \right) \right) \qquad (10)$$

where P_c, T_c and V_c are cell pressure, temperature and volume respectively. The air mass flow during suction and discharge processes may be obtained by applying the one dimensional compressible flow equation across the flow area assuming that this areas behaves like an orifice, i.e.

$$\dot{m}_{or} = \frac{P_u}{\sqrt{RT_u}} A_{or} \sqrt{ \frac{2\gamma}{\gamma - 1} \left(r^{\frac{2}{\gamma}} - r^{\frac{\gamma+1}{\gamma}} \right) } \qquad (11)$$

where,

$$r = \frac{P_d}{P_u} \qquad (12)$$

Equations (1) and (11) were solved simultaneously and equations (9) and (10) were integrated using Merson's version of a Runge-Kutta integration technique. Figure 4 shows that the agreement between the predicted and measured results (9) was satisfactory.

The simulation study allows the performance of a machine to be assessed and the effects of changing design parameters on the performance may be observed i.e. the free air delivery and the amount of energy consumed. The use of a simulation model together with an optimization algorithm allows the selection of a combination of design parameters which gives an overall optimum performance for a prescribed specification to be achieved. A general optimization study may be represented as follows :-

$$\text{optimise} : FOPT = f(x_i), i = 1,,,,N \qquad (13)$$

N is the number of free variables. In any optimization study, the choice of independent variables must be made with care and parameters which have little influence on the outcome of the optimization should be discarded. Any reduction in the number of independent variables brings benefits by way of a reduction in the number of function evaluations and a reduction in computing time.

subject to :

$$\text{(i)} \quad L_{E_i} \leq E_i \leq H_{E_i} , \quad i = 1,....,N \qquad (14)$$

$$\text{(ii)} \quad L_{G_j} \leq G(x)_j \leq H_{G_j} , \quad j = 1,....,Z \qquad (15)$$

$$\text{(iii)} \quad L_{I_k} \leq I(x)_k \leq H_{I_k} , \quad k = 1,2,3 \qquad (16)$$

Equations 14,15 and 16 represent the constraints which are applied to a problem and their choice is crucial. E_i represents the explicit constraints imposed on the free variables where L_{Ei} and H_{Ei} are the lower and upper limits of the free variables.

$G(x)_j$ are called geometrical constraints in which each constraint is usually a function of one or more of the free variables. They describe geometrical relationships peculiar to the type of design under consideration and ensure that the combination of a particular set of variables yields a practical configuration.

$I(x)_k$ are implicit constraints and represent the outcome which a particular calculation may have to satisfy.

4 OPTIMIZATION TECHNIQUE

The Complex Method used in the present study is a modification of the Simplex optimization technique developed by Spendley et al. (12). In its original form the Simplex technique requires that the regular shape of the Simplexes be maintained. This was found to be a disadvantage particularly when the optimum lies on a surface which is difficult to characterise for example at a narrow valley. The version of the Simplex method which is most popular today results from modifications by Nelder and Mead (13) whereby an irregular Simplex which can adapt itself onto the geometry of the search region is allowed.

However, in their basic forms, neither the original version nor the modified version could handle constraints. In principle any unconstrained optimization technique can be modified to handle a constrained optimization problem by the introduction of penalty functions or barrier functions into the objective function. The constrained optimization thus becomes an unconstrained optimization problem but with a modified objective function. This feature introduces complications especially when the constraints themselves are complicated inequalities and are possibly non-linear. In 1965 M.J. Box (14) introduced the version of the Simplex technique which is called Constrained Simplex or Complex technique which could handle constraints in a much better and simpler way and avoided complicated transformation of the original objective function. The method has been used extensively since its development by Box because of its basic simplicity and adaptability to suit individual optimization problems (15), (16) and (17).

Basically the technique begins by specifying a first Complex which satisfies all the imposed constraints and follows by setting up an additional (K-1) initial Complexes in a pseudo-random manner according to,

$$x_{i,j} = v_j + r_{i,j}(h_j - v_j) \qquad (17)$$

where $x_{i,j}$ is any free variable

$r_{i,j}$ is the pseudo-random number in the interval 0,1.

h_j is the upper limit of the independent variable.

v_j is the lower limit of the independent variable.

K =(N+1), where N is the number of free variables involved in the study.

The search strategy begins by successive comparisons of the objective function values of the Complexes and the worst Complex is rejected by reflecting it through the centroid of the remaining Complexes. This process is repeated until any of the constraints is violated. If an explicit constraint is violated the trial point is moved a small distance inside the boundary of the constraint. If any of the geometrical or implicit constraints have been violated the trial point is moved half way towards the centroid of the remaining complexes.

Convergence is assumed to have occurred when for a specified number of consecutive successful iterations, GAMMA, the objective function at a new point which satisfies all the above conditions lies within a preset value BETA, of the value of optimising function of the best Complex. In the present study, GAMMA is set to 5 and the BETA is set to 0.001 (i.e. about 0.04% of the function value)

5 COMPRESSOR OPTIMIZATION

Compressor designs were optimised for their thermodynamic and mechanical performance under a prescribed operating condition. Thus whilst meeting a required free air delivery the minimum shaft power input was sought and the objective function was chosen to be the throughput divided by the power input to the compressor (l/kWs).

To assist the optimization algorithm at the decision making stage by causing rejection of any design which exhibited unwanted behaviour, a penalty function was introduced into the objective function. The objective function was then modified to be the following expression:-

$$FOPT= FAD/P_{in} - ABS(FLOWL)$$

In the design of a sliding vane compressor for a specified operational condition, some 18 geometric parameters may be identified, these are Rs, Rr, ε, Lr, Nv, Lv, Hv, tv, Rt, Ds, Ws, Cs, β1, β2, Ld, β3, β4 and Sd. If the suction port is sited on the stator circumference, the axial length (Ls) of the port may also be considered. A given design must achieve a specified free air delivery.

The 11 variables which were allowed to vary in present optimization study are:- Rs, Rr, ε, Hv, Lr, β1, β2, β3, β4, Ls and Ld. The number of vanes (Nv) can clearly be varied but optimizations were only performed for specified vane numbers to avoid difficulties encountered with the optimization algorithm in respect of integer variables.

Detail of the various constraints applied during the present study are given in table 1 and 2 and the geometric constraints are explained as follows:-

1. To ensure that there is always a sealing arc existing between the minimum pressure region and the highest pressure region.

2. To ensure that the stator radius is greater than rotor radius.

3. To ensure that the suction port closing angle is greater than its opening angle.

4. To ensure that the discharge port closing angle is greater than its opening angle.

5. To ensure that rotor radius is always greater than the height of the vane, this is obviously necessary since vanes are housed in the slots in the rotor. The the height of the vane was not allowed to be greater than 85% of the radius of the rotor.

6. To ensure that the maximum vane extension is less than 85% of the vane height. The experience of sliding vane compressor manufacturers indicates that greater vane extensions may cause jamming of vanes and may cause instability of vanes in the slots.

7,8. To ensure that for an individual cell there is only one main flow process occurring at a given time.

9,10 To restrict the maximum possible axial length of the discharge or suction ports to a length less than that of the rotor unit.

11. To ensure more positive sealing between the high pressure region and low pressure region of the machine, the sealing arc angle is maintained at an angle greater than a cell angle. This condition ensures that at least one vane will always be present in the sealing arc region.

12,13 To ensure that the absolute values of the arc cosine function is not greater than unity in the calculation of the non-radial vane parameter.

Three implicit constraints were used in the present study:- these were free air delivery, indicated power and the difference between the induced and discharged air mass. Details of the constraints are shown in table 3 and each constraint is explained as follows:-

1. Free air delivery (FAD)
    The design has to meet a specified minimum free air delivery. To prevent excessively large free air deliveries from influencing size considerations an upper constraint was in fact imposed on this item.

2. Indicated power (Pi)
    The indicated power is restricted to a positive value.

3. FLOWL
    This constraint was introduced in order to minimise wasteful computation. It recognises that in a true steady state operation the machine must discharge as much fluid as is drawn in during the suction process. With some combinations of the free variables there was a significant mismatch between the induced and discharge air masses and by introducing this constraint as a penalty function it was possible to reduce the number of thermodynamic cycle, and optimization function evaluations. FLOWL is calculated as the difference between the induced and the discharged air mass.

6 RESULTS AND DISCUSSION

The techniques outlined in the previous sections were applied to three cases:-

CASE 1. An optimization study of a rotary sliding vane compressor having circular-arc rotor-stator geometry and 8 radially disposed vanes under a fixed operating condition.

CASE 2. An optimization study similar to that in case (1) above, but with a compressor having a different number of vanes. The number of vane was varied from 4 to 16.

CASE 3. An optimization study which was similar to that in case (1), but with several different compressor designs each of which described a compressor with 8 vanes of differing angle of vane inclination. This is referred to as the optimization of non-radial vane compressors.

This paper presents the results for CASE 1 and CASES 2 and 3 will be the subject of future papers.

6.1 Sliding vane compressor with 8 vanes

Variations of the parameters of a radial vane machine fitted with 8 vanes were plotted against the successful search number. The latter item being the number of times that the simulation model was used with a particular set of free variables and producing results within all the imposed constraints. The whole process required more than 700 simulation model executions but only 270 lay within the feasible region. The calculations required more than 70 minutes of cpu-time, on VAX-780 computer.

The results have been presented non-dimensionally with respect to the dimension of the first design Complex (an existing design). An examination of figures 5(a) to 5(k) shows that dimensions may increase or decrease.

The optimum values for the stator and rotor radii were smaller than those of the first feasible design see figures 5(a,b). The variation of the rotor-stator centre offset is out of phase with the variation of the length of the rotor-stator unit. This implies that a machine can produce the same output by having a combination of large rotor-stator centre offset and a short machine length or vice-versa.

Variations of the suction and the discharge port positions are shown in figures 5(h,i,j,k). These parameters have a very close relationship with the offset between the rotor-stator centres and the length of the sealing arc. Generally speaking the port positions have marked effects on the performance of the machine. The axial length of the discharge and the suction ports converged to smaller values than that of the initial design, see figures 5(e,f).

It was noticed that although the frictional power dissipation increased at the optimum design, a decrease in the indicated power, produced a net reduction in the power input.

The variation of the frictional power dissipation was believed to have a close relationship to the variation of the height of the vane (H_v). For a given angular position the absolute location of the centre of the gravity of the vane varies with the height of the vane, and this causes changes in the vane inertia forces.

The free air delivery figure 6(b) converges to a value close to the lower constraint value. It may be seen that the value of the objective function increases with the number of successful searches and finally converges after about 270 such searches. There was an 8.0% increase in the predicted specific free air delivery. The rapid increase in the cpu-time at the end of the search was caused by the shrinking strategy of the optimization technique while the reflection strategy was not effective during this stage.

6.2 Results for 4 to 16 vane compressors

Figure 7 shows optimization results for models fitted with a different number of vanes. The values of the objective function generally increased with a reduction in the number of vanes. There was a 15% difference between the lowest and the highest function values when normalised by the highest function value. The difference was caused by the reduction of the frictional energy dissipated by the machine fitted with the smaller number of vanes.

This figure also shows results where the total power is plotted against a parameter which represents the volume of a machine. It is akin to a power density, i.e. the measure of the power input per unit volume of the machine and is reasonably constant for machines fitted with 8 to 12 vanes, it increased when the number of vanes reached 16.

Figure 7 also shows a parameter which might be used to indicate the manufacturing cost of a machine. By assuming that the cost of a machine increases with the volume of the machine because a big machine requires more material and generally possesses larger machining surfaces and longer cutting paths it was decided to plot a parameter which was formed by dividing the objective function by an effective machine volume. Since the cost of a machine is generally assumed to be proportional to the parameter Rs^2Lr the parameter $FOPT/Rs^2Lr$ could be imagined as equivalent to the **specific free air delivery divided by the cost of the machine**. This parameter increased with a reduction in the number of vanes.

7 CONCLUSIONS

The work reported in this paper shows that modelling and computer aided design techniques are powerful tools for the compressor designer. Significant performance improvements have been predicted by the use of these techniques and a corroborative experimental programme will be required to validate the predictions. Such a programme is currently in hand. The paper suggests that sliding vane machines require fewer vanes than many manufacturers currently employ.

8 REFERENCES

(1)   THE BIRD MANUFACTURING CO. LTD. Improvement in and relating to Rotory Compressors and/or Vacuum Pumps and the like. 1949-51, Patent spec. 653295.

(2) MACLAREN, J.F.T. The Influence of Computers on Compressor Technology. Proc 6th Compressor Technology Conference, Purdue University, 1982.

(3) LA FRANCE, L.J. AND HAMILTON, J.F. Computer controlled Optimization of a Rotary Vane Compressor. Proc. 3rd compressor Technology Conference, Purdue University, 1976.

(4) COATES, D.A. AND COHEN, R. Using Digital computer Simulations for Compressor Design. Proc. 2nd compressor Technology Conference, Purdue University, 1974.

(5) COATES, D.A. Design Technique for Performance Optimization of a Small Rotary-Vane Compressor. Ph.D thesis, 1970, Purdue University.

(6) EDWARD, T.C. AND MCDONARD, A.T. Analysis of Mechanical Friction in Rotary Vane Mechines. Proc. 1st compressor Technology Conference, Purdue University, 1972.

(7) LINDEMANN, H. AND KAISER, H. KUEVER, M. AND KRUSE, H. Optimisation of a Special Shaped Rotary Vane Compressor Comparison of Theoretical and Experiment Results. Proc. 6th compressor Technology Conference, Purdue University, 1982.

(8) PICKSAK, A. AND KRUSE, H. Mathematical Simulation of Lubrication Conditions in Rotary Vane Compressor. International Compressor Conference, Purdue University, 1986.

(9) CHANG, K.Y. A Theoretical and Experimental Study of an Oil-flooded Rotary Sliding Vane Compressor (Vol. 1). Ph.D thesis, 1983, Mechanical Engineering Department, University of Strathclyde.

(10) PETERSON, C.R. AND MCGAHAN, W.A. Thermodynamic and Aerodynamic Analysis Methods for Oil-Flooded Sliding Vane Compressors. Proc. 1st compressor Technology Conference, Purdue University, 1972.

(11) SMITH, C. Oil Cooling of Sliding-vane Rotary Compressor. Scientific Lubrication, August, 1959.

(12) SPENDLEY, W., HEXT, G.R. AND HIMSWORTH, F.R. Sequential Application of Simplex Designs in Optimization and Evolutionary Operation. Technometrics, November, 1962.

(13) NELDER, J.A. AND MEAD, R. A Simplex Method for Function Minimisation. The Computer Journal (Vol. 7), 1964-65.

(14) BOX, M.J. A New Method of Constraint Optimization and Comparison with Other Methods. The Computer Journal (Vol. 8), 1965-66.

(15) MITCHELL, R.A. AND KAPLAN, J.L. Non-linear Constrained Optimization by a Nonrandom Complex Method. Journal of Researrch of the National Bureau of Standards - C. Engineering and Instrumentation. Vol. 72C No. 4 Oct-Dec, 1968.

(16) MICHAND, G.H. AND MODREY, J. A Direst Search Algorithm for Constrained Non-linear Design Optimization. ASME 75-DET-100, 1975.

(17) DEMPSTER, W. M., TRAMSCHEK, A.B. AND MACLAREN, J.F.T. Optimization of a Referigeration Compressor Valve Design Using a Modified Complex Method. I.I.R., Paris, 1983.

9 ACKNOWLEDGEMENT

The authors wish to express their thanks to the Hydrovane Compressor Company for the inspiration of and support for the work reported.

Table 1 Explicit constraints

i	L_{Ei}		E_i		H_{Ei}	Unit
1	30	$\leq$	Rs	$\leq$	70	mm
2	30	$\leq$	Rr	$\leq$	70	mm
3	1×10^{-6}	$\leq$	ε	$\leq$	15	mm
4	$0.5(360/Nv)+1$	$\leq$	$\beta1$	$\leq$	120	°
5	130	$\leq$	$\beta2$	$\leq$	180	°
6	300	$\leq$	$\beta3$	$\leq$	$360-0.5(360/Nv$	°
7	$360-0.5(360/Nv)$	$\leq$	$\beta4$	$\leq$	355	°
8	10	$\leq$	Hv	$\leq$	70	mm
9	50	$\leq$	Lr	$\leq$	500	mm
10	30	$\leq$	Ld	$\leq$	Lr	mm
11	1.0	$\leq$	Ls	$\leq$	Lr	mm

Table 2 Geometrical constraints

j	L_{Gj}		$G(x)_j$		H_{Gi}	Unit
1	1×10^{-6}	$\leq$	$(Rr+\varepsilon-Rs)$	$\leq$	60	mm
2	1×10^{-6}	$\leq$	$(Rs-Rr)$	$\leq$	60	mm
3	1×10^{-6}	$\leq$	$(\beta2-\beta1)$	$\leq$	360	°
4	1×10^{-6}	$\leq$	$(\beta4-\beta3)$	$\leq$	360	°
5	1×10^{-6}	$\leq$	$(0.85Rr-Hv)$	$\leq$	60	mm
6	1×10^{-6}	$\leq$	$(Rs+\varepsilon-Rr)$	$\leq$	$0.85(Hv)$	mm
7	$(360/Nv)$	$\leq$	$(360-\beta4+\beta1)$	$\leq$	360	°
8	$(360/Nv)$	$\leq$	$(\beta3-\beta2)$	$\leq$	360	°
9	1×10^{-6}	$\leq$	$(Lr-Ld)$	$\leq$	1×10^{20}	mm
10	1×10^{-6}	$\leq$	$(Lr-Ls)$	$\leq$	1×10^{20}	mm
11	$(360/Nv)+1$	$\leq$	(SEALANG)	$\leq$	360	°
12	1×10^{-6}	$\leq$	X_{12}	$\leq$	1×10^{20}	
13	-0.99999	$\leq$	X_{13}	$\leq$	0.99999	

Table 3 Implicit constraints

k	L_{Ik}		$I(x)_k$		H_{Ik}	Unit
1	14.5	$\leq$	FAD	$\leq$	30	l/s
2	0.0001	$\leq$	Pi	$\leq$	1×10^{20}	kW
3	-0.017	$\leq$	FLOWL	$\leq$	$+0.017$	l/s

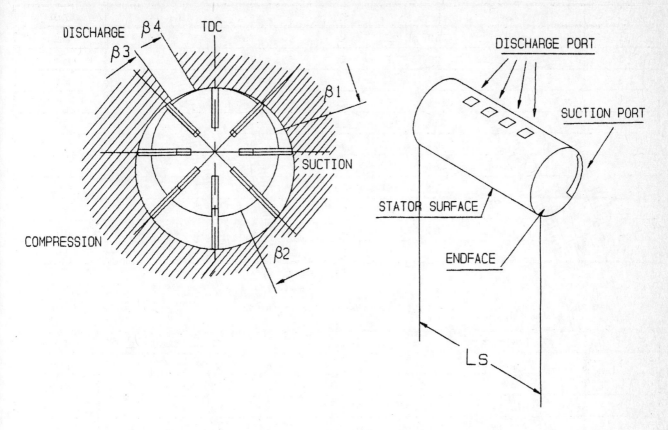

Fig 1   Schematic diagram of compressor

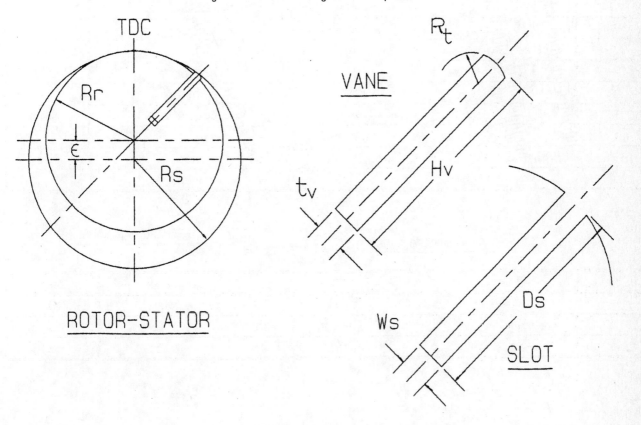

Fig 2   Basic dimensions of a compressor

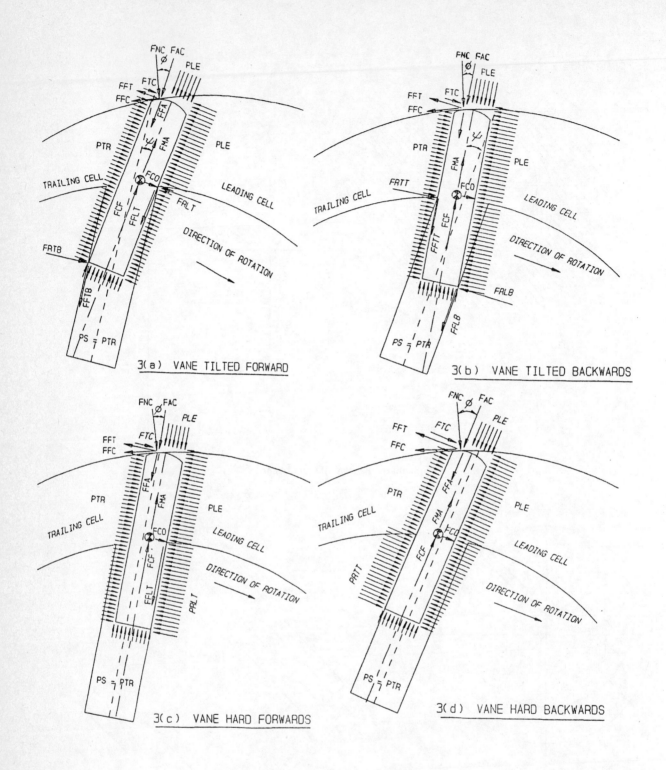

Fig 3   Vane modes

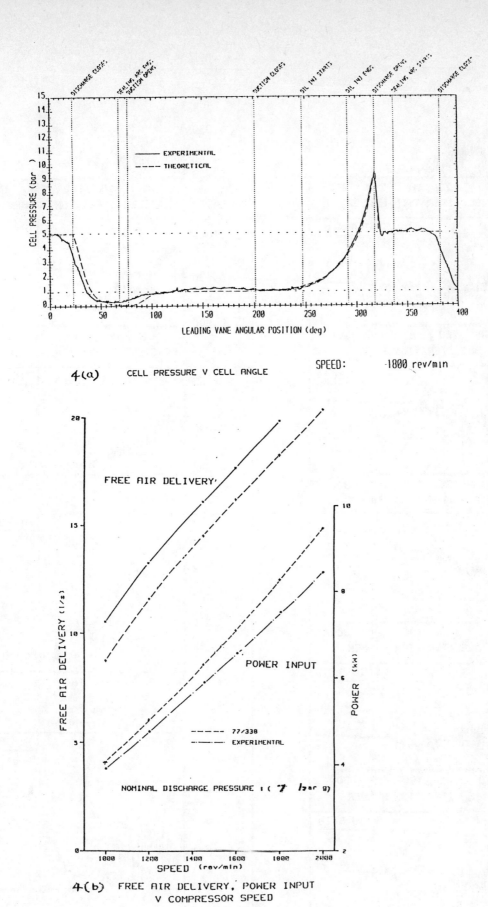

4(a) CELL PRESSURE V CELL ANGLE

SPEED: 1800 rev/min

4(b) FREE AIR DELIVERY, POWER INPUT
V COMPRESSOR SPEED

Fig 4 Comparison of theoretical and experimental values

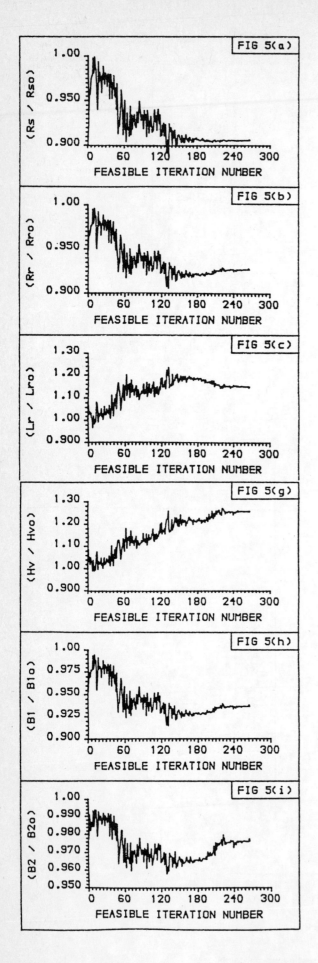
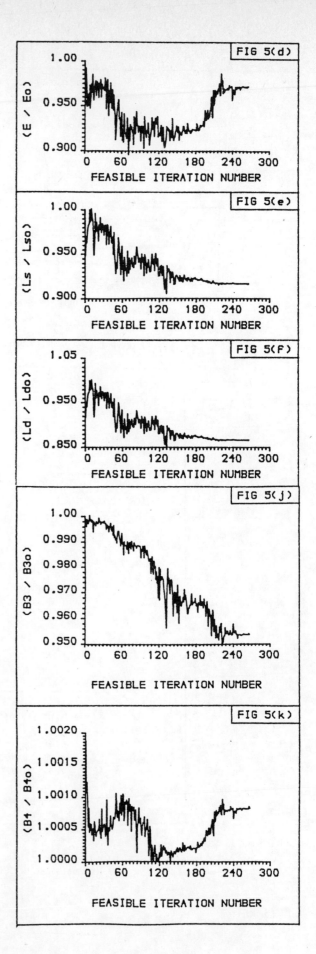

Fig 5   Variation of design parameters with iteration number

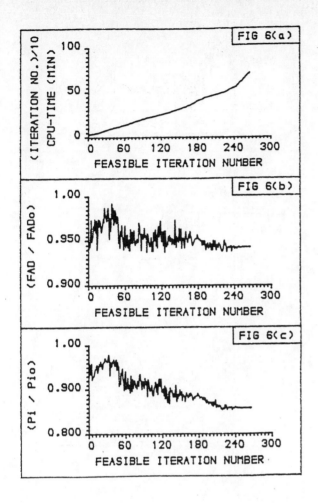

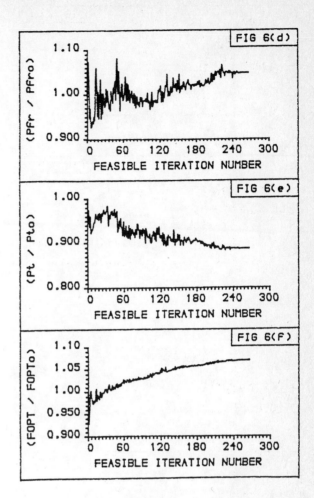

Fig 6   Variation of computational and optimization parameters with
         iteration number

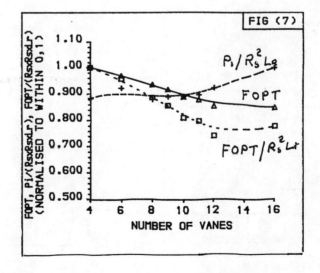

Fig 7   Optimization results for varying vane numbers

C390/011

A theoretical and experimental investigation of the flow of gas through reciprocating compressor valves

J S FLEMING, BSc, PhD, CEng, MIMechE, MRAeS, **A B TRAMSCHEK**, BSc, PhD, CEng, MIMechE, FInstR and **J M H ABDUL HUSAIN**
Department of Mechanical and Process Engineering, University of Strathclyde, Glasgow

SYNOPSIS: The flow of gas through compressor valves is investigated by making use of the PHOENICS program to compute pressure distribution, gas force and velocity. Comparisons are made with measured values of gas force and velocity and the importance of modelling turbulence and compressibility in regions of flow separation and high velocity is discussed.

1 INTRODUCTION

This paper is concerned with developing methods of predicting the behaviour of gas flowing through the valves of reciprocating compressors. Very recently, attempts have been made (1) to adapt these machines to operate flexibly; ie to handle variations in suction pressure, gas molecular weight and crankshaft speed. In reciprocators designed as they normally are to function in conditions which do not vary with time, the design of the valves, which are the most vulnerable components in an otherwise robust machine, has been found to be a process which requires a combination of practical knowledge and scientific technique. When the operating conditions vary, valve design becomes a much more serious problem due to the valves passing through and perhaps dwelling in, resonant-like dynamic conditions which can cause a drastic reduction in the flow efficiency of the valve, in addition to reducing its service life, due to the increased violence of the impacts the moving element makes with the stop when opening and the seat when closing.

Even in a normal non-resonant valve action the valve impact velocity is difficult to determine accurately due to the problem of computing the gas force driving the moving element. The difficulty is caused by the nature of the geometry of the flow path through the valve, featuring as it usually does sharp corners and abrupt changes of orientation and cross-section. In addition, at particular displacements of the relatively simple valves considered here the flow is especially difficult to model due, the writers believe, to the presence of a large eddy behind a sharp corner.

The valves in a compressor operating in the normal way open and close once per revolution of the crankshaft. As a consequence, the flow passageway geometry varies with time. However, in most compressors the maximum speed of the valve motion is of the order of a few metres per second. It has been found (2) that although the valve motion and the flow are transient, the gas force and by implication the flow efficiency, are the same as they would be if a succession of steady state flow regimes existed at fixed increments of valve displacement. The evidence suggests that only in high speed (i.e. small) reciprocating compressors is it necessary to consider departing from a steady state representation of the flow regime, and even here the difference in the gas force due to transient effects may be as little as 15% or less.

Before a compressor valve opens the gas in close proximity to the valve is stationary. As the valve moving element moves from fully closed to fully open in an opening action, the gas accelerates from rest and moves through a gap which is increasing in cross-sectional area. The gas is driven by a pressure difference which increases with time. The pressure difference reaches its maximum value at the maximum displacement of the valve. Hot wire measurements of gas velocity (2) have shown that the period of laminar flow following the instant at which the valve plate first loses contact with the seat is very brief. Hence, for most of the opening action the flow is turbulent at all cross-sections of the flow path. As a consequence, consideration must be given to modelling turbulence if the computations are to have a realistic prospect of giving useful predictions. Two turbulence models have been used in the work reported here; a constant value of eddy kinematic viscosity and the K-epsilon model.

The flow studies described here are relevant to determining valve gas forces and flow (efficiency) characteristics but are also of general interest in the area of computational and experimental fluid mechanics.

2 COMPUTATIONS OF THE FLOW

Since the ultimate objective of this work is the development of computational methods capable of predicting the behaviour of valves and compressors, valves were chosen for which a realistic prospect existed of achieving a computed solution. That is valves having a geometry which is not too complex but is similar to that of real valves. Success with this modelling will be followed with a systematic increase in the complexity of the cases handled, so that eventually all real cases can be modelled successfully.

The PHOENICS program due to CHAM Ltd. (4) of London was used to compute streamlines, velocity vectors and pressure distributions and hence the aerodynamic force on the valve plate. The poor agreement between computed values obtained by earlier methods (5) and measured values is believed by the authors to be due to the manner in which viscosity-related phenomena like wall friction, compressibility and turbulence were dealt with in the computations. In the computations presented here turbulence was modelled in two ways: firstly by assuming that the same value of eddy kinematic viscosity exists everywhere in the flow field (a relatively crude approximation) and secondly by making use of the K-epsilon model, a model which depends on assumptions concerning the rate of generation and dissipation of eddies in the flow (6).

3 MEASUREMENTS

Valves were manufactured to match the computational model. They consisted of a plain disc concentrically situated over a round valve port with the planes of the disc and the seat maintained parallel at all times (Figures 1 and 2). A range of valve displacements was set and flow of the gas (air) through the valve was induced by applying a range of pressure differences comparable to that which occurs across the suction valve of an operating reciprocating compressor. Measuring the force exerted by the gas on the disc while the gas is in steady flow through the valve driven by a constant pressure difference is straightforward and has been described elsewhere (3).

4 DISCUSSION OF COMPUTED AND MEASURED VALUES

The computations of the gas force acting on the valve plate were obtained by integrating the plate pressure distribution with respect to the plate area. Figure 3 (valve lift 0.04 mm) and figure 4 (valve lift 0.4 mm) show the pressure distributions predicted by PHOENICS for valve A (drawn to scale for a lift of 0.4 mm in figure 1) for two values of eddy kinematic viscosity and also for the K-epsilon model for an overall pressure difference of 20.7 kN/m² (3 lbf/in). As yet there are no experimentally determined pressure distributions against which to compare these predictions. For such a small valve they would be difficult to obtain. However, plans are in hand for making these measurements on a larger valve.

For the combination of pressure difference and valve displacement pertaining to figure 3 the agreement between measured and computed values of gas foce is good for the K-epsilon model but less good for the assumption that a constant eddy kinematic viscosity exists throughout the flow field. It seems fairly likely that this lack of agreement is due to the crudity of this assumption. Figure 4 is for the case where the valve lift is ten times greater than in figure 3. For this displacement neither model of turbulence gives good agreement on total gas force as can be seen in figure 5 in which measured and predicted values of gas force are plotted against valve lift for valve A for an overall pressure difference of 20.7 kN/M² (3 lbf/in²). Figure 6 gives the same information for the same valve when the pressure difference across the valve is doubled to 41.4 kN/M² in.

Figures 5 and 6 both indicate that computed and measured values of gas force agree reasonably well for valve A at small and large values of valve displacement but do not agree well at intermediate values of displacement. The writers formed the opinion tht this may be due to the passageway geometry at intermediate values of displacement being such as to cause a large eddy to form behind the sharp edge in the overlap region. This is clearly capable of greatly affecting the pressure distribution in the overlap region and hence the gas force. If PHOENICS were failing to predict the size and shape of the eddy it would give the wrong pressure distribution for the overlap region and hence the wrong value of gas force overall.

In order to investigate the predictive capacity of PHOENICS the writers introduced valve B, identical in every respect to valve A except that a rounded edge replaces a sharp one as shown in figure 2. Such a valve should present less of a challenge to the computational power of PHOENICS. Figures 7 and 8 indicate that this is so, with the agreement between measured and computed values of gas force being considerably improved and the correct shape being predicted for the curves where it is not for the sharp-edge valve.

To investigate the flow behaviour of valve A further, hot wire measurements of velocity magnitude of the flow at the valve exit were made (conditions as in figure 6; valve displacement 0.4 mm). Using this value of velocity and, as a first approximation, assuming incompressibility in the flow, the following Reynolds numbers were calculated: 4356 at exit, 11500 in the port and 2880 in the throat of the valve. These values should of course be treated as a guide, especially that for the throat where a local velocity of mach 0.64 is indicated, suggesting that compressibility effects in that region may be of equal or greater importance than those of turbulence.

The computed solutions presented here are for incompressible flow. This discussion suggests that they should be extended to take compressibility into account together with the use of an adequate model for turbulence. Fortunately, Reynolds stress models of turbulence are now becoming available in PHOENICS which have the prospect of being superior to the K-epsilon model.

REFERENCES

(1) MOES, D. New valve design for flexible operation of reciprocating compressors. Purdue Compressor Engineering Conference, Purdue University, 1988.

(2) FLEMING, J.S. Gas force effects on compressor valves in the early stages of valve opening. PhD Thesis 1983, University of Strathclyde, Scotland.

(3) FLEMING, J.S. The measurement of aerodynamic forces as an accelerating valve. 10th IMEKO Congress, Prague, April, 1985.

(4) SPALDING, D.B. & MALLIN, M.R. PHOENICS-84 Reference Handbook, CHAM Report UK/TR/100, Imperial College, London, United Kingdom.

(5) HALLAM, W.W. Gas forces during the rapid opening of disc valves. PhD Thesis 1981, University of Strathclyde, Scotland.

(6) ECKERT, E.R.G. & DRAKE, R.M. Analysis of heat and mass transfer. McGraw-Hill, 1972.

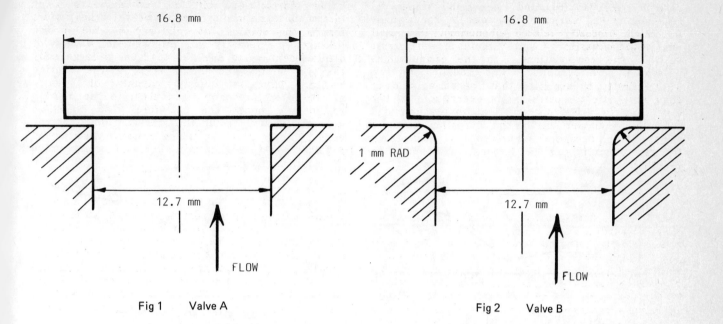

Fig 1   Valve A

Fig 2   Valve B

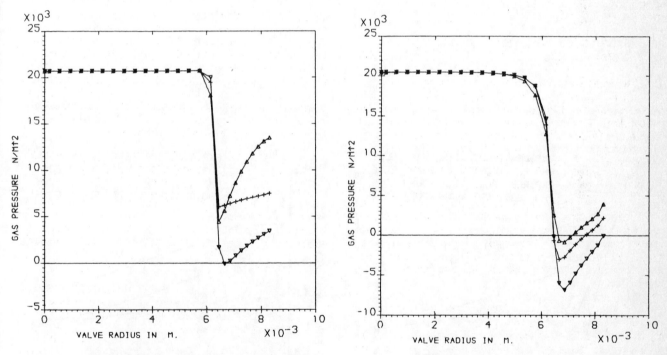

Fig 3   Distribution of gas pressure on valve upstream
side, lift = 0.04mm
△ EKV = $1.E^{-2}$
▽ EKV = $1.E^{-3}$
+ K_E Model
Valve A — pressure difference = 20.7 kN/m²

Fig 4   Distribution of gas pressure on valve upstream
side, lift = 0.40mm
△ EKV = $1.E^{-2}$
▽ EKV = $1.E^{-3}$
+ K_E Model
Valve A — pressure difference = 20.7 kN/m²

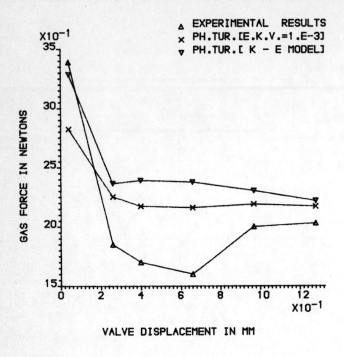

Fig 5   Valve A – pressure difference = 20.7 kN/m²

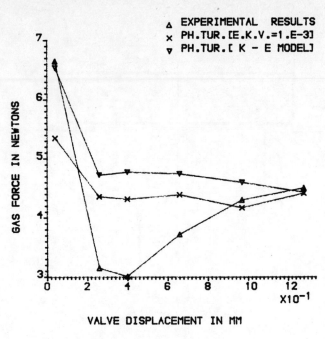

Fig 6   Valve A – pressure difference = 41.4 kN/m²

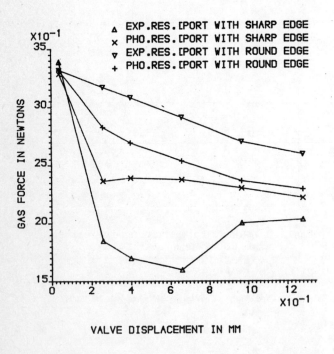

Fig 7   K–ε model – pressure difference = 20.7 kN/m²

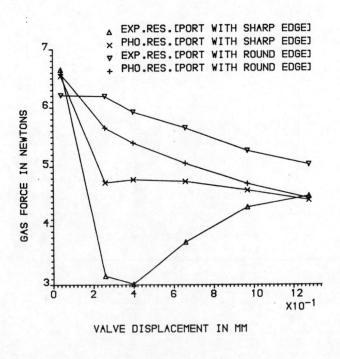

Fig 8   K–ε model – pressure difference = 41.4 kN/m²

C390/012

The mechanisms for lubricant failure in reciprocating and rotary vane/screw air compressors

P H D MATTHEWS, J GRISDALE and R H WALKDEN
Shell Research Limited, Thornton Research Centre, Chester

SYNOPSIS The prediction of the behaviour of a lubricant for reciprocating and rotary air-compressors is of paramount importance in enabling the selection of the correct lubricant for a trouble free operation. Reasons for premature failures are discussed and suggestions for overcoming these problems are put forward.

1 INTRODUCTION

The consistent production of 'clean' compressed air is frequently a vital element in many industrial applications. It is of paramount importance that the machines used for the production of air should run reliably for long periods, but a variety of types of lubricant and machinery failures have been observed.

The purpose of this paper is to share some of our experiences with the reader and to attempt to provide possible remedies. We will discuss the problems experienced in both reciprocating and rotary machines. Whilst the trend for the supply of new equipment certainly favours the rotary machines, there are still many reciprocating compressors in service. It is with this latter category of machines that we shall begin the discussion.

2 RECIPROCATING COMPRESSORS

The lubricant in these machines is expected to protect bearings, pistons, liners etc without causing the excessive formation of carbonaceous deposits on either exhaust valves or in the exhaust trunking leading from the compressor. Temperatures experienced in the multi-stage machines are generally much lower than for the single-stage, high compression machines. Even so, the combination of a high air delivery pressure and moderate operating temperatures in the delivery valve zone can lead to the formation of carbonaceous deposits on valves and in the trunking. In extreme cases such as that illustrated in Fig. 1, the trunking pipe can suffer severe build-up of carbon. When hot, high pressure air containing oil vapour passes over the glowing carbonaceous deposit a 'dieseling effect' can result which, in extreme cases, can be followed by an explosion. More often the formation of carbonaceous-deposits on-valves has a "nuisance effect". Quite apart from the increased cost of maintenance and the possibility of the expensive loss in production, fouled compressors run inefficiently. A typical example of this type of problem is illustrated in, Fig. 2, which shows the air delivery valves from a machine lubricated by oil A.

Having illustrated that carbonaceous deposits are a problematic with this type of machine, what guidance does the customer receive in order to select the lubricant that will perform well in his application?

2.1 Specification

We have described in a previous paper (1) how historically the earlier German DIN 51506 and more recently the International Standards Organisation (ISO) in the ISO-L classification DAA, DAB and DAC specification (Table 1) were derived. The ISO-L-DAB category would be considered appropriate for a premium quality mineral oil. An oil is classified as meeting ISO-L-DAB by performance in a series of laboratory tests designed to measure resistance to oxidation and corrosivity, and for water-shedding capability as well as pour points (Table 2). If we return to the failed valves, illustrated in Fig. 2, and explain that the compressor was serviced with a mineral oil that easily meets the DAB classification, then clearly changes will have to be made in the structure of the proposed ISO specification if it is to reflect service conditions. Our studies have shown that it is absolutely essential to carry out tests in a variety of compressors, both 'in-house' and in field trials in order to establish the suitability of a lubricant for a particular application.

2.2 Assessment of lubricant performance

We have illustrated above how the current specifications are not always capable of rating lubricants in line with their known field performance. In order to develop suitable lubricants, we have devised both rapid screening and longer-term rig tests that are known to rate lubricants in the same order as their performance in the field. The details of these rig tests have been fully documented in a previous paper (1) and it is appropriate to summarise only the salient points here.

The Compair Broomwade 2050H is a single-stage, air-cooled, twin-piston compressor in which lubrication is by pump feed to the bearings and by an oil-mist generated in the crankcase to the cylinder walls. Excessively high air delivery temperatures are generated during continuous operation and we have found that at an air delivery temperature of 300°C we can differentiate between a poor performer and a good performer within 200h of continuous operation. Candidate formulations that perform well in the screening test are further evaluated in a longer-term test. This uses the Compair Reavell VHP 15 machine - a four-stage machine fitted with water inter-coolers in which lubrication to stages 1 and 2 is by 'splash' lubrication similar to the Broomwade, whilst stages 3 and 4 receive new lubricant from a separate reservoir on a once through basis. The test conditions detailed in Table 3 were agreed with the original equipment manufacturers (OEM) as being a realistic test, running under conditions that would be experienced in service.

Using the Broomwade screening test and the longer-term Reavell tests we have been able to confirm that the oil meeting the ISO-L-DAB specification, but performing badly in service (Fig. 2) gave substantial amounts of carbonaceous deposits in each of these machines.

Having established what constitutes a poor performer, what can be done to improve the performance of a lubricant? The formation of carbonaceous deposits on valves and in the trunking leading from the machines is a complex subject involving the decomposition of the lubricant by free radical mechanisms and chain reactions. Our studies have shown that, in the case of mineral oil based products, solvency (the ability to hold thermal and oxidation products in solution) coupled with the selection of suitable anti-oxidants can significantly improve the performance of products. The increased solvency characteristics of naphthenic based products are preferred over the paraffinic equivalents. This effect has been clearly demonstrated by comparing naphthenic and paraffinic-based products in the Reavell compressor test mentioned earlier. During the test the valves were removed every 100h, examined and photographed. After 500h test duration using Oil A (paraffinic) the test had to be terminated as the build-up of deposits was so severe that it was considered unsafe to continue. In contrast, at the same test time Oil B (naphthenic) showed little sign of deposit (compare Figs. 3 and 4) and ran for over 2000h with the formation of very little carbonaceous deposit.

In order to understand more fully the effects of solvency and anti-oxidants, we have carried out a series of experiments with a naphthenic basestock in which the solvency characteristics have been reduced by the manufacturing process (Oil C), and some interesting results have been obtained. We have used the modified Wolf Strip Test, DIN 51392, previously discussed (1), as a thin film thermal/oxidation test, to measure the tendency for a lubricant to give deposits. Under the test conditions of 12h at 250°C the method has shown excellent correlation with the Broomwade and Reavell compressor rig tests.

The results from the current series of experiments are summarised in Table 4. Briefly, they show that it is possible to counter-balance a moderate reduction in solvency characteristics of a naphthenic basestock by an increase in the treat-rate of anti-oxidant additives. In fact,

in this case doubling the treat-rate of this type of additive gave an equivalent Wolf Strip deposit to the original formulation and this was subsequently confirmed by rig tests.

But even when the product is properly formulated and the basestocks are carefully selected, there are a limited number of operating conditions for which mineral oils are not suitable. We would not, for example recommend that a mineral-oil based product be used when machines such as the Broomwade are operating continuously and air delivery temperatures in excess of 300°C are observed. Our experiences with the Reavell VHP 15 compressor have indicated that a properly formulated mineral oil based product will operate successfully at 180°C and 310 bar, but increasing the temperature to in excess of 200°C could lead to thermal degradation of the product. Under these conditions a synthetic lubricant is required.

2.3 Synthetic lubricants
The term synthetic lubricant covers a wide spectrum of base fluids each type with its own inherent characteristics, which we shall discuss below. The types of fluids that have been tested are based on:-

(a) polyalphaolefin (PAO)
(b) polyol ester   (PE)
(c) aryl ester   (AE)

PAO based fluids suffer from a severe lack of inherent solvency, which would appear to be required for this type of application. Our experiences with predominantly PAO-based products in the Broomwade rig, Wolf Strip Test and field trials have been to say the least disappointing (Oil F in Table 5) to such a degree that we would actively discourage the use of this type of product in ISO-L-DAC applications.

Polyol esters would be expected, from experience in the aviation industry, to offer distinct advantages over the PAO's. Unfortunately, the increase in viscosity required to lubricate reciprocating air compressors, typically ISO 100 viscosity grade, necessitates structural changes of the base fluid to meet, for example, the low temperature requirements. Hence, these base fluids cannot withstand the equivalent thermal/oxidative stresses that their lower viscosity counter-part would successfully endure.

The third and final type of synthetic fluids to be considered in this section are the aryl esters - either di-esters, based on phthalic acid or tri-esters, based on trimellitic acid. Our studies have shown that, whilst improvement in thermal/oxidative stability over mineral-oils is achievable by careful selection of the base fluid and anti-oxidant additives, there are other areas in which potential problems exist. For example, high nitrile rubber or Viton elastomers must be used as seal materials and the materials used in filter bowls and sight glasses must be tested for compatibility with the candidate lubricants. In addition, synthesised fluids such as aryl esters are generally fairly pure compounds containing only carbon, hydrogen and oxygen and have little inherent anti-wear capability that is associated with complex mixtures such as mineral oils. Consequently, we have experienced some wear problems when no additional anti-wear agent is used in the formulation. Equally unacceptable are products which incorporate the sulphur/phosphorus type of additives that are used for their e.p. properties in gear oil applications. This type of formulation has exhibited two types of failure; the acidic nature of the e.p. additive can lead to an acceleration in hydrolysis of the ester-based fluid (Table 5), thus causing a rapid increase in the acidity of the lubricant leading to severe rusting of components. In addition, the aggressive nature of the sulphur/phosphorus additive, which causes a rapid 'run-in' with gears can cause excessive wear in the surface contacts between the piston rings and cylinder wall, resulting in 'blow-by'. We would recommend the use of less aggressive phosphorus containing additives in formulations for this type of application.

2.4 Mechanical failure

Reciprocating compressors generally run at higher air delivery temperatures and pressures than the corresponding rotary machines. Thus maintenance, or rather lack of maintenance, can have a more significant effect on the performance of the reciprocating machines. It is to be hoped that the selection of a suitable lubricant based on a knowledge of the air delivery temperatures and pressures will minimise the build-up of carbon on valves, but mechanical failure can lead to the premature shut-down of machines. We shall describe below some problems that we have encountered in field trials and 'in-house' testing.

The most common form of failure concerns the valves. On several occasions we have observed mechanical failure such as breakage of the diaphragm retaining-pin. This has the effect of restricting the air exit from the valve, thus causing the temperature to rise and promoting thermal degradation of the lubricant. Similarly, failure of valves to seat correctly or the leakage of elastomeric seals can over work certain compression stages with a similar effect on the lubricant.

Many compressors operate in hostile environments in which airborne abrasive particles are present. Ingress of this type of material into the sump can accelerate wear in, for example, the crankshaft and cylinder walls, piston rings etc. This is in addition to wear that can be caused by incorrect selection of anti-wear additives, as described in Section 2.3.

Failure of pressure maintaining valves can occur in each type of machine, through the formation of deposits. Likewise build-up of water in the lubricant can lead to premature bearing fatigue in either type of machine.

2.5 Conclusions from this section

Lubricants for use in reciprocating machines can be exposed to extreme thermal and oxidative stresses. Specially formulated products should be used which have good solvency and anti-oxidation properties. Mineral oil based products may be used providing temperatures and pressures are not excessive (eg upto 180°C at 310 bar). When synthetic-based aryl ester products are required, care should be taken to ensure that components such as the elastomeric seals used are compatible. Other problem areas include rusting and wear. The use of predominantly PAO based products should be avoided in these applications.

3 ROTARY VANE AND SCREW COMPRESSORS

As we discussed earlier, the temperature to which the lubricants are subjected in this type of compressor are much lower than in the corresponding reciprocating machine. The lubricant would rarely encounter temperatures in excess of 100°C and typically the temperature would be in the region of 80°C. Lubricants in these rotary machines are expected to protect bearings and gears, to act as sealant, to remove heat and in the case of rotary vane machines to assist the sliding motion of vanes in the rotor and to reduce wear between the vane tip and the stator elements. The period between the lubricant charge replacement is generally governed by the time to block air/oil separator filter elements. Our experiments, although not complete, have indicated that different mechanisms are involved dependent on base fluid and formulation. We shall describe below some of the experiments and the implications of the results.

3.1 Separator blockage

Initially the Hydrovane 13PU and more recently the 23PU rotary vane compressors were used as the test rigs at an elevated sump temperature of 120°C and an air delivery pressure of 5.4 bar (80 lbf/in^2). As a rule of thumb it is considered that, within certain limits, the oil life halves for every 10°C rise in temperature, thus an oil with a life of 1000h @ 120°C would be expected to operate for some 16,000 h or 2 years continuously at a normal running temperature of 80°C. Our experiments have involved different formulations in mineral oils and polyolphaolefins. Various properties of the lubricant measured during the test were:- change in viscosity and acidity, and the increase in differential pressure across the air/oil separator element. Typically, a premium-quality, properly formulated mineral oil based product (Oil H) would show a gradual increase in viscosity, acidity and differential pressure across the separator element during the test. The end of test is indicated by a sudden increase in the differential pressure. Our studies have attempted to determine the mechanism for failure. In the above case, once the separator element had become blocked it was subjected to analysis by the scanning electron microscope (SEM). The normal technique of washing the area of filter to be analysed with heptane to remove oil, followed by carbon cooling prior to SEM examination, showed little evidence for deposit on the surface of the separator element, but a solvent extracted sample when examined by Infrared analysis showed the presence of polymerised products from either the basestock or the additives. A recently introduced SEM technique of freezing the section of filter under examination in liquid nitrogen at-150°C and gold plating prior to examination in the apparatus at-150°C has proved to be more successful. The blocking material remained on the surface of the filter (Fig. 6) and it was shown to be mainly organic in nature.

In other instances the failure of a lubricants can be more dramatic! For example a mineral oil product (Oil J) ran successfully in the Hydrovane rig @ 120°C for 2678h (Table 6) and when the machine was last examined the measured parameters gave little indication of failure. The next time the machine was examined at 2818 h the oil was found to be nearly solid, the acidity was 123 mg KOH/g and the rig itself was in a seized condition. The test on a duplicate machine lubricated by the same product was terminated at 3060h. At this time the acidity was 45 mg KOH/g, the viscosity at 40°C had increased by over 400%, but rather surprisingly the differential pressure across the separator element had not changed. These results would represent a very long life of the lubricant under normal operating temperatures but we are investigating the reasons for the sudden failure.

The properties of the base fluids can, of course, play an important part in the performance of the lubricant. To illustrate this point, consider Oil I, which is based on PAO. This lubricant was tested in the Hydrovane rig under the conditions described above and completed 1760h with little change in viscosity, or acidity, but the separator became blocked (Fig. 5). It would appear likely in this case that because of its poor solvency characteristics, the PAO would not dissolve the products of oxidation, hence there was premature blocking of the separator element. Our studies in this area are continuing.

3.2 Bearings and gears

Bearing failure can be caused by too low a viscosity at the working temperature or by the presence of slugs of water in the lubricant. The bearing manufacturers vary in their opinion concerning the minimum viscosity at the operating temperature; some prefer 10 cSt, whilst others consider 7 cSt to be adequate. The latter value would equate to an ISO 46 viscosity grade at a viscosity index (VI) of 100 and a temperature of 100°C. When the operating temperatures rise above this value a more viscous grade or a lubricant with a higher viscosity index would be required.

Very occasionally metal/metal contact problems can arise in compressor with gear drives, giving scuffing. In these circumstances, if it is unacceptable to use a higher viscosity grade, than a lubricant with mild e.p. properties, say FZG load stage failure of 8 or 9, would be expected to overcome the problem.

3.3 Low temperature operation

Low temperature operation can cause problems in both vane and screw compressors. In the case of rotary vane machines, a very high oil viscosity at start-up can reduce the sliding action of the vanes in the rotor, causing a free-wheeling effect. As the temperature of the oil rises then the vanes begin to operate spasmodically, which can result in vane bouncing and may cause excessive wear to the stator unit and the vanes themselves.

In the case of the screw machines, an increased viscosity caused by low temperature can increase the flow response time of the lubricant. Thus at start-up, the machine is starved of lubricant for the first 20 to 30 seconds operating resulting in a rapid rise in temperatures which could (and has) on occasion led to an explosion by auto-ignition. There are several ways that the problems associated with low ambient temperature on start-up can be overcome:-

(a) install an oil reservoir heater
(b) use an oil with a high VI having good low temperature properties.
(c) use a low viscosity grade
(d) in the case of the screw compressors, redesign to ensure that the lubricant is pumped prior to the operation of the compressor.

3.4 Effects of water

As we mentioned in Section 3.2. the presence of large slugs of water in the lubricant can lead to premature bearing failure through fatigue. In countries such as Japan, where air discharge temperatures are maintained below 60°C and the ambient air has a high humidity, then water which can build-up in the lubricant could be quite significant. Clearly under these conditions, good water shedding properties are essential and this type of machine in operation in these countries are often fitted with automatic water shedding devices. The additives used in these systems (in common with those used in steam turbine lubricants) must not be soluble in water and should be tested for water washout.

In European compressors, where the operating temperatures are higher and the amount of water present in the lubricant is therefore lower, we favour the use of the dispersant type of additives. These formulations have the effect of dispersing water and oxidation products, thus reducing the harmful effects of slugs of water and increasing the life of the separator element.

The presence of water in countries operating where there is a low ambient temperature could be harmful and pre-heating of the oil would be recommended under these conditions.

3.5 Air release and foaming

Good air release and low foaming properties of a lubricant are required for successful operation. Each property is temperature and viscosity dependent; lowering the viscosity and raising the temperature improves the properties. During the compression operation air can be entrained in the lubricant and poor air release properties have been shown on occasion to cause problems of excessive foaming at the separator element, resulting in increased oil carry-over. Certain types of additives used to control foaming eg. silicone containing, can have a serious, detrimental effect on the air release properties and their use should be restricted.

3.6 Specification

The specifications to be applied to lubricants for use in this type of machinery have not yet been completed. The issue is currently under review by the International Organisation for Standardisation (ISO), Panel TC 28/SC4/WC2 and by the British Standards Institute (BSI), Panel PTC 7/6/2.

3.7 Conclusions from this section

Lubricants for use in rotary vane and screw compressors do not have to endure the high temperatures experienced in the reciprocating machines. Problems are generally associated with air/oil separator elements and the lubricants used must be capable of preventing oxidation products from causing premature blocking of the separator elements by having good solvency properties or by the use of a dispersant agent in the formulation or preferably both. Surface properties, such as air release and foaming, can have a significant effect on oil carry-over and care should be taken to formulate lubricants with acceptable performance in these areas. Good water shedding properties become of paramount importance in machines operating under conditions of high humidity and low oil reservoir temperatures.

4 REFERENCE

(1) MATTHEWS, P.H.D. 'The lubrication of Reciprocating Compressors' 6th International Colloquium, Esslingen, January 12th-14th, 1988, Vol. 11 p.14.3 (Herausgebers/ Wilfried J. Bartz).

Table 1 ISO-L Specifications reciprocating oil-lubricated air compressors

Duty	Symbol		Operating conditions
Light	DAA	Intermittent operation	Sufficient time to allow cooling between periods of operation (for example 5 min continuous running in 20 min)
		Continuous operation	a) discharge pressure $<10^3$ kPa(10 bar) discharge temperature $<160°C$ stage pressure ratio $<3:1$ or b) discharge pressure $>10^3$ kPa(10 bar) discharge temperature $<140°C$ stage pressure ratio $<3:1$
Medium	DAB	Intermittent operation	Sufficient time to allow cooling between periods of operation
		Continuous operation	a) discharge pressure $<10^3$ kPa(10 bar) discharge temperature $>160°C$ or b) discharge pressure $>10^3$ kPa(10 bar) discharge temperature $>140°C$ but $<160°C$ or c) stage pressure ration $> 3:1$
Heavy	DAC	Intermittent or continuous operation	As for "medium" when conditions a), b) or c) above are fulfilled and where severe coke formation in a discharge system might be anticipated as a result of previous experience with a medium-duty oil.

Table 2 Specifications of mineral oil based lubricants for air compressors - Categories L-DAA and L-DAB

Category	ISO-L-DAA					ISO-L-DAB					Method of test
ISO viscosity grade (VG)	32	46	68	100	150	32	46	68	100	150	ISO 3448
Kinematic viscosity at 40°C, mm²/s ±10% at 100°C, mm²/s ±10%	32 46 68 100 150 Typical value to be stated by supplier					32 46 68 100 150 Typical value to be stated by supplier					ISO 3104
Pour point max. °C	-9	-9	-9	-9	-9	-9	-9	-9	-9	-9	ISO 3016
Corrosiveness to copper (3h. at 100°C max rating	1	1	1	1	1	1	1	1	1	1	ISO 2160
Emulsion characteristics < 3ml after temperature °C	No requirement					30min 54	30min 54	30min 54	30min 82	30min 82	ISO 6614
Rust preventing characteristics	No requirement					Rusting absent					ISO 7120 Procedure A
Oxidation stability 1 Properties after ageing with a stream of air at 200°C a) evaporation loss max % (m/m) b) increase in Conradson carbon residue max. % (m/m)	15 1.5	15 1.5	15 1.5	15 1.5	15 1.5	Not applicable					ISO 6617 Part 1
2 Properties after ageing with a stream of air at 200°C in the presence of iron oxide a) evaporation loss max, % (m/m) b) Conradson carbon residue max. % (m/m)	Not applicable					20 2.5	20 2.5	20 3.0	20 3.0	20 3.0	ISO 6617 Part 2
Properties of the residue that remains after distilling off 80% (v/v) a) Conradson carbon residue max. % (m/m) b) ratio of kinematic viscosity of residue to that of new oil at 40°C max.	Not applicable					0.3 5	0.3 5	0.3 5	0.3 5	0.6 5	ISO 6616 with ISO 6615 and ISO 3104

Table 3 Operating conditions for the Reavell VHP15 4-stage air compressor'

Stage	1	2	3
Delivery pressure, bar	3.1	19.6	84.5
Delivery temperature, °C	140	179	146
Compression ratio	3.1:1	6.3:1	4.3:1

Table 4 Wolf strip results showing effects of basestock and treat-rate of anti-oxidants

	no additives	standard anti-oxidant treat-rate	twice anti-oxidant treat-rate
Naphthenic Oil B	150	20	-
Naphthenic Oil C	300	150	20

Table 5 Results for formulated synthetic fluids

Test		Oil D aryl ester	Oil E aryl ester	Oil F PAO	Oil G PE
Hydrolytic Stability (96h @ 93°C) ASTM-D 2619 (mod).					
acidity of oil					
before test.	mg KOH/g	0.47	0.06	0.36	0.10
after test.	mg KOH/g	1.00	0.09	0.20	0.50
change.	mg KOH/g	+0.53	+0.03	-0.16	+0.40
weight change, Cu strip.	mg	-0.01	-0.01	-0.05	-0.08
total acidity water	mg KOH/g	3.45	0.01	0.40	0.32
Demulsibility @ 82°C ASTM-D 1401 Oil, water, emulsion (minutes)		43,27,0(25)	43,37,0(15)	40,40,0(5)	40,40,0(15)
Four-ball, IP 239, 1500 r/min					
Weld load,	kg	160	110	220	130
Wear scar diameter, (40kg for 60mm)	mm	0.31	0.90	0.30	1.0
Wolf Strip, 12h @ 250°C DIN 51392					
deposit	mg	4	4	285	146
Rubber swell, 14 days @ 120°C Low nitrite, change in:					
flexibility	%		no change	no change	
volume	%		+33.5	-5.2	
hardness	%		-20.0	+10	
high nitrile, change in:					
flexibility	%		no change	no change	
volume,	%		4.2	-2.2	
hardness,	%		-1.0	+4	
Viton, change in:					
flexibility,	%		no change	no change	
volume,	%		2.4	-0.6	
hardness,	%		-2.0	0	
Differential scanning calorimetry, 230°C induction period,	min		14.2	2.0	0.6

P.A.O. = polyolphaolefin, based on a trimer of 1-decene (hydrogenated)
P.E. = pentaerythrityl ester (ISO C_{10})

Table 6 Hydrovane rig test - change in viscosity for Oils H, I and J (see Fig. 6 for description of oils)

Test duration, h	% change in viscosity @ 40°C		
	Oil H	Oil I	Oil J
200	3.5	3.0	-2.5
500	6.6	3.0	-0.7
700	9.2	3.0	-
1000	17.5	3.3	2.9
1137	23.3	-	-
1500	-	3.3	6.25
1760	-	3.3	-
2000	-	-	10.2
2678	-	-	10.8
2818	-	-	oil almost solid

Table 7 Hydrovane rig test - change in acidity for Oils H, I and J (see Fig. 5 for description of oils)

Test duration, h	Change in acidity of oil, mgKOH/g		
	Oil H	Oil I	Oil J
200	0.50	-0.27	-0.50
500	0.50	-0.27	-0.40
700	0.60	-0.26	-
1000	2.40	-0.20	-0.40
1137	3.50	-	-
1500	-	0.01	-0.10
1760	-	0.20	-
2000	-	-	-0.3
2678	-	-	0.3
2818	-	-	120

Fig 1   Carbonized trucking pipe leading from a reciprocating compressor

Fig 2   Showing carbonaceous deposits on air-delivery valves

Fig 3   Heavy-coking of Reavell VHP 15 compressor, stage 2, lubricated
by oil A (paraffinic)

Fig 4   Low-coking of Reavell VHP 15 compressor, stage 2, lubricated
by oil B (naphthenic)

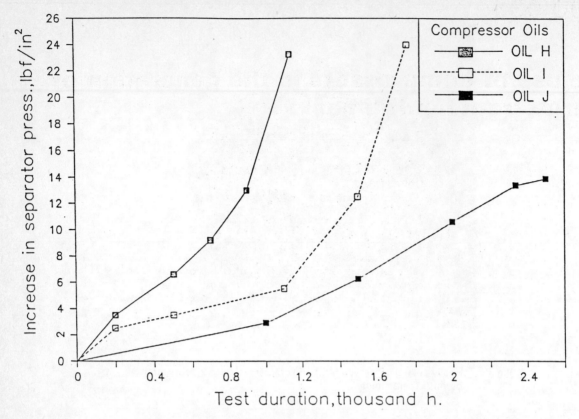

Fig 5   Hydrovane rig test — increase in dp across separator element
Oil H – premium quality mineral oil based product
Oil I   – PAO-based product
Oil J   – mineral oil based high additive treat-rate

Fig 6   SEM at –150°C showing blockage of separator element in
Hydrovane rig test

C390/033

The use of compressors in the generation of energy from landfill gas

B W LAMB, CEng, MIMechE and **D HOUGH**, BTech, CEng, MIProdE, MIMechE
NEI-Allen Limited, Belliss and Morcom, Birmingham

SYNOPSIS The utilisation of landfill gas for the generation of power through a gas turbine has been proved a viable proposition, which will achieve increasing importance in the power generation program of many industrialised countries. This paper covers one aspect of the system, namely the compressor used to boost the low pressure gas from the site collection system, to the higher pressure required to feed the gas turbine. This paper also discusses selection parameters, compressor control methods, and experiences gained from various landfill gas installations.

Modern man produces a great deal of rubbish and this has to be disposed of in an economical manner - a common method used is to excavate large areas of waste ground and effectively 'bury' the rubbish; this results in the landfill sites so common in the U.K. and other countries.

This is a fairly effective means of waste disposal but there is an important aspect to consider - many of the components of the rubbish that has been buried are biodegradable and a by-product of this break-down is methane gas. There have been several well publicised instances of explosions on filled sites where gas has collected in pockets and then in some way been ignited.

One solution to this problem is to flare off the landfill gas and this simple approach is quite frequently adopted even to this day. This total loss system means however that a significant potential energy source is lost and over the last few years much thought has been given to ways of utilising the gas produced naturally in these sites.

There are two main approaches to using the landfill gas which are attracting attention at present, particularly in the U.K:-

i   The direct use of the gas as a fuel in kilns, ovens etc. for firing bricks or similar products.

ii The indirect use of the gas to fuel gas turbines which in turn drive electrical generators. The power generated can either by used to satisfy local industrial/commercial electricity requirements or be exported to the National Grid.

The first approach is being adopted successfully in many industries and the use of landfill gas in this way is expected to increase in the next decade - compressors/blowers do find use in these installations.

However, it is felt that the second approach i.e., the utilisation of landfill gas for energy generation through a gas turbine, as shown in Fig.1, has even greater potential (particularly in the U.K. if privatisation of the Electrical Supply Industry takes place). Several projects have been completed which indicates the viability of this method of power generation. It is this use of landfill gas therefore that is considered.

The complete power generation installation is a fairly complex one and this paper concentrates on one aspect of the system - namely the compressor unit necessary to provide the gas turbine with gas at suitable, usable inlet conditions.

The compressor is an important part of any viable, landfill generation scheme since it provides the link between the energy source (landfill gas) and energy user (gas turbine).

The landfill gas as it comes from the site collection system can vary significantly in pressure due to ambient conditions, contents of the landfill etc. In addition the pressure will be fairly low - rarely much above atmospheric.

In this form the energy source cannot be utilised by the turbine which requires gas at a predictable and much higher pressure to operate efficiently and satisfactorily (typically 14/22 Bar g depending on the make and size of the turbine used).

The compressor supplies this link by drawing the required quantity of gas from the collection points and compressing it to a controlled, predictable delivery pressure. With suitable aftercooling this compressed gas can be rendered suitable for use in the turbine which in turn drives the electrical generation equipment.

At this stage it might be useful to discuss in more depth the characteristics required for successful gas compression and the economics of machine type selection.

First consider the gas input to the compressors - this can vary from sub-atmospheric to just above atmospheric pressure and the compressor must be capable of accommodating this variation both in respect of the change in volume flow this implies (to maintain a given mass flow to the turbine) and in respect of the change of overall compression ratio this results in, whilst maintaining the required pressure into the turbine.

The variation in volume flow can be accommodated by sizing the compressor inlet capacity to give the turbine requirement at the lowest expected gas inlet pressure and then reducing compressor capacity at higher inlet pressures to match the mass flow requirements of the turbine. The control system has a significant influence on the economic operation of the whole installation and the possible methods of control are discussed in detail later.

The variation in overall compression ratio can be considerable over a period of time and is an unavoidable aspect of landfill gas compression which can have a significant bearing on the selection of compressor type particularly where flexible economic performance is important.

Another very important area to be considered is the total power absorbed by the compression train. This includes the power requirements of ancillary equipment such as closed circuit cooling water systems if fitted

but the main source of power usage is of course the compressor itself. The importance of having the most economical method of gas compression will become evident when it is realise that the only commercially useful electricity energy generated by the turbine installation is that available for use either on the site or for export to the national network - thus any power used by the gas compression system is "parasitic" in nature and if this parasitic power is excessive then the viability of the whole project will be in question.

It is the importance of all these parameters in both combination and isolation that has placed emphasis on the use of high quality reciprocating gas compressors in this application. A more detailed treatment of all these aspects is given below.

1 INLET GAS TREATMENT

The condition of the gas handled by the compressor will obviously influence the reliability and performance of the gas compression unit and the possible need for actual treatment of the inlet gas should be considered. Practical experiences in this direction will be discussed later and general comments will suffice at this stage.

The composition of the gas produced will depends on the nature of the landfill used so that the importance of pre-treatment will vary from site to site. Certainly all available information of site constituents should be obtained and a typical gas analysis would be most useful. See Table 1 for typical composition.

2 WEATHER PROTECTION/NOISE REDUCTION

Most landfill sites tend to be in fairly open areas and this means that equipment could be subject to inclement weather conditions. Again, each site should be assessed on its particular merits and the approach varied to suit. In some cases the site operator may house the equipment in purpose-made buildings - this could be expensive in itself although the equipment would not then require weatherproofing (suitable enclosures for electrical motors, protection/control switches etc. to operate in a potentially hazardous environment would still be required however).

If the equipment is required to operate outdoors then all electrical equipment should be suitably weatherproofed and all openings, breathers etc. should be appropriately protected. A simple canopy could be fitted over the installation to protect it from direct rainfall although some weatherproofing would still be advisable.

If the site is in an environmentally-sensitive area or close to residential property then the noise aspect should also be considered. A watercooled reciprocating gas compressor is in itself fairly quiet but the effect of any cooling fans or other ancillary equipment should also be included in the assessment.

The treatment of noise can prove a delicate area in any circumstance but this is particularly so in the case of landfill gas generation installations since the demands of local noise regulation and/or environmental or residential pressure groups have to be weighed against the very considerable cost of a high degree of noise control. Very effective acoustic enclosures can be designed for this type of equipment and these can incorporate hazard warning, fire control and other systems but the considerable capital cost may well effect the viability of the project. With careful selection of fans, low noise motors etc. a compromise noise emission level can often be achieved.

3   VARIATION IN INLET VOLUME FLOW

For a given load, a gas turbine requires a certain energy input from the fuel gas and this in turn represents, for a given gas calorific value, a particular mass flow requirement. In order to achieve this the compressor has to provide a consistent volume flow of gas commonly measured in Nm^3/h. This volume is referred to NTP (usually taken as 0^oC 1.013 Bar A dry gas). It will be evident from this that since landfill gas is almost certainly water saturated, the gas temperature will usually be significantly above 0^oC and the inlet gas pressure could be below atmospheric, then the actual inlet gas volume flow that the compressor needs to handle will invariably be appreciably larger than the reference flow corresponding to the mass flow. Furthermore there will be day to day variation in the gas inlet conditions which will again result in variation of the inlet volume requirement.

As stated earlier the usual approach is to size for the maximum

likely volume requirement and rely on the control system to take care of the variation. This matching is facilitated by the use of reciprocating compressor systems where different cylinders (and combinations of cylinders) can be fitted on one crankcase of the appropriate power capability. This means that different sites with their differing gas inlet conditions and turbine requirements can be accommodated by simply altering cylinder sizing whilst retaining the main components. This has considerable advantages in servicing and spares particularly if one operator has several sites each with differing characteristics.

Additionally, if there was over a long period of time a significant change in the properties of the landfill gas and/or a drastic change in the site requirements, the modular design reciprocating compressors could be amenable to an on-site cylinder change to match more accurately the new conditions. This is a somewhat drastic approach but the very fact that it is possible indicates the flexibility of this system. Because of the importance of economical operation it should be re-emphasised that the modular approach on reciprocating gas compressors allows optimisation of efficiencies, speeds, temperatures etc. for each individual site. No other type of compressor has this total flexibility which is so vital for the successful operation of this type of installation.

4   VARIATION IN OVERALL COMPRESSION RATIO

As with any natural product, landfill gas can be subject to considerable variation of ambient temperature, variation in composition of different areas of landfill and/or variation in call-off of the gas. In addition the method of gas collection may have some influence.

One of the parameters which will be subject to variation as a result of the above is the pressure of the gas at the compressor inlet. In some cases this will be slightly above atmospheric pressure but quite often it will be significantly sub-atmospheric. There will of course be variations in pressure from site to site which can be accommodated by appropriate cylinder matching as discussed previously. Of more significance however is the variation in pressure which occurs from day to day (or even hour to hour) at any particular site. This variation may well be large so that, even with a constant delivery pressure, the compressor is required to accommodate a fluctuating overall compression ratio.

This of course is a most undesirable state of affairs for any fixed ratio type of machine - or indeed a dynamic machine with its relatively limited ratio capability. With either of these types any significant variation of compression ratio from the rated value will result in less-than-optimum operation.

In marked contrast to this, the reciprocating gas compressor has a high tolerance of overall compression ratio variation particular with the modular arrangement of crankcase/cylinder previously discussed. When the initial selection is being performed, the likely limits of inlet pressure (and if applicable, delivery pressure) are taken into account and the cylinder arrangement selected to give good operation characteristics over the compression ratio range. This selection takes into account all the aspects resulting from the compression ratio variation such as volumetric efficiencies, stage delivery temperatures, line loadings, stage working pressures etc. as applicable so that adequate service margins can be maintained, thus ensuring reliability as well as good overall performance.

5 COMPRESSION TRAIN POWER

This has been referred to earlier and is obviously extremely important, having as it does a real bearing on the long term economic viability of the installation - all power used here represents wasted energy that cannot be utilised on the site being served by the generation unit or exported to the grid.

The actual numbers and types of components on the compressor train which use power of course depend on the exact layout proposed. In many cases the landfill site is isolated and therefore a closed circuit cooling water system is provided. This system uses fans and pumps with a consequential use of electrical power. There may in addition be other minor users of electricity but the main user is of course the compressor driving motor. The emphasis is clearly on good specific power characteristics.

The actual power absorbed by the compressor does of course depend on the duty requirements of the particular installation. Factors which have an effect are the required mass flow (and therefore volume flow) of the turbine, the gas pressure necessary for satisfactory operation of the turbine and gas inlet conditions.

Again in this area the high quality reciprocating gas compressor does enjoy significant advantages since for a given combination of capacity/inlet pressure/delivery pressure, this type will absorb significantly less power than any other. The margin is difficult to quantify since it depends on individual circumstances but assuming alike-for-like comparison and similar tolerances for capacity and power being used a value of 10/15% is considered likely. This should of course be coupled with the already stated flexibility of operation for a complete assessment. See Table 2 for compressor reference list.

6 VARIATIONS IN RECIPROCATING COMPRESSORS FOR OPTIMUM PERFORMANCE

If the pursuit of economical power generation is to be carried as far as possible then, assuming that a reciprocating compressor is decided upon, the next step is to investigate in more depth the type of machine to be used and the detailed specification of ancillary equipments etc.

The initial move is to consider the number of stages of compression to be adopted - this depends on the particular site requirements/ parameters and normally can be one, two or three. In the case of landfill gas applications, the relatively low inlet pressure (giving as a consequence a relatively high overall compression ratio) normally results in two or three stage compression being necessary although if a gas engine rather than gas turbine is being employed a single stage machine could be a viable proposition.

General guidelines are as follows:

6.1 Single stage

Usually used on the lower compression ratios (say up to 5 to 1) this is the simplest form of compressor with no intercoolers or other complications.

Fairly large capacities can also be handled since each cylinder contributes to the inlet volume. Specific power tends to be inferior to multistage machines although the relative difference and the importance does depend on the particular requirements.

Other limitations which become apparent as the compression ratio increases are:-

(a) Relatively rapid reduction in volumetric efficiency with consequent fall-off of inlet capacity.

(b) Relatively rapid increase in delivery temperature. Gas inlet temperature obviously also has a significant effect on single stage machines.

In addition there can sometimes be difficulties in selection particularly at the higher compression ratios when load limitations and capacity requirements can sometimes conflict. Consequently there may be cases when a two stage machine represents the more viable proposition even though the compression ratio does appear to be in general within the orbit of single stage compression.

6.2   Two stage

Compression ratios up to 22 to 1 and above can be considered although at the higher end there is an overlap with three stage machines - the cut off point is ill-defined and depends entirely on the particular application. As always, in order to achieve optimum results each case is taken on its own particular merits.

The two stage machine is more expensive then the single stage because of the intercooler system required. Also, due to the sharing of stages between cylinders the inherent inlet volume capability is less for a given crankcase configuration. This sharing does however also have an advantage in so far as line loads and delivery temperature do not increase directly with the increase in compression ratio/pressure difference over the machine.

The specific power is good over a relatively wide range of conditions.

The two stage compression allows for optimisation to be carried out to any degree felt desirable in the particular application and there is plenty of scope for balancing site performance requirements with

economical selection of components such as intercoolers, aftercoolers etc. The modular approach of a fixed number of crankcases with differing power capability, each having a group of interchangeable cylinders which can be used in any required combination help to facilitate the optimisation process.

6.3   Three stage

This can be used satifactorily over a wide range of compression ratios and in landfill gas applications there is significant overlap between 2 and 3 stage machine. Again, the choice depends on the circumstances prevailing.

The three stage machine does tend to be the most expensive due to the fairly complicated interstage arrangements and the fact that the necessary three cylinders require the larger crankcase sizes to accommodate them. There are occasions however when this represents the most economical and satisfactory approach. Again the specific power is good over the range of compression ratios likely to be encountered in landfill application.

There are other aspects to be considered which can have a bearing on the satisfactory operation of the compressors and some of these are discussed below:-

6.4   Cooling systems

The majority of gas compressors, particularly in the larger power ranges, have water cooled cylinders so water has to be provided. As mentioned earlier, the closed circuit cooling water system with its air cooled radiator and water pumps is commonly used on landfill sites which are by definition often somewhat isolated and without easy access to the mains supply.

On most instances aftercooling is necessary as most turbines have a maximum permitted fuel gas inlet temperature. In addition, multistage compressors also require intercoolers.

There are several different appraoches to this aspect and the one adopted in any particular case depends on the circumstances peculiar to that case but some typical layouts and their advantages are discussed briefly below.

Water cooled aftercoolers are commonly used in industrial gas and air compression installations and have the advantage of being compact and capable of high specification/performance and if site water is readily available this would be the most satisfactory solution. The cooled gas will typically be 5/15°C above cooling water inlet temperature depending on the specification of the cooler – the higher the performance of the cooler the higher the cost and careful assessment is necessary to obtain the optimum balance between performance requirements and economical purchasing/operation.

If site water is not available and a closed circuit system is employed, water cooled aftercooling could have some disadvantage since the gas outlet temperature is dependant on the circuit cooling water temperature which in turn is dependant on the efficiency of the radiator and the ambient temperature at the site. As a consequence, in certain circumstances, the gas outlet temperature could be unacceptably high although each application should be examined on its merits – with moderate ambients prevailing, the compact water cooled unit (with its noise-free operation) may well still be considered the best solution.

If however the water cooled unit is not suitable then an aircooled aftercooler can be considered. This can either take the form of a separate air blast unit or be incorporated as part of the radiator block. In either case, the gas outlet temperature is only dependent on the prevailing ambient. The separate unit may have advantages in flexibility of installation and ease of arranging the gas delivery system but the combined radiators/aftercooler is obviously the more compact unit.

In either form air blast aftercooling tends to be more bulky than the comparable water cooled unit and of course any cooling fans used contribute to the overall noise level of the installation.

Intercooling is not applicable on single stage machines but where multistaging is necessary water cooled units are invariably employed on account of their compact design which facilitates incorporation into the interstage pipework system.

7 METHODS OF COMPRESSOR CONTROL

It will by now be obvious that the high quality reciprocating gas compressor, carefully engineered and tailored to suit the particular site, is ideally suited to provide a flexible and economic source of pressurised gas for landfill gas electricity generation installations. In order, however, to take full advantage of this flexibility and good specific power, careful consideration must be given to the compressor control system. The most commonly used systems are briefly discussed below.

7.1 Step control

In this control method, suction valves are unloaded in sequence to reduce capacity. The usual number of steps are two or three with double acting reciprocating compressors. This is a cheap and effective means of capacity control which is chiefly used on air compressors. It would rarely be used in landfill applications and is included mainly for completeness.

7.2 Bypass

This is a very common method for gas compressor installations of all types whereby any excess capacity is diverted back to the compressor suction via a suitable aftercooler or bypass cooler. This is a very cheap and effective modulating control system and, if the operating conditions are relatively stable, this is probably the most cost effective means of control and would be totally suitable for landfill applications. It does suffer from a very significant drawback however, namely that the absorbed power of the compression train remains unchanged even if most of the gas is being recirculated. Obviously therefore if variable conditions exist this is not the most economical means of control and does not allow full advantage to be taken of the reciprocating compressor's characteristically good specific power.

7.3 Variable speed drive

This is another modulating control method. In this case the capacity is adjusted by variation of the rotational speed of a variable speed motor. This method gives good capacity matching and has the advantage of giving a power reduction which follows fairly exactly the reduction in capacity. The main disadvantage of this system is the very high capital cost, but in addition care has to be taken, particularly if a large speed range is required, to provide sufficient flywheel inertia and lubricating oil pump capacity for the low speed end of the operation. Also one must be aware of the increased possibility of torsional peaks occuring somewhere in the speed range.

If the other problems can be satisfactorily addressed then the question of capital cost remains - a comparison of the likely saving in running costs with this might show that the pay-back period is acceptably short. Over the next few years the cost of this system may well fall in which case variable speed drive would be a very attractive possibility for landfill generation installations.

Throttle control

This again is a modulating system of control and in this case the compressor is equipped with a suction throttle valve which reduces the inlet pressure in response to a reduction in capacity requirement. This is a relatively cheap and simple system but it suffers from the fact that the power reduction is not directly proportional to the capacity reduction (typically a 55% inlet capacity corresponds to approximately 70% full load power). Further difficulty is the suction depression which occurs as a natural consequence of the inlet throttling. When the gas pressure is little if any above atmospheric pressure (as occurs in landfill installations) this results in the ingress of air into the system. If the critical air/gas ratios occur then the installation could be at hazard in some circumstances.

7.5 Stepless reverse flow (Hoerbiger)

This is a proprietary system for gas compressor which works on the principle of keeping the suction valve of a reciprocating compressor open for a controlled, variable portion of the delivery stroke thus modifying the indicator diagram and reducing the gas volume delivered accordingly. The power and volume reductions are approximately proportional. The initial costs are fairly high and this system has not been used specifically on landfill gas, but pay-back periods are likely to be fairly short and it is felt that there is potential for this method of modulating control in landfill applications.

8 EXPERIENCES GAINED ON A LANDFILL GAS INSTALLATION IN THE MIDLANDS

Many of the areas of attention have already been referred at some length previously but some additional comments can usefully be made.

(a) Much of the initial problems encountered were due to active chemicals being introduced into the gas stream by the inlet scrubber which had been fitted in order to remove the H_2S which was believed to be present in the landfill gas - in fact the conten was inconsequential and caused less problems than the projected cure. This experience emphasises the importance of carefully checking the constituents of the landfill gas to be handled and, based on this, deciding whether any inlet gas treatment is in fact necessary.

(b) Another area of initial difficulty was again connected with the nature of the landfill gas - the dropping out of water and heavy hydrocarbons at various points in the cycle. This problem has been resolved by altering the gas/cooling circuits to ensure that the gas remains above dew point at all times.

(c) The initial material specification for the compressors has proved basically satisfactory with Ni resist cylinder liners, stainless steel rods and valves and coated carbon steel interstage pipework although there is some feeling that maybe a lower carbon stainless steel than the 316L presently used could given even greater corrosion resistance.

(d) Drain traps have proved very susceptible to blocking up and a move has been made toward level controlled automatic discharge valves where applicable.

This installation is now operating satisfactorily but the experiences gained emphasise the importance of taking great care in the initial conceptual stages to ascertain as precisely as possible the operating conditions likely to prevail, particularly with regard to the landfill gas composition. Also it is imperative that suppliers of component and ancillary items such as coolers, compressor valves etc. are kept fully informed as to the likely conditions and are allowed where possible to make recommendations - obviously these should be fully implemented where possible.

Another interesting aspect of this installation is the fact that the calorific value of the landfill gas has recently improved which has meant that the gas pressure requirement at the turbine has reduced. The reciprocating gas compressors used in this installation can satisfactorily handle this reduction in overall compression ratio (which is quite drastic) with a consequent reduction in parasitic power absorbed. This has result in more power being available for export to the national grid - a good example of the flexibility of reciprocating compressors allowing full advantage to be taken of any beneficial change of conditions that may occur.

9 THE FUTURE OF ENERGY GENERATION FROM LANDFILL GAS

As the need for energy throughout the world increases and the traditional resources start to fail, sources of energy such as landfill gas will gain in importance.

It is visualised that more small factories or industrial estates will take their electrical supply from an adjacent landfill site by incorporating a gas turbine generation unit utilising this gas.

A further extension of this may be the use of gas engine generator sets for smaller electrical output requirements. The gas pressure required by a typical gas engine is much less than that required by a turbine and single stage compressors can be considered.

Advances will be made in control methods and condition monitoring and both turbines, engines and compressor will progressively improve their efficiency making this form of energy generation increasingly attractive.

Rubbish seems to have a promising future!!

Table 1   LANDFILL GAS COMPOSITION

Component	Typical Value (mature site)	Maximum Values
Methane	63.8	75.0
Carbon Dioxide	33.6	80.0
Nitrogen	2.3	60.0
Oxygen	0.16	5.0
Hydrogen	0.05	15.0
Carbon Monoxide	0.001	0.005
Saturated Hydrocarbons	0.003	0.05
Unsaturated Hydrocarbons	0.009	0.02

TYPICAL RANGE OF DUTIES AT PRESENT

BEING HANDLED

LANDFILL BIO GAS/SEWAGE GAS

Single Stage

Capacities: From 3.95 m^3/min to 48.5 m^3/min

Inlet Pressures: Sub-atmospheric to 2.0 Barg

Delivery Pressures: 2.4 Barg to 4.5 Barg

Higher capacities and Inlet/Delivery pressures can be accomodated within the compression ratio limitations of Single Stage compression.

Multi Stage

Capacities: Up to 58.5 m^3/min

Inlet Pressures: Sub-atmospheric to Atmospheric

Delivery Pressures: 15.5 Barg to 21.0 Barg

The use of two or three stages is dependent on the compression ration. Again, the use of appropriate cylinder sizings other capacities and pressures can be accomodated.

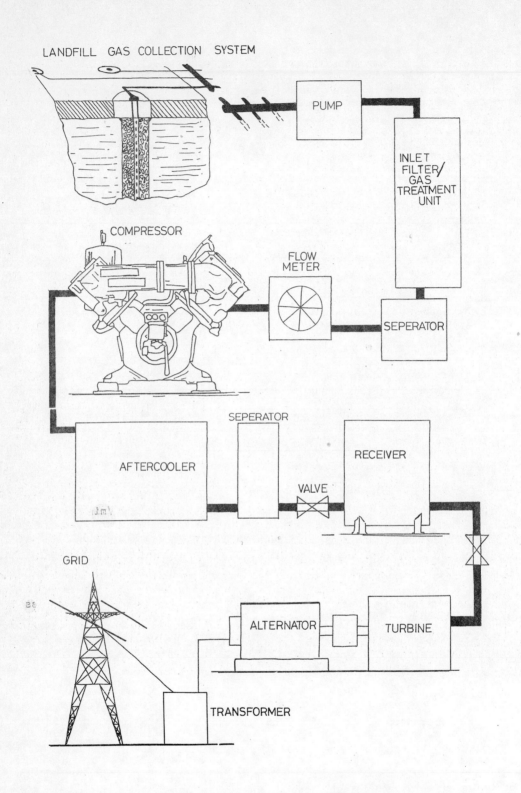

Fig 1   Simplified landfill gas power generation system

Fig 2   Three-stage landfull gas compressor

C390/020

Compressor installations to meet current relevant specifications for medical and breathable air

R M FIELDING and **C T BILLIET**
Domnick Hunter Filters Limited, Chester-le-Street, Co Durham

ABSTRACT

The revised specification for Medical Compressed Air Plant (C11) (Ref 1) which replaces in part HTM22 (Health Technical Memorandum 22) for product specification (not code of practice), has been developed through thirteen (13) discussion drafts and finally published in May 1988. HTM22 is recognised in many overseas markets due to the absence of any other standards, so C11 will be of interest in both the UK and overseas.

This paper reviews the principal technical requirements of the Compressed Air Plant which involves duplication of all equipment required to compress, store, treat and distribute air at 7 bar g for surgical use in operating theatres and 4 bar g for respirable use.

The maximum permissible limits of contaminants are reviewed and advice presented as to the most efficient method of achieving them.

The requirements for protective devices and indicators are considered together with requirement for compressor control including cyclical sequence operation.

Filtration and drying equipment is discussed and advice given on installation, control and servicing.

INTRODUCTION

The extent of C11 Specification relates only to product specifications and is not intended as a Code of Practice. On review of the Code it has become apparent that anomolies still exist and there are points for further informed discussion although at the time of writing it is not known if a further review of the document is underway.

C11 will prove to be an invaluable document for those people responsible for the provision of high quality air for medical applications.

These principles can be applied to other areas, such as instrumentation, pharmaceutical, electronic manufacture and especially breathing air. Consideration must also be given to the Control of Substances Hazardous to Health Regulations (COSHH) which are due for implementation in the UK in 1989 with particular reference to air purity when required for breathing purposes, and the validation thereof.

The selection of a compressor/air treatment package which includes the necessary purification to comply with not only the C11 specification but also BS 4275 (Ref 2) and BS 4001 (Ref 3) will become a major issue in the near future. Reliability, cost effectiveness, ease of maintenance and performance efficiency will be the paramount criteria when procurement is considered.

Trials have been conducted both in-house and in actual installations. Techniques and product specifications, with performance validation are outlined in this document, for the provision of air whose purity exceeds any known related standard.

The requirement stated by C11 is lited below:-

Dry particulate - 0.01 mg/m^3
Oil - 0.5 mg/m^3 Liquid aerosol and vapour
Water - 115 mg/m^3 (dewpoint minus 40°C atmospheric pressure)
Carbon Monoxide - 5.5 mg/m^3 (5ppm)
Carbon Dioxide - 900 mg/m^3 (500 ppm)

DESCRIPTION OF SYSTEM

The Medical Compressed Air Plant comprises element 04 of the code and includes 22 Clauses.

The configuration of the plant may be schematised as in Figure 1. comprising as a minimum : two identical compressor/aftercooler units; one air receiver; Duplex filtration/Dryer system; non-return valves, isolating valves, gauges and differential pressure switches; a plant operating and status indication system; plant intake system and multi-purpose test point; and an emergency/reserve manifold. Employed downstream of the regulating valve is an air sterilizing filter, suitable for complete bacteria removal.

COMPRESSOR TYPE AND CAPACITY

The capacity of the plant must provide a minimum of the Average Continuous Demand (ACD) specified by the user with one compressor a stationary unit, and needs to produce a minimum of 5 m^3/K Wh (4 scfm/Hp) at a continuous plant flow rate of 100% and 10% of the ACD over a 6 hour period. The system pressure must be capable of

achieving 7 bar g downstream from a minimum pressure valve, and the compressors are normally operating at about 10 bar g. The compressor type is not specified and may be of both Oil Lubricated or Non-lubricated types. Previous custom has been to specify Oil Lubricated Compressors based on technology available in 1972.

There appears still to be a reluctance in the industry to accept the use of compressors using Flourocarbon coated sealing faces due to the possibility of the polymer pyrolysing in a compressor overheat situation. The likelihood of this ever happening is extremely remote and the reliability of such machines has improved over the past decade.

However, with the relatively high capital cost and service outlay associated with this type of compressor the use of an oil

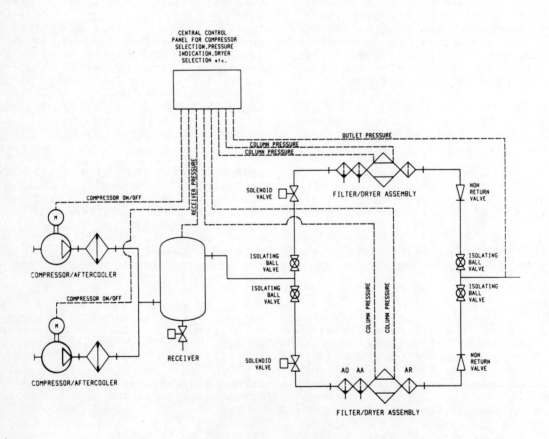

Fig 1   Description of system

lubricated unit combined with suitable high efficiency coalescing/adsorption filters dictate that the air quality cannot be improved upon from this configuration. Ambient levels of hydrocarbon from unburnt fuels from Transportation and Industrial Manufacturing processes have been shown to be significantly higher when compared with the air purity required in the specification (Ref 4). This fact alone means that High Efficiency Filtration is a definite requirement to guarantee compliance with the specification.

CONTAMINATION

The common contamination levels of compressed air have been well documented (Ref 5) but as a review the major ones are tabulated (Table 1) below with their typical relative concentration levels.

regulated by use of sonic nozzles situated at the inlet of each independant purification train. This will ensure that as the system pressure fluctuates between the high and low levels the contact times required during the adsorption and chemisorption/catalytic stages are not exceeded.

The nozzle is situated downstream from the pre-filter which will provide air with a maximum remaining oil aerosol content of 0.5 mg/m^3 with 100% removal of particulate matter removal down to 1 micron. The function of the receiver therefore is to provide sufficient volume to run the plant until the plant emergency condition is achieved due to low pressure.

Table 1. Level of contaminants to be expected

Contaminant	Source	Typical Concentration
Dirt particles	Atmosphere	up to 140×10^6/m^3
Carbon	Burnt Oil	up to 10 mg/m^2
Water	Atmosphere	up to 11 g/m^3
Rust	Pipework	up to 4 mg/m^3
Oil	Compressor lubricant	5 – 50 mg/m^3
Oil/water emulsion	Mixture of oil and water	up to 11 g/m^3
Vapour	Gaseous oil	0.05 – 0.5 mg/m^3
Micro-organisms	Atmosphere	up to 3,850/m^3 [2]
Unburnt hydrocarbon	Atmosphere	up to 0.5 mg/m^3

After compression, aftercoolers typically of the air-blast type are employed to reduce the outlet temperature of the compressed air to a maximum of 15°C above the local ambient temperature, further water cooled aftercooler units may be used if the delivery temperature to a desiccant dryer is expected to be above +50°C.

An air receiver, with adequate drainage facilities is required with a minimum water capacity of 50% ACD. The system pressure is regulated from this receiver with pressure sensing dictating the load/off load sequence of the compressors.

AIR PURIFICATION

A duplex air treatment/purification package is situated downstream from this receiver and it is recommended that the volumetric flow through this package is

A further high efficiency filter, with particle removal down to 0.01 micron and oil aerosol removal to 0.01 mg/m^3 will protect the twin adsorption columns which will reduce the water vapour content to a maximum of 115 mgm^3 (dewpoint of -40°C at atmospheric pressure).

Such a package is shown schematically in Figure 2 combining both manual isolating ball valves and electrically operated solonoid valves for duty dryer or standby dryer deployment, subject to the status of the control circuitry and the condition of the alarm safeguards installed. The solenoid valves are designed as fail safe, i.e. inlet normally open and purge valves normally closed.

Experience has shown by the use of an upstream water separator utilising mechanical separation, the fibrous pre-filter is adequately protected from surges of oil or water 'slugs' which may occur following a possible drain malfunction upstream or following a period of de-commissioning allowing condensate accumulation in upstream pipework. Figure 2 depicts a package supplying 120 scfm @ 7 bar g ANR and gives an indication of the compactness of such a design.

can be 'snowstorm' filled gives each desiccant particle its minimum potential energy or maximum packing density. Sensitive work on fixed adsorption beds utilising this facility, it has been shown to have the effect (by truncation of the adsorption isotherm) of increasing the adsorptive capacity of the column by a factor of 5 times a conventionally filled column.

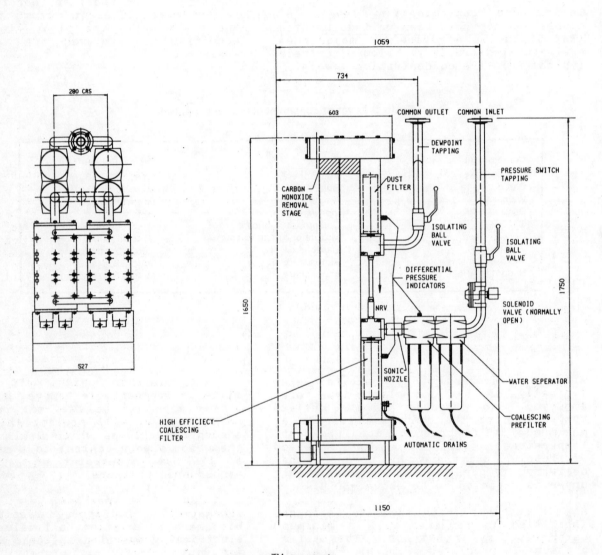

Fig 2   Pneudri^{TM} (duplex)

The dryer itself is based upon a very successful modular design (Pneudri^{TM} range of desiccant dryer) which utilises a twin tower extrusion and is shown in conjunction with control valves in Fig. 3. (Ref 5). The controlled air flow distribution through the columns allows for extremely efficient adsorption profiles to be achieved, and the fact that the columns

146

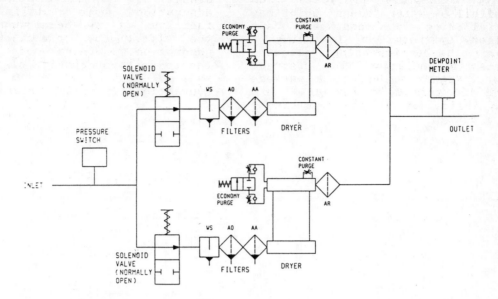

Fig 3   Standby and duty dryer configuration

The adsorbent chosen for this application is a selected grade of Molecular Sieve 13X (spherical bead 2.5 - 4 mm diameter). This has been shown to give optimum pressure loss characteristics with respect to the length/diameter ratio. The selectivity of this adsorbent, when used in a heatless pressure swing (PSA) mode has also been shown to effectively remove completely the remaining hydrocarbon content of the compressed air thus obviating the requirement for an activated carbon stage in the purification train. This is also a major benefit when servicing or maintenance of the dryer is being considered.

Toxic gas removal is mainly confined to the removal of carbon monoxide (CO) through chemisorption and catalysis utilising a compacted granular hopcalite bed. In this design the catalyst is housed in the same common extrusion and enjoys the benefit of identical volumetric flow conditions through each column, regulated by the uniform packing density of the adsorbent in the main section of the column. Provided contact times are not exceeded, the catalytic bed will totally remove incident carbon monoxide levels, but during the process, which is by oxidation of CO to carbon dioxide (CO_2) outlet levels of CO_2 should not exceed the specified amount of 900 mg/m^3 (500 ppm).

Again, by using a heatless PSA dryer, selective adsorption of CO_2 on the molecular sieve has been achieved. This has the effect of reducing the CO_2 content of the outlet air - this can only be achieved because of the relatively fast cycle times of the dryer.

DRYER CONTROL

By use of outlet non-passive check valves in conjunction with air operated purge valves, the PSA process is timed pneumatically using an air motor and cam timer driving pilot valves over typically a 2.5 minute half cycle. This ensures that the Mass Transfer Zone (MTZ) within the drying column is confined to a relatively small portion of the adsorbent bed at the inlet, of the column, allowing adsorption selectivity to occur. The dryers are thus totally automatic and will commence functioning when air pressure (min. 4 bar g) is available.

Energy costs are regulated by two methods:-
a) Dewpoint sensing
b) Purge shut-off during compressor unload periods

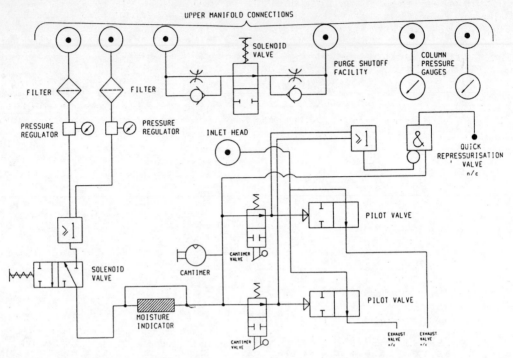

UPPER MANIFOLD CONNECTIONS

FILTER FILTER SOLENOID VALVE PURGE SHUTOFF FACILITY COLUMN PRESSURE GAUGES

PRESSURE REGULATOR PRESSURE REGULATOR INLET HEAD QUICK REPRESSURISATION VALVE n/c

PILOT VALVE

CAMTIMER VALVE CAMTIMER

SOLENOID VALVE

MOISTURE INDICATOR

PILOT VALVE

CAMTIMER VALVE EXHAUST VALVE n/c EXHAUST VALVE n/c

Fig 4   Dryer control circuit

Circuit and valving is shown in Figure 4. The valves employed are failsafe, for example, the purge control valves are normally shut so there is no possibility of rapid depressurisation during a power failure event.

a) Dewpoint sensing is achieved by taking a small bleed of air (0.5 Lmin⁻¹) from downstream of the outlet high efficiency dust removal filter and traversing it across a silicon chip based Hygrometer. This type of Hygrometer has been selected because of its rapid speed of response at low dewpoint temperatures. The output from this device is monitored via a small DC jack and will automatically switch the duty dryer to the standby dryer if the outlet dewpoint becomes wetter than -26°C (500 mgm^{-3}). An alarm is activated as a plant emergency condition should this event occur. The other plant emergency alarm will activate should the system pressure fall to 0.5 bar below the standby compressor cut in pressure.

b) Purge shut-off facility: This is necessary to ensure the energy loss in purge requirement is linked directly to the mass flow through the dryer. With all designs of PSA drying systems not requiring additional energy inputs in the form of heat, the amount of purge air required is a minimum of the same volumetric flow throughput of air during the drying cycle. For example, if there has been a 50% utilisation of drying column at 7 bar g then the dryer during its half cycle regeneration will require 50% of its purge volume to regenerate the bed.

With traditional dryers employing two fabricated vessels as the twin columns, there is generally more purge requirement because of the uneven flow distribution through the bed caused by channelling of the desiccant due to unfavourable packing densities being achieved in assembly.

With this pneumatic control system, as the compressor unloads during low demand periods, a normally closed solenoid valve is activated and the purge is stopped. When the compressor loads, indicating there is a flow demand through the dryer, the purge is re-instated and the dryer, because of the inherent memory in the form of air motor/cam timer, is not subjected to overloading the adsorption capacity of the desiccant beds. This facility ensures the Mass Transfer Zone created by the water vapour isotherm does not traverse the length of unused bed at the dryer outlet and the emergent dewpoint does not detriorate.

The status indicators of such a dryer unit are depicted in Figure 5, and are colour coded to comply with the C11 specification.

The plant pipework upstream of the NRV should provide for a multi-purpose test point to allow for air purity checks to be made.

Monitoring of dewpoint in this manner has been shown to have a correlation with the air purity in terms of other contaminants, notably oil, in these critical applications.

Should malfunction of the compressor occur, causing threat to the coalescing filter integrity for example an 'o' ring seal failure, then a snowstorm filled desiccant bed will effectively remove the majority of these by-pass aerosols by impaction. The result of this is the sites available in the zeolite (desiccant) lattice become choked with oil and progressively prevent the adsorption of water vapour onto the desiccant. As the water vapour isotherm will always travel in front of oil contamination, the first indication will be breakthrough of this isotherm causing the outlet dewpoint to deteriorate. The alarm condition therefore, set at -26°C ADP will activate long before the oil contamination can breach the desiccant bed. Also, the catalytic stage which is poisoned by water vapour, will remain active for a period after this dewpoint is reached, so the carbon monoxide impurity will be successfully oxidised and risk to the user eliminated.

OTHER CONSIDERATIONS

There are a number of issues relating to the provision of breathing air for which there is no definitive solution as yet. The purpose of this section is to highlight some of these issues to enable further consideration to be given:-

.   The use of PTFE ring or oil lubricated compressors - with advances in design of both types, the possibility of the pyrolysis products of oil or flourocarbon polymers inside the compression chamber must be extremely remote. Should this occur though, the pyrolysis products of PTFE depend upon a number of factors, such as the nature of the intact polymers, temperature, atmosphere and pyrolysis vessel. To predict the type or multiplicity of these PTFE decomposition products is a difficult task thus design of a purification filter to cope with all permutations is not feasible.

.   Oil manufacturers or suppliers will not recommend the use of their mineral oils or some synthetic blends in breathing applications. More investigation should be placed on such oils as Polyalphaolefins, of which some highly saturated versions are approved for this purpose.

.   There is contradiction in the amount of water vapour that can be present in breathing air. C11 advocates the use of -40°C ADP, but a study of relevant documentation generally deprecates any form of drying.

.   The use of humidifiers downstream of compressed air filtration is controversial, due to the possibility of water reservoir stagnation in poorly maintained systems and large droplets or 'slugs' of condensate or re-intrained aerosols appearing at the point of expansion causing discomfort to the user.

From the experience of the authors, the use of air at the low dewpoints specified has not caused any discomfort to the user and in some circumstances, particulary full hood or suit supplies, the dry air has significantly improved comfort by reducing humidity and excess perspiration within the confines of the suit.

.   Oxygen depletion by use of membrane separation systems has given cause for concern. Trials on the desiccant materials molecular sieve 13X grade and activated alumina have shown there is no detectable reduction of the delivered oxygen concentration downstream of this particular dryer. One should be aware however that if other grades of molecular sieve are used (e.g. 5A) then oxygen concentration will vary.

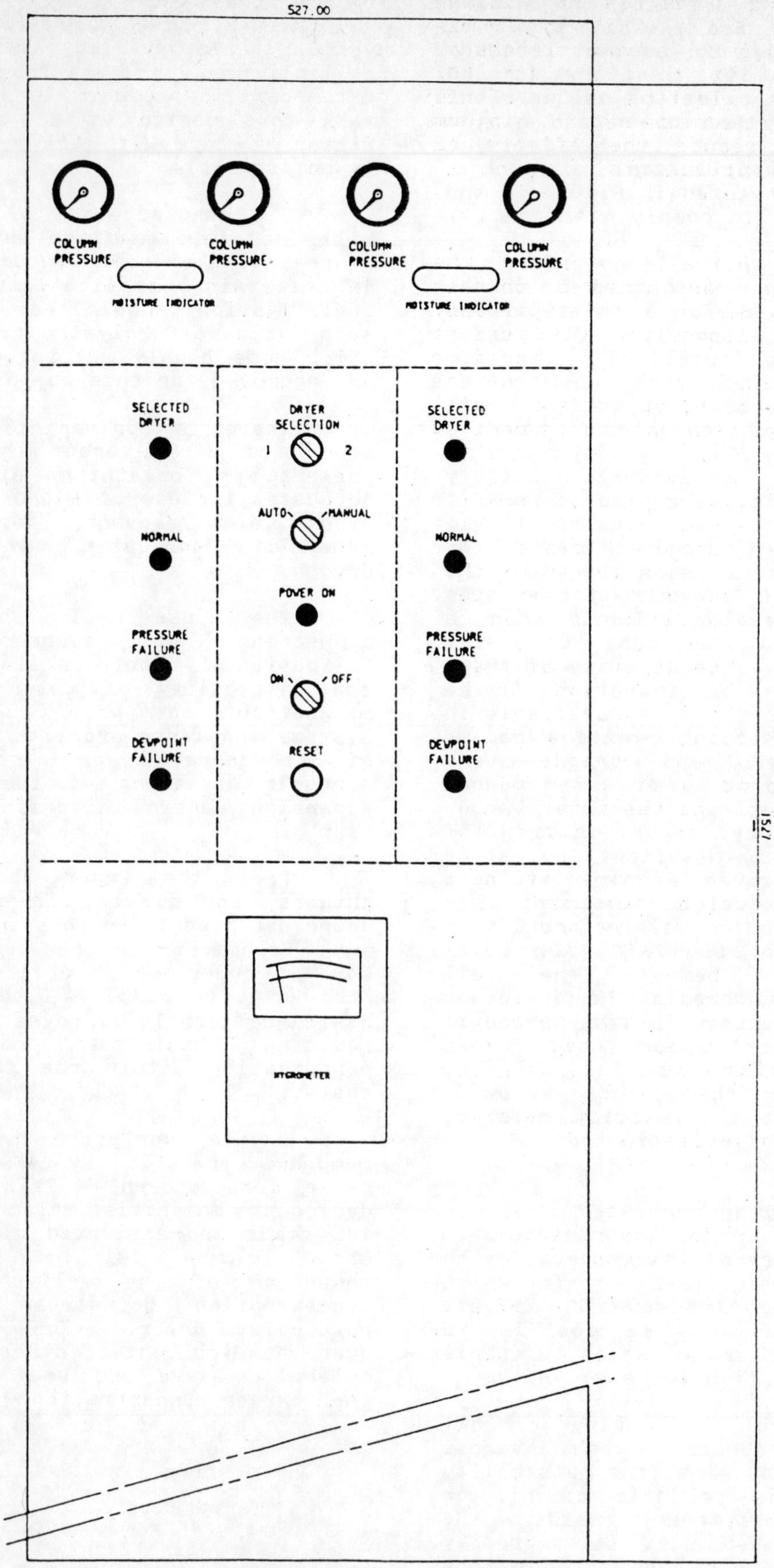

Fig 5   Dryer status facia

. Maximum levels of CO_2 are quoted in standards but there is no minimum requirement for B.A. This system is designed to reduce the ambient levels of CO_2 by 25 - 50% to allow for CO_2 addition through oxidation of CO. It is considered important to retain minimum CO_2 levels to reduce the effects of possible hyper-ventilation.

SUMMARY

By compliance with the C11 standard, the recommendations contained therein relating to design, installation, maintenance and inspection will ensure that correctly specified compressor equipment combined with the correct choice of air treatment package, will provide high quality air for medical use.

The emphasis should not be allowed to rest there and the standards relating to the air purity requirements for breathing air need review to take into account improved legislation and state of the art filtration products.

REFERENCES

1. National Health Service Model
    Engineering Specifications
    C11 - Medical Gases May 1988
    (Wessex Regional Health
     Authority)

2. BS 4275 : 1974 'Recommendations
    for The Selection Use and
    Maintenance of Respiratory
    Protective Equipment'.

3. BS 4001 : Part 1 : 1981.
    Recommendations for the Care and
    Maintenance of Underwater
    Breathing Apparatus.

4. Department of the Environment
    Statistical Bulletin (87)1 -
    Air Quality (May 1987)

5. Billiet CT : Compressed Air
    Purification for Instrumenta-
    tion in the High Technology
    Industries.
    Publication Ref 32/86/UK DHF Ltd

C390/036

Nitrogen separation from air by permeable membranes—a new application for industrial air compressors

K E NICHOLDS
Consultant, Fladbury, Worcestershire
J K R PAGE
Calor Gas Limited, Datchet, Slough, Berkshire

SYNOPSIS The availability of advanced hollow fibre membranes for air separation process also presents the compressor industry with a major new opportunity. The technical requirements of air compressors for use in systems providing an on-site nitrogen service are explained and aspects of performance are identified where improvements would be of practical benefit.

INTRODUCTION

The separation of a gaseous mixture into its constituent parts by selective filtration or diffusion has been known for many years. A notable example using permeable membranes was the separation of the isotopes of uranium hexafluoride to produce concentrated U_{235}. The process has traditionally required a very high differential pressure to drive the desired molecules selectively through the permeable media in sufficient quantity to give a worthwhile yield. Consequently both the capital and operating costs have been high. This has made the process unattractive for air separation compared with alternative methods.

Industrial nitrogen, which is being increasingly used in many applications is usually produced by the liquefaction of air, followed by fractional distillation of the cryogenic liquid to separate the oxygen from the nitrogen and the other permanent gases. (Water, CO_2 and hydrocarbons will have been removed before liquefaction.) The nitrogen may be supplied to the point of use as a liquid, or it may be compressed to around 150 bar and supplied in bottles. Both routes require a distribution system, except for very large users where on-site generation by liquefaction may be used. Alternatively, on-site production may be achieved by the dissociation of ammonia, although this requires the NH_3 to be supplied. There is also the pressure-swing process, wherein columns of molecular sieves are alternately pressurised and de-pressurised with compressed air which has just been thoroughly treated to remove water vapour. The differential adsorbtion-desorbtion rates create a nitrogen-rich stream.

In recent years permeable membranes have been developed which can operate effectively at pressures within the range of ordinary industrial air compressors, and enable nitrogen to be generated on-site very economically. This is a significant development in view of the increased usage of nitrogen in applications ranging from inertion in areas of high fire risk, to the preservation of food and the dispensing of beverages.

THE SEPARATION MEMBRANES

The permeable membranes are produced as very small-bore hollow fibres in plastic materials, with controlled micro-porosity walls. These are packed as bundles and the ends of the fibres are sealed externally into resin plugs as shown in Figure 1. The tube bundle is then sealed into a metal tube using static pressure seals. Air under pressure is fed to one end of the assembly and passes freely down the fibre bores with little loss of pressure. Each gas in the air has a characteristic permeation rate that is a function of its ability to dissolve and diffuse through the fibre wall membranes. This characteristic rate allows 'fast' gases such as oxygen and water vapour to be separated from 'slow' gases such as nitrogen and argon.

Residence time within the fibres is important in determining the purity of the yield, and the vent point along the assembly also has an effect on the performance. The relative permeation rates of the different constituents is also shown in Figure 1.

PERFORMANCE PARAMETERS

Interaction between inlet air pressure, inlet temperature and flow rate, determines the quality of the gas. This is shown in Figure 2. The effect of temperature is to increase the permeability of the hollow fibre walls for all the species of gas in the supply air. The net result is generation of higher purity nitrogen at a given outlet flowrate, but this is at the expense of higher input air flowrate because more nitrogen (and argon) are being lost to the permeate stream.

Generally temperatures between +45°C and +50°C at inlet are desirable. Minimum supply pressures should be 10 bar, although 7-8 bar operation is still feasible.

Because water is a "fast" gas, the nitrogen is extremely dry, the pressure dewpoint being -60°C for a 95% purity output, and as low as -75°C for a 99% purity output.

THE SUPPLY SYSTEM

A flow chart of a typical system based on a rotary oil-flooded compressor is shown in Figure 3 (the system based on a reciprocating compressor is very similar). A point to note is that the aftercooler, normally provided to knock out free water, is needed here to reduce the temperature of the air to below the upper limit of tolerance for the air filtration system and the membranes. A heater is provided, with thermostatic control, to ensure that the temperature of the air and the membrane is also being maintained at the selected operational level.

The membrane is tolerant to oil vapour, and the degree of protection shown is strictly only necessary where food, pharmaceuticals or electronic materials processing demands oil-free gas. For inerting applications, the purification system could be simplified, but these standard Air Separator packages are always fitted with the three stages of filtration in particle, aerosol and odour removal when used in lubricated compressors. If an oil-free compressor is used, then the aerosol removal stage is omitted.

TYPES OF COMPRESSOR

Dry and lubricated reciprocating, oil-flooded rotary vane, and oil-flooded rotary screw compressors have been used successfully in installations ranging from 1.0 to 200 hp. The greater durability of oil-flooded machines gives them an edge over dry reciprocating machines in unattended applications where reliability is essential.

EXAMPLES OF APPLICATIONS

Numerous applications will arise due to the convenience and economics of on-site generated nitrogen.

BEER DISPENSING

The provision of an over-pressure on keg or bulk stored beer or lager in a public house cellar both provides a driving force for dispensing at the tap, and also prevents deterioration of the beverage by oxidation. In practice a mixture of nitrogen and CO_2 is used. Figure 4 shows a practical installation. Note the miniature rotary compressor developed for the air supply, the Air Separator unit, and the gas mixture metering valve. This plant is provided with downstream receivers to cope with peak demands, but would be capable of dispensing beer at a rate of 170 pints per hour continuously; there is also a smaller unit with a continuous 40 pint per hour capability.

FOOD STORAGE

Nitrogen is now used to provide a controlled atmosphere for the preservation of vegetables in storage, and for keeping the quality of perishable vegetables such as lettuce whilst in transit. There is also a growing trend towards presenting packaged food in transparent containers. By using controlled permeability wrappings and Nitrogen/CO_2/O_2 gas fills, many foods can be preserved for much longer than is possible with close wrapped refrigerated food packs.

Note, however, that while the process does inhibit the growth of aerobic bacteria, presentation in a refrigerated cabinet is still essential for controlling anaerobic bacteria.

INERTING AND PURGING

Figure 5 shows the type of equipment which is in service in North Sea oil rigs to provide inerting nitrogen gas. Similar systems are used off-shore for purging of storage holds in tanker vessels. The convenience of on-site generation from portable Air Separator systems has been found ideal for purging land-based fuel tanks and underground gas pipelines.

TYRE INFLATION

Air-filled pneumatic tyres which are subjected to high temperatures in service - including conduction of heat from e.g. disc brakes - are prone to sudden failure as a result of rubber oxidation, corrosion of steel wall bracing, intra-wall pressurisation and, more rarely, explosive hydrocarbon air mixtures being developed. These hazards are minimised by using nitrogen for tyre inflation, and this is now mandatory for aircraft tyres, where inflation pressures of up to 17 bar would otherwise increase the oxygen content by that factor. The production of nitrogen on-site on an airfield to provide a local supply for tyre inflation considerably eases the logistics of aircraft maintenance, particularly on remote fields. Recompression into bottles would be necessary for the larger aircraft.

METALLURGY

Processes such as furnace brazing, sintering and heat treatment, benefit from the use of nitrogen as an inert blanketing and heat transfer medium.

OPERATING COST INDICATIONS

Capital, maintenance and power costs together determine the economics of nitrogen produced by membranes. Figure 6 shows, for a large single membrane assembly, the unit cost for various levels of purity against the annual total of operating hours. The cost reduces considerably as the utilisation increases, but increases as the purity increases. This is because the yield reduces as the residence time needed to produce higher purity increases. If the demand level is greater than that from the largest single tube assembly available it is possible to manifold single tube assemblies into a parallel array. This has a potential cost advantage in that:
- the capital cost element of the compressor tends to reduce as a specific cost as compressor size increases.
- the operating efficiency of compressor plant tends to increase as its size does, so that operating costs reduce.
- the number of stand-by compressors (if any) can be reduced.

THE NEEDS OF THE FUTURE

These state of the art hollow fibre membranes as described above, are both stable and robust, with life expectancy in excess of 7 working years. Furthermore the Air Separators incorporating the membranes contain no complex or moving components: the gas purity is simply determined by regulation of its flowrate.

Clearly, for such systems, compressor performance is now the key issue determining overall reliability, efficiency and cost.

In this new area of application for air compressors, screw machines are clearly preferred for power levels above about 20 kW but, below that level no single compressor type is currently seen to be capable of dominating over others.

The aspects of compressor development required specifically to benefit the Air Separation process with membranes are:-

- CONVERSION EFFICIENCY - At any level of purity, the process costs are largely determined by the cost of the power input, hence the need to use compressors with a genuine high conversion efficiency, expressed as M^3/kWh. The present level of around 7 at 10 bar needs to be increased, particularly because the membrane recovery factor reduces the overall yield rate.

- PRESSURE - Process economics indicate that the required supply air pressure for membranes, currently 10 bar minimum, will tend to increase in future to, say, 13-14 bar. There is a challenge here to the industry to improve conversion efficiency at higher compression ratios. Bearing in mind the purity/flow characteristic of membranes, perhaps an even greater challenge is the desirability of up to 30% turn-down in air flowrate from a given compressor at the constant nominal set pressure without sacrificing efficiency or needing to include a bulky air receiver in the supply line.

- SIMPLICITY - For many, if not all applications, the duty of a given system will be of constant flow demand. The normal industrial compressor has modulating controls developed for conventional air supply systems which add complexity and cost, may compromise reliability, and could perhaps be dispensed with for the process described.

- DURABILITY AND RELIABILITY - In the applications listed, the reliability of the system is of paramount importance. The compressors - including drive, cooling system, control ancillaries - because they are machines with moving parts, are most likely to be the cause of breakdown. Compressors generally have a good reputation for reliability, but difficulty has been experienced in forecasting the statistical reliability from manufacturers. Ideally, an MTBF of 10,000 hours is needed, with a tolerance of $\pm$ 1,000 hours at the 99% confidence level.

- CLEAN DISCHARGE - Of the "contaminants" in the discharge from a lubricated compressor - particulates, water condensate, oil vapour and oil aerosol (water presents no problem for membranes of polysulphone hollow fibres). Indeed, gas from these membranes will be at least as dry as that obtained from bulk liquid nitrogen supplies.

Particulates and oil aerosol are both detrimental to membrane performance, and are generally highly undesirable in the product gas. Fortunately modern filtration technology has resulted in efficient devices for removing these species, but nevertheless there is real benefit in reducing the frequency and cost of filter maintenance by minimising the levels of solids and aerosol in the compressor discharge.

The present standard of air intake filters is not generally adequate, especially for reciprocating machines. While oil-flooded machines are effective in trapping ingested particles, the intake filters are seldom designed to survive for the full service intervals.

Oil vapour in the discharge from flooded or lubricated compressors is reduced initially by aftercooling and finally by activated charcoal filter stages.

The total, i.e. aerosol + vapour emission from the compressor also represents depletion of lubricant in the machines, so low emissions - measured before the aftercooler - are therefore desirable to minimise the need for attention to oil levels.

The capabilities of certain classes of compressors have enabled Air Separation using the modern hollow-fibre membranes to become economically attractive in a wide variety of applications. The challenge to the compressor industry, as this paper has explained, is that there is scope for improvement in some operational features of these machines which would further increase the viability of this form of on-site Nitrogen generation.

K E Nicholds, C.Eng., Fellow, is a consultant to Calor Gas Ltd. He retired as Engineering Director of The Hydrovane Compressor Company in 1988.

J K R Page is the Research Manager for Calor Air Separation, a division of Calor Gas Ltd. He was formerly Senior Research Manager at Fulmer Research Laboratories.

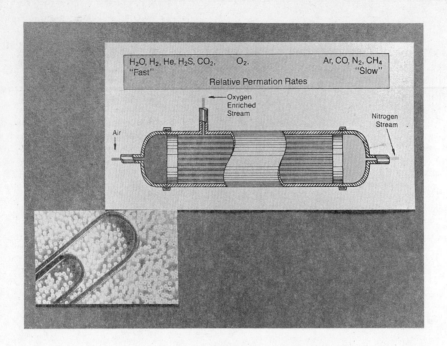

Fig 1 Gas membrane principles

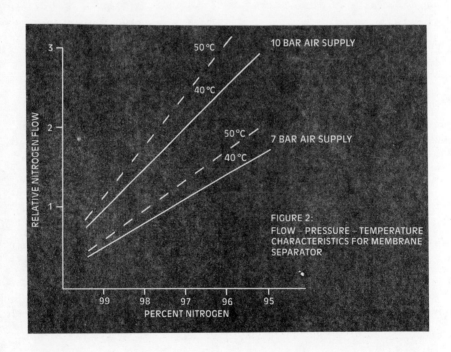

Fig 2 Flow—pressure—temperature characteristics for membrane separator

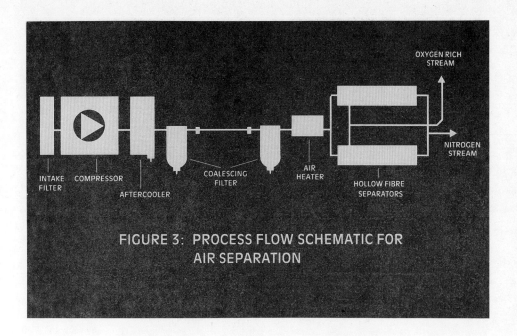

Fig 3   Process flow schematic for air separation

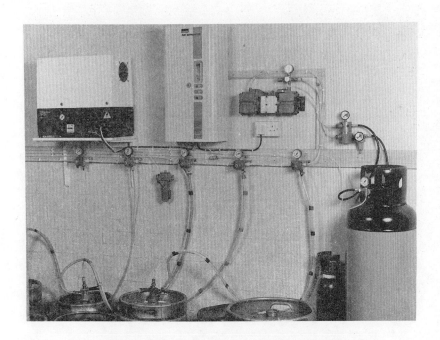

Fig 4   On-site nitrogen generator system for beer dispensing

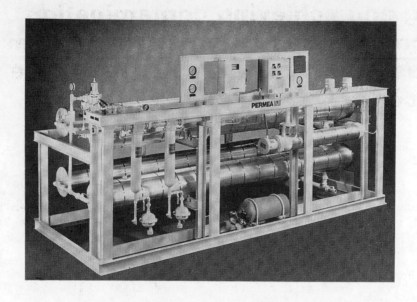

Fig 5   Membrane system for inerting

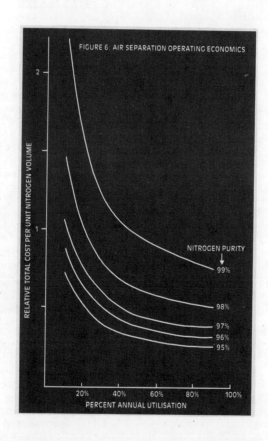

Fig 6   Air separation operating economics

C390/021

Specifying and achieving contamination levels in compressed air using the system of quality classes—with particular reference to humidity control

C T BILLIET
Domnick Hunter Filters Limited, Chester-le-Street, Co Durham

ABSTRACT

The provision of purification equipment
to meet the highest requirements of the
recently introduced ISO/DIS 8573.1
"Compressed Air For General Use" :
Quality Classes Part 1 and ISO DP 7183.2
"Compressed Air Dryers - Specification
and Testing" are discussed.

INTRODUCTION

To an increasing extent users of
compressed air and particularly those in
advanced industries such as
Pharmaceuticals and Electronics are
specifying air cleanliness required by
the use of Quality Class specifications.

The system of Quality Classes allows the
users to employ a simple numerical
reference to indicate the maximum
acceptable contamination levels for
Solids - Water Vapour - Oil and was
originally developed by PNEUROP and
published in 1984. A draft
International Standard ISO/DIS 8573.1 is
firmly based on PNEUROP Recommendation
6611/1984 "Compressed Air for General
Use - Part 1 Quality Classes" (**Ref 1**).

ISO 7183.1 "Compressed Air Dryers -
Specifications and Testing" is planned
to be supported by a Part 2 which will
deal with guidelines for selection.
Theoretically as many as 120 different
quality classes can be specified but in
practice as the paper explains the
actual number of practicable
possibilities is very much less.

The methods for removal of
contaminants - Solids - Water and Oil
are well understood as are the methods
of measuring the actual remaining levels
of contamination in the compressed air
(**Ref 2**).

There is however a high degree of
misunderstanding about acceptable levels
of water vapour and whilst pressure
dewpoint is generally accepted as a
means of specifying such levels it is
frequently more important to control the
humidity of the compressed air at normal
ambient factory conditions than it is to
be concerned about its actual dewpoint.

**Pressure dewpoint is the
temperature at a given pressure at
which water vapour begins to
condense.**

Consequently drying equipment is
often underspecified resulting in
unsatisfactory humidity levels

The paper reviews the available main
methods of satisfactorily controlling
humidity levels and provides guidance
to the users on the best and most
economical methods of obtaining
compressed air of the correct Quality
Class for their particular
applications.

CONTAMINANTS

Contamination can enter a compressed
air system from three sources. These
are namely, the atmosphere, the
compressor and the piping system.
Taking the atmosphere first; in a
typical metropolitan environment
there are something like 140×10^6
dirt particles per m^3 (4 x
10^6/cu.ft.). Approximately 80 per
cent of these are less than 2
micrometres in size (a um is one
millionth part of a metre or
approximately 0.04 thousandths of an
inch) and are not removed by the
compressor intake filter. In
addition to this, there are
contaminants such as hydrocarbon
vapours (from unburnt fuels and
industrial processes), micro-
organisms and water vapour. All of
these are drawn into the compressor
and their concentration increased by
the compression process.

Inside the compressor, wear particles
and lubricating oil are added to the
air. The amount of oil contamination
depends on the type of compressor and
its condition but can typically vary
between 5 and 50 mg/m^3. To put this
into context, a 280 L/s- A.N.R.* (600
scfm) compressor carrying 30 mg/m^3

* Atmosphere Normale de Reference,
  indicates that the rate of flow
  is free air at standard reference
  atmosphere conditions.

(25 parts per million) of oil during an operational period of 6,000 hours will deposit approximately **212 litres** (47 gallons) of oil into the system. It is never an advantage to have oil from a compressor in the system as this oil is inevitably degraded and oxidised after the heat of compression. Usually it is acidic and can appear as a varnish like substance possessing properties completely opposed to lubrication. If synthetic oils are being used these can cause chemical attack on downstream components such as seals and polycarbonate parts. Carbonisation of the lubricating oil in a reciprocating compressor is not uncommon, due to the temperature of compression, and the presence of 'hotspots' results in deposits of carbon which are again carried over. It is worth taking note at this point that even using a non-lubricated compressor does not necessarily generate 'oil free' air as quite large amounts of hydrocarbons can be drawn in from the atmosphere. A carefully designed oil lubricated compressor and filter system can result in less oil being present than a non lubricated compressor without filters.

After compression the air then passes into the piping system. Normally, aftercooling reduces the amount of water vapour contained in the air but further cooling in the system causes more water to condense. Pipe-scale and rust are also present and when these contaminants mix together with the oil, carried over from the compressor, they form an abrasive, creamy sludge.

This combination of contaminants causes costly problems with both the equipment and the product. These can be eliminated by suitably treating the compressed air using an effective filtration system.

Water vapour itself is a particular problem and may not be tolerated in any amount, in which case a dryer is also necessary. When the air is discharged from an air cooled aftercooler at say $30^{o}C$ and enters a compressed air system it will cool to the ambient temperature of say $20^{o}C$ and as a result and assuming a pressure of 7 bar gauge (100 psig) about $1.6 \ g/m^3$ of water vapour will condense and present a real problem to all users of compressed air. In the earlier example of a 280 L/s A.N.R. (600 scfm) compressor over 6,000 hours, more than **9,680 litres** (2,130 gallons) of water will enter the system and must be removed.

CONTAMINATION LEVELS

The anticipated levels of various contaminants that may be expected to be present in a cubic metre of air at atmospheric pressure in an industrial environment are given in **Table 1** and an investigation into available standards and specifications for instrument quality air covering the four main contaminants oil, water, dirt and vapour produced the results summarised in **Table 2**. (Ref 3)

Table 1   Level of contaminants to be expected

Contaminant	Source	Typical Concentration
Dirt particles	Atmosphere	up to $140 \times 10^6 / m^3$
Carbon	Burnt oil	up to $10 \ mg/m^3$
Water	Atmosphere	up to $11 \ g/m^3$
Rust	Pipework	up to $4 \ mg/m^3$
Oil	Compressor lubricant	$5 - 50 \ mg/m^3$
Oil/Water emulsion	Mixture of oil and water	up to $11 \ g/m^3$
Vapour	Gaseous oil	$0.05 - 0.5 \ mg/m^{3(2)}$
Micro-organisms	Atmosphere	up to $3850/m^3$
Unburnt hydrocarbon	Atmoshpere	up to $0.5 \ mg/m^3$

Table 2   Summary of international standards on contamination

Solids	Water	Water Vapour	Oil Mist/Vapour
0.2 micron	Nil	$-40^{o}C$	less than $1 \ mg/m^3$

ISO/DIS 8573.1 specifies quality classes for the 3 main contaminants (Fig. 1) to enable users to specify their precise quality requirements.

To determine what quality of air users should specify we have to consider what a particular system can tolerate, what equipment is providing satisfactory protection and what equipment is available.

It is academic to attempt to determine system or equipment tolerance to impurity levels since systems vary tremendously whilst at the same time there is equipment commercially available fulfilling the needs of users at acceptable cost.

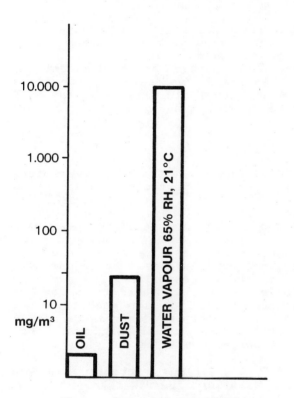

Fig 1   Atmospheric contamination

The biggest pollutant is water in the form of condensate for not only can it combine with other contaminants to form abrasive sludges and sticky emulsion but it can also freeze in cold conditions preventing systems operating at all. In order to have an adequate safety margin the pressure dewpoint should normally be at least 10°C below the anticipated ambient temperature (**Ref 4**). Refrigerated dryers are only suitable where the ambient will always exceed approximately 15°C. A pressure dew point of -40°C can only be achieved commercially by the use of chemical dryers using adsorption materials which in themselves require protection from bulk oil and water to prevent pollution of the adsorption surface, additionally, particulates shed from the adsorption material exist which, while generally sub-micron in size, are in sufficient quantity to be unacceptable.

Bacterial growth takes place when relative humidity exceeds 10% (-18°C pressure dew point) and resultant acidic waste speeds up corrosion and will contaminate food and pharmaceutical products. Until the relative humidity is reduced to below 2% (-36°C pressure dew point), corrosion will take place.

The only sure way to avoid contamination by water is to reduce the pressure dewpoint of the air to a temperature that is unlikely to be reached in practice. The general recommendation is that the dewpoint should be at least 10°C lower than the lowest anticipated ambient temperature.

WATER VAPOUR CONTENT IN AIR

Ambient air always contains to some extent water vapour, when it is compressed its capacity to hold water in vapour form is affected by both temperature and pressure. If we assume a compressor discharges air at 7 bar g and 35°C it will contain approximately 5 g/m³ of water vapour and will be saturated. Saturated means the maximum possible vapour content is being held by the air at specific conditions of temperature and pressure. Air at an ambient condition of 1 bar absolute pressure and temperature of 20°C at say 65% relative humidity will contain approximately 17 g/m³ of water vapour, so 12 g/m³ of vapour will condense at the aftercooler and be removed by the water separator. (Figure 2.)

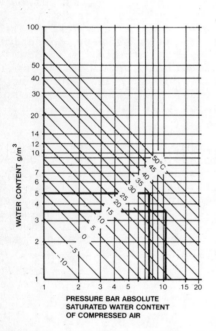

Fig 2

As the air flows into the compressed air system further cooling will result and more condensation will form, e.g. 7 bar g and 20°C a further 2.8 g/m³ of water vapour will condense. At higher pressures for a given temperature less water vapour will be present for a given volume in free air conditions, e.g. at 11 bar absolute and 35°C only 3.6 g/m³ of water vapour will be present.

QUALITY CLASSES

Both the field of application and the type of component being supplied with compressed air need to be considered when deciding upon the maximum amount of contamination that can be accepted. The final choice will be governed by which ever criterion is the most stringent.

The Quality Class is simply specified by three figures XXX arranged in the order. Solids - Water - Oil and, if for any particular contaminant it should not be necessary to specify a maximum level, the figure is replaced by a hyphen.

SOLIDS

ISO/DIS 8573.1 selected four choices of dirt particle size and concentration, related as closely as possible to achievable filtration limits, using readily available commercial products, and to the degree of cleanliness demanded by typical applications. Solid particle sizes and concentrations are given in Table 3 which is based on a maximum penetration of 5% for each size and the concentration assumes a cubic metre of air at standard reference atmosphere conditions.

TABLE 3 Maximum Particle Size and Concentration (ISO/DIS 8573.1)

Class	Particle Size	Concentration
	m	mg/m³
1	0.1	0.1
2	1	1
3	5	5
4	40	10

WATER

The ISO Committee recommends six classes which differ from the original PNEUROP Recommendation and these are given in Table 4.

TABLE 4 Pressure Dewpoint °C (ISO/DIS 8573.1 and ISO/DP 7183.2)

Class	ISO Proposal	Water Vapour ppmv (7bar)
1	-70 or less	0.3
2	-40 or less	15.9
3	-20 or less	127.9
4	+3 or less	940
5	+7 or less	1240
6	+10 or less	1500

These particular dewpoint levels were selected since the first three classes are typical of dewpoints achieved by desiccant dryers and the last three can be theoretically obtained by refrigeration dryers without pushing them to the limits of their performance. -70°C pressure dewpoint is specified by users, particularly in the electronics industry.

It is evident that in order to comply with the recommendation of a pressure dewpoint at least 10°C below lowest ambient that a refrigeration dryer will only perform satisfactorily down to about 15°C i.e. the minimum temperature normally permitted within a factory building. However, rapid expansion of the compressed air through control valves and orifices will cause further condensation.

OIL - MINERAL AND SYNTHETIC

With oil lubricated compressors it is inevitable that the compressed air contains some oil and even with the so-called 'oil free' compressors (which should be more accurately titled 'non-lubricated') complete freedom from oil and oil vapour cannot be positively guaranteed as hydrocarbon vapours are frequently drawn in by the compressor and leaked across oil seals from the gear box.

Oil will exist in the system in three categories - bulk liquid, oil aerosol and oil vapour. However, with a proper selection of lubricant and a well designed aftercooler, the amount of oil vapour present is likely to be small and unlikely to exceed 0.1 mg/m³ at 20°C compressed air temperature and below 0.5 mg/m³ even at 40°C (**Ref 5**). Mineral oil vapour is not considered a health hazard (may not apply to synthetic oils) and levels as high as 500 mg/m³ can be tolerated (**Ref 6**) although the odour may be unacceptable. It is suggested that 0.3 mg/m³ is the odour threshold (**Ref 7**) and as indicated above, a well maintained and operated system will normally be below this level.

Because oil vapour content is low with normal compressor lubricants and industrial operating temperatures and oil vapour is not a hazard except when involved in food, beverage, pharmaceutical and similar applications, the ISO Committee decided against separate specifications for liquid and vapour contaminion levels.

By specifying only total oil content, the user and supplier of filtration equipment could decide whether vapour removal was required. **Table 5** shows the recommended maximum levels.

TABLE 5 Maximum Total Oil Content mg/m³ (ISO/DIS 8573.1)

Class	ISO Proposal
1	0.01
2	0.1
3	1.0
4	5
5	25

OBTAINING HIGH QUALITY COMPRESSED AIR

For all critical applications, a desiccant dryer should be specified and this automatically provides a high degree of efficiency in removing solids and oil.

Where extremely clean air is required to a Quality Class better than 111, the resulting air treatment equipment assembly has, in the past, been extremely bulky - (**Fig 3**). For high air flow rates the size of the dryer columns becomes important and once a dryer size is chosen, there is no easy solution, except complete replacement, if additional air demand requires a larger compressor installation.

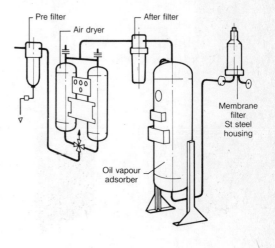

Fig 3

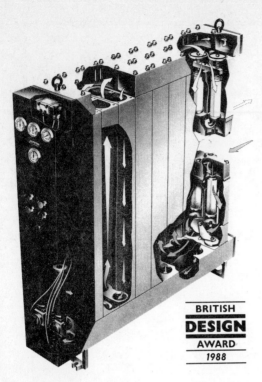

BRITISH
DESIGN
AWARD
1988

Fig 4

Fig 6

A better and modern alternative system **PNEUDRI** is shown in **Fig 4**. This is of modular construction and incorporates, within the confines of the dryer module, pre-filters and after-filters. If required, outlet 0.2 micrometre membrane filtration with stainless steel specially cleaned outlet manifold can be provided. Because of the modular construction, a dryer originally manufactured as a single bank with two pairs of columns can be expanded to a quadruple bank with 32 pairs of columns. This covers the flow range from 76 L/s A.N.R. up to 1220 L/s A.N.R. - **(Fig 5)**

This principle extends downwards to cover the flow range from 1.4 L/s A.N.R. up to 76 L/s A.N.R. - **(Fig 6)**. However, considerations of cost made it preferable to use newly available bolt-on *OIL-X filtration equipment rather than integrating them within the dryer housing. The operating advantages offered by this particular design have been described elsewhere and can be summarised. Very low dewpoint; special desiccant filling techniques to give optimum packing density and freedom from channelling; pressure swing or heat activity regeneration; optimum bed length to diameter ratio; simple changeover valving and, with the pressure swing design, all pneumatic operation as standard to allow for minimum installation expense and allowing unrestricted operation in hazardous areas.

Fig 5

* OIL-X and PNEUDRI - Trade Marks of Domnick Hunter Filters Ltd

INDUSTRIAL APPLICATIONS

Whilst fluid power equipment can tolerate quite high levels of contamination, in many cases the environment in which it operates cannot. The biggest pollutant is water in the form of condensate. It is now common practice to fit some form of dryer to a modern compressed air system and the choice really comes down to two systems.

REDUCED DEWPOINT SYSTEM (FIG 7)

Where dewpoint is not required to be less than +3 to +10°C and ambient temperature is always at least 10°C above the required dewpoint, e.g. inside well heated factories.

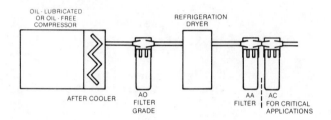

Fig 7

In this system a refrigerated dryer is used. It is protected against bulk liquid, aerosols and dirt by a general purpose coalescing filter. Downstream a high efficiency coalescing filter removes fine oil aerosols, an activated carbon filter may additionally be employed for critical applications.

The air quality according to ISO/DIS 8573.1 would be:

Contaminant	Class	Concentration
Dirt	1	0.1 mg/m^3
		(0.1 micrometre)
Water	4/5/6	+3/+7/+10°C P.D.P.
Oil (total)	2	0.1 mg/m^3
	1**	0.01 mg/m^3

** Activated Carbon filter fitted

LOW DEWPOINT SYSTEM (Fig 8)

Where dewpoint must be extremely low e.g. instrumentation, external pipework, rapid expansion of compressed air.

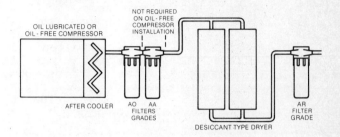

Fig 8

This system uses a desiccant dryer which is protected upstream by a high efficiency coalescing filter and pre-filter to provide a high level of protection to the desiccant dryer. Downstream a dust filter is employed to remove particles of dust shed by the desiccant.

The air quality according to ISO DP 8573.1 would be:

Contaminant	Class	Concentration
Dirt	1	0.1 mg/m^3
		(0.1 micrometre)
Water	1/2/3	-70/-40/-20°C P.D.P.
Oil (total)	2	0.1 mg/m^3
	1**	0.01 mg/m^3

** Activated Carbon filter fitted

MAINTAINING COMPRESSED AIR QUALITY

It can be seen from Fig 1. that water is by far the major contaminent present and it therefore follows that monitoring the pressure dewpoint of the treated compressed air provides a simple way to guarantee the overall compressed air quality (Ref 8).

Water vapour should always be the first of the contaminents to breakthrough, and since pressure dewpoint measurement is with care relatively straight forward a pressure dewpoint meter can provide a simple and effective indication of the overall compressed air quality whatever the source of compressed air.

CONCLUSIONS

In the past, especially where equipment was operated by medium and heavy industry, the equipment supplier had to ensure that his products would function satisfactorily on low quality compressed air since the great majority of compressed air systems were, and too many still are, of very low quality with high levels of solid and liquid contamiation. This resulted in additional expense to the user since, in order to ensure satisfactory continuous operation, each penumatic tool or device needed protection and lubrication by local air treatment equipment.

A large part of the medium and heavy industrial demand for Compressed Air has vanished. Its use is now being focussed to an increasing extent in high technology applications where new standards of air purity not previously required are essential.

With the advent of an International Standards 8573 and 7183 this knowledge will become more widespread and companies specialising in installing compressors and compressed air systems will need to be aware of the Quality Class systems.

Air treatment equipment in the form of aftercoolers, filters and dryers is readily available today in compact and easily installed form which is capable of ensuring a compressed air supply to the highest I.S.O. quality class 111.

REFERENCES

1. PNEUROP 6611/1984 - Compressed Air for General Use

   Part 1 Quality Classes
   Part 2 Testing

   Published by British Compressed Air Society, London.

2. Quality Specifications For Compressed Air For General Use And How To Achieve Them. C.T. Billiet - 8th International Fluid Power Symposium, Birmingham, England - 19-21st April 1988

3. Compressed Air Purification For Instrumentation In The High Technology Industries. C.T. Billiet - Institute of Mechanical Engineers Conference - October 1985.

4. API Recommended Practice 550, Manual on Installation of Refinery Instruments and Control Systems Part 1 Process Instrumentation and Control Section 9 - Air Supply Systems. American Petrolium Institute 1980.

5. A Test Procedure to Determine the Integrity and Performance Of Activated Carbon Filters used In Compressed Gas Applications. R.M. Fielding - 4th World Filtration Congress, Ostend, Belgium. - 22-25 April 1986.

6. Methods for the Determination of Atmospheric Concentration of Oil Mist - Institute of Petroleum Occupational Hygiene Sub-committee - Annual of Occupational Hygiene Volume 18 Pages 293/297

7. DD97 Part 1 - Respiratory Protective Equipment - Part 1 Glossary of Terms. Draft for Development Published by the British Standards Institution

8. A New Innovative Approach To The Provision of High Quality 'Oil Free' Compressed Air. C.T. Billiet - Power International Nov/Dec 1986

Enhanced turbocompressor anti-surge control

H T DEARDEN and S I MAALOUF
Foxboro Great Britain Limited, Redhill, Surrey

Synopsis

This paper reviews the conventional control system used in surge prevention on turbo-compressors and describes the advanced techniques which have been incorporated into a modern digital controller developed by the Foxboro Company.

1.0 Introduction

Turbo-compressors (axial and centrifugal) are vulnerable to the phenomenon known as surge. This arises when the operating point of a machine reaches a position on the characteristic curve where stable operation can no longer be maintained. The result is a severe cycling of pressure and flow, usually in the frequency range of 0.5-10Hz, which can cause serious damage or even catastrophic failure. Damage is caused through the cycling of thrust on the impeller and the high temperatures and massive vibrations which are induced. Since there is no nett forward flow of gas, all power is absorbed in accelerating the impeller and heating the same mass of gas which is cycling through the machine. Accelerations of 2000 rpm/sec and temperatures of 1100C have been observed.

Even if obvious damage does not occur, the internal clearances of the machine may be affected, causing a permanent loss of efficiency. Repeated surge will cause an accumulative drop in efficiency, reduced component lifetimes and more frequent and expensive maintenance bills. The implications for efficiency and the potential threat to production means that effective surge prevention is a prime requirement.

To prevent surge, a feedback controller has been traditionally employed to open a recirculation or blow off valve, to maintain stable operation and prevent the operating point crossing the surge curve.

Since recirculation of gas is wasteful of energy, it should be the objective of every energy conscious operation to keep this to the minimum consistent with maintenance of machine protection.

Pneumatic analogue controllers were originally (and still are), employed for surge prevention, but the advent of digital equipment has led to the development of a more advanced controller which offers enhanced machine protection and improved efficiency of operation through reduced recirculation.

2.0 Conventional Control Techniques

In order to place the latest developments in context it is necessary to review the traditional control scheme, (described in detail in ref.1) in which a conventional Proportional and Integral (P+I) controller with batch action is used:

The surge curve of a centrifugal compressor is usually considered to be parabolic because of the square law relationship between pressure rise across a compressor and the volumetric flow through the machine. This parabolic curve translates into a straight line relationship between pressure rise and the flow element differential pressure. (Fig 1.)

The controller set point is usually defined as a constant (ratio setting) times the pressure rise across the machine. This relationship is shown as a straight control line on the plot shown in fig 1. The control line is placed at a predetermined margin from the surge line by selection of a suitable ratio setting. Displacing the control line to the right reduces the possibility of an excursion into surge. However, if the control line is placed too far to the right, gas will be recirculated unnecessarily and power will be wasted. The selected position of the control line forms a compromise between these two conflicting considerations.

The proportional band (PB) or gain setting of the controller can be represented as a band of flow (or rather flow element differential as shown in fig 1) on the machine characteristic. The position of the machine operating point within this band determines the controller output and corresponding valve position. The upper boundary of this band corresponds to 100% valve opening, the lower boundary to 0% opening.

The position of the band itself is determined by the integral action of the controller; when flow is below set point the integral action will move the band to the left causing a progressive closure of the valve as the operating point approaches the lower band boundary. The converse is true when the flow is greater than set point. The rate at which the band moves is determined by the integral setting of the controller and the difference between set point and measurement. (Controller error)

During normal operation the operating point of the machine is well away from the control line. This sustained deviation of measurement from set point would cause the integral action to move the proportional band to the left until the controller saturated (integral wind-up). This would leave the PB on the other side of the control line so that the operating point would have to cross the control line before it could enter the PB and cause the valve to open.

This overshoot of the control line before the controller can respond is unacceptable in anti-surge control and batch action is provided to reposition the proportional band with its upper boundary (100% open) lying on the control line. This means that the operating point will enter the PB, and the controller will respond, before the operating point reaches the control line. The batch action is triggered (and the PB repositioned) when the controller output falls to zero.

3.0 Advanced Control Techniques

There follows a review of the advanced control techniques which have been integrated into a single device which is dedicated to machine protection.

3.1 Asymmetric control

Conventional controllers are symmetrical in that their response is the same for a given increase or decrease in flow. Their speed of response upon approach to surge, is determined by the proportional band and integral action time settings. Just as with any feedback control loop, there is a limit to which these settings may be adjusted, and control tightened, beyond which loop instability will arise. This places a fundamental limit on the speed of response of the controller.

Asymmetric control provides direction dependent control action. Effectively this places a rate limit on the output of the controller in one direction only; the recirculation valve will open unimpeded, but may only close at less than a predetermined rate. This allows the selection of controller gain settings which will give a faster response than possible with a conventional symmetrical controller, without compromising loop stability.

Fig 2 illustrates the difference in the open loop response of the two types of controller to successive transients towards surge.

Note also that the symmetrical response of the conventional controller may be unable to prevent persistent cycling if surge should occur. The cycling of flow due to surge can cause a corresponding cycling of the valve because of the proportional response of the controller which will act to re-close the valve as flow recovers. This may prevent the controller from effectively damping the flow oscillations. This possibility is eliminated with the asymmetric controller since the recirculation valve is prevented from immediate closure in response to the recovery of flow.

3.2 Surge Curve Characterization

As described earlier, the surge curve of a centrifugal compressor is usually considered to be parabolic, and this transforms into a straight line on a plot of pressure rise against flow element differential. This has led to the use of a straight control line to maintain a margin to surge.

Note however that the actual surge curve of a machine may well deviate significantly from this theoretical relationship (and will certainly do so with an axial flow machine). Curve fitting of the actual relationship allows a closer match to the individual compressor surge curve . This allows a given margin to surge to be maintained throughout all operating conditions, avoiding excessive recirculation and maintaining machine protection.
The effect is illustrated in fig 3.

3.3 Non-Linear Control

When the operating point crosses the control line and enters the control margin, the error seen by the controller changes polarity. By characterizing the controller error as shown in fig 4, the error seen by the controller is amplified when the operating point lies within the margin to surge. This results in an increase in the effective proportional and integral action of the controller and accelerates the controller response.

3.4 Computation Capability

The surge characteristics of a compressor may vary with temperature, pressure or gas composition (and inlet guide vane position when these are fitted). If there is no means of compensating for possible variations in process conditions (or compressor operation), the control line must be placed far enough to the right to cater for the worst possible conditions. This inevitably means excessive recirculation at other conditions. The computational capability of modern equipment allows continuous correction for these variations and avoids the need to compromise efficiency.

3.5 Enhanced Batch Action

As described earlier in section 2.0, the upper boundary of the proportional band of conventional controllers is tied to the control line whenever the operating point lies below the proportional band lower boundary (i.e. output is 0%). This means that if an excursion towards surge occurs, the controller response is delayed until the operating point enters the PB.

With enhanced batch action, the controller tracks the compressor operation and maintains the lower

boundary of the PB at the operating point as long as this point moves at less than the integrating rate of the controller. This eliminates the delay incurred with conventional controllers. When an excursion towards surge occurs which is faster than the integrating rate of the controller, the operating point will immediately enter the PB giving an immediate proportional action response. This feature is illustrated in fig 5.

3.6 Noise Handling

The advanced controller has the facility to apply 2nd order digital filters to measurement inputs. These can be used to attenuate high amplitude, high frequency noise. However, it is important not to slow the control action by the introduction of excessive filtering lag. A further feature eliminates the effect of residual noise without sacrificing speed of response. This is achieved with the specification of a noise band; flow variations within this band are ignored by the controller, but any excursion beyond this band is acted upon immediately.

3.7 Detection of Operation in Vincinity of Surge Limit

A further technique provides protection against transmitter drift, variations in uncompensated parameters or changes in compressor characteristics due to wear or fouling. These influences may lead to discrepancies between the actual and measured operating points and between the actual and programmed surge curves. These discrepancies may result in operation with a reduced margin to surge which would remain undetected in a conventional controller. The advanced controller provides enhanced protection by monitoring the flow measurement noise amplitude. Flow noise is known to increase as a machine approaches surge. (Fig 6) This phenomenon is exploited in the advanced controller, which detects increased noise amplitude and progressively opens the recirculation valve until the noise level returns to its normal level. This protection is not affected by the displacements of the operating point or surge line due to the above influences.

3.8 Feedforward Logic

A feedback control scheme cannot respond to sudden changes in load, which may arise due to plant status changes, until the controller measurement has been influenced. The feedforward logic capability of the advanced controller allows immediate opening of the recirculation valve in response to contact input changes. For example, a compressor may supply air to a number of process units. These units may be subject to random and rapid shutdowns through protection system trips. If a contact is available to indicate a shutdown, the controller may be configured to immediately open the valve by a pre-determined amount or to move the valve to a pre-determined position.

With a conventional controller, sufficient margin to surge has to be maintained to allow the feedback loop to protect against the extreme transients associated with plant trips. This may lead to excessive recirculation during normal operation. The feedforward aspect of the advanced controller provides an immediate response to these events, allowing safe operation with a reduced margin.

3.9 Transmitter Failure

Since the controller set point is established from a measurement of pressure rise across the machine, a failure of the transmitter will cause the setpoint of a conventional controller to fall to zero. (The control line becomes the Y-axis) This leaves the machine unprotected. To prevent this, the advanced controller detects transmitter failure and drives the set point to a safe, conservative position. (The control line becomes a vertical line, well to the right of the surge line)

4.0 Conclusions

This paper has described a variety of control techniques which are incorporated into an advanced anti-surge controller developed by the Foxboro Company. This controller offers improved efficiency of machine operation and enhanced protection. Some of the techniques detailed here have been previously implemented in earlier generation equipment, (ref.2) but the latest microprocessor based, single station devices allow a more elegant implementation and provide a more appropriate equipment architecture which can be dedicated to machine protection.

The potential payback from reduced recirculation can be estimated from the power consumption at a nominal operating point: Machine performance maps will typically show a variation in machine efficiency of 75-85%, but this takes no account of the losses associated with gas recirculation. In terms of operational efficiency, the proportion of gas flow which is recirculated will waste a corresponding proportion of the drive power.

As a first approximation, machine efficiency can be assumed to be constant at the value corresponding with the nominal operating point. On this basis any reduction in gas flow will yield a proportional saving in power:

$$P_s = \frac{F_r \times P_o}{F_o}$$

P_s : Power Saving
P_o : Operating point power
F_o : " " flow
F_r : Reduction in recirc flow

Further savings are realized by the preservation of the actual machine efficiency, which might otherwise be degraded by damaging transients. Each 1% drop in machine efficiency would of course increase power consumption by a corresponding 1%.

The controller can be adapted to handle a variety of machine and instrument configurations, some of which are illustrated in fig 7. Computer aided design tools facilitate the preparation of fully engineered solutions customised for individual machine characteristics.

References

1. White M.H., Surge control for Centrifugal Compressors, Chem. Eng., Vol.79, No.29, Dec. 25, 1972.

2. Ferhervari W., Asymmetric Algorithm Tightens Compressor Surge Control, Control Engineering, October 1977, 63-65.

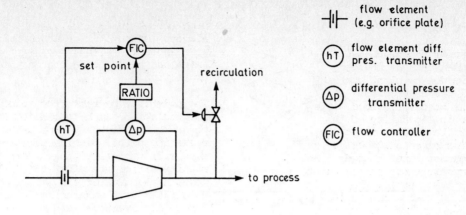

flow element
(e.g. orifice plate)

(hT) flow element diff.
pres. transmitter

(Δp) differential pressure
transmitter

(FIC) flow controller

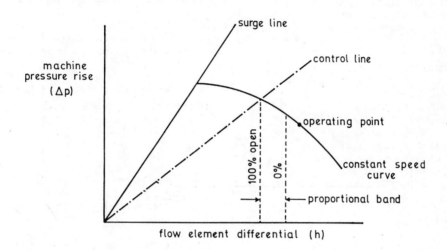

Fig 1

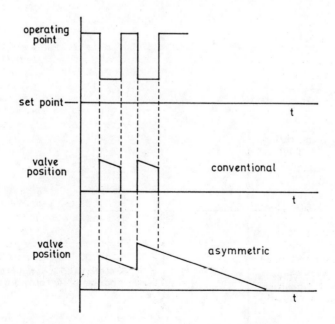

Fig 2

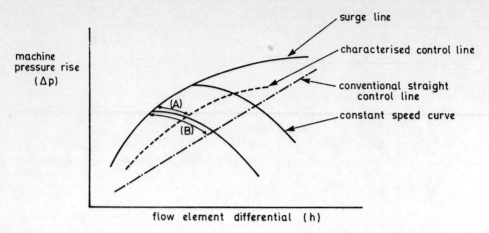

(A) appropriate margin maintained
with curved control line.

(B) excessive margin with
straight control line.

Fig 3

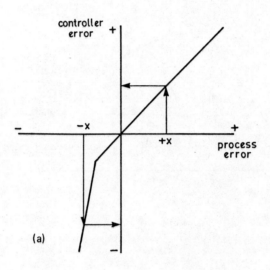

(a)

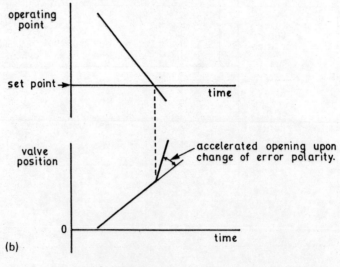

(b)

Fig 4

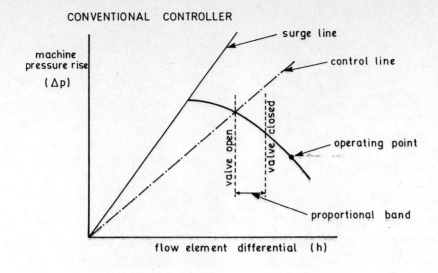

CONVENTIONAL CONTROLLER

machine pressure rise (Δp)

surge line

control line

valve open

valve closed

operating point

proportional band

flow element differential (h)

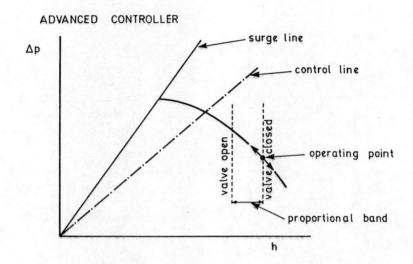

ADVANCED CONTROLLER

Δp

surge line

control line

valve open

valve closed

operating point

proportional band

h

Fig 5

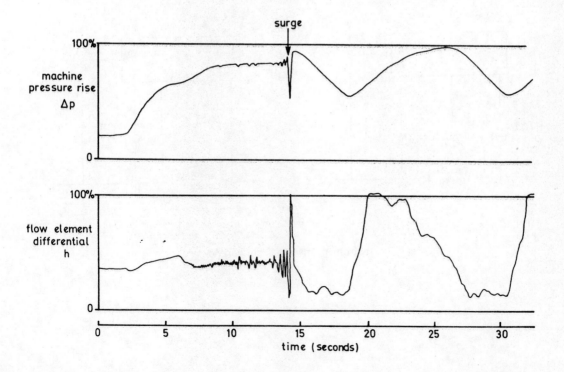

surge

100%

machine pressure rise Δp

0

100%

flow element differential h

0

0   5   10   15   20   25   30

time (seconds)

Fig 6

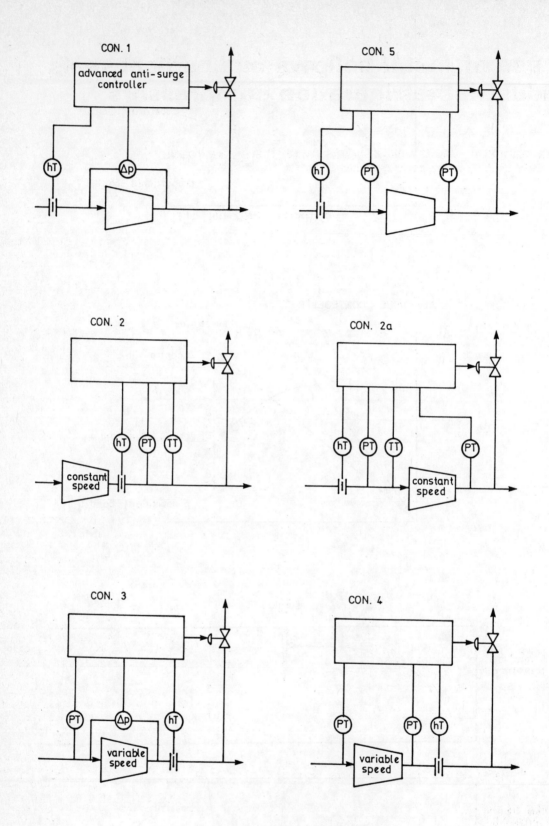

Fig 7   Instrument/machine configurations

C390/028

The use of metal bellows mechanical seals in industrial refrigeration compressors

J M PLUMRIDGE, CEng, MIMechE, MIProdE, MRAeS, **P WAKEFIELD** and **R YOUNG**
E G and G Sealol, High Wycombe, Buckinghamshire

SYNOPSIS

Conventional methods of sealing the rotating shaft in oil lubricated compressors include various rubber bellows and pusher seals, manufactured either by the OEM or commercially sourced.

After generally good early life performance, these conventional seals often deteriorate rapidly resulting in high oil leakage. Cause of failure is normally chemical/thermal elastomer deterioration together with classical "hang-up" of pusher seals preventing proper face lubrication.

This paper presents a case for using metal bellows seals which eliminate these primary causes of failure, and gives detail of seal pedigree, construction, in-house testing and type approval/monitoring by compressor manufacturers and users.

1. INTRODUCTION

There are three types of industrial refrigeration compressor where metal bellows seals are either supplied in production or presently under evaluation. These comprise:

Piston Compressors. The majority of metal bellows seal installations are fitted to Piston Compressors. A single seal is installed at the drive end of the shaft.

The sealed fluid is generally mineral oil saturated with the refigerant, usually R12, 22 and 502 (dichlorodifluoromethane and dichlorotetrafluoroethane), which in the sealing area is in the form of a foam. Rotational speeds are commonly 1000 to 1800 r/m but in some cases to 3000 r/m. Normal operating pressures at the seal are 2 to 10 atmospheres with maximum operating conditions (generally at shutdown), quoted to 20 atmospheres. Temperatures are 60 to 90°C.

Seals have been installed and tested on shafts ranging from 18 to 105mm diameter. Some 20 configurations of Piston Compressors sealed with metal bellows seals are known to the authors.

Vane Compressors. Experience is more limited on these machines, but metal bellows seals have been successfully tested on compressors ranging from 25 to 45mm diameters. The medium being sealed is similar to that described under Piston Compressors, but running conditions are more severe. Running test conditions are 3000 r/m, 25 atmospheres, and temperatures to 120°C.

Screw Compressors. Running conditions are typically 3000 r/m, 25 atmospheres on shaft sizes from 50 to 80mm.

The use of metal bellows to improve sealing performance in industrial refrigeration compressors is a fairly recent change in approach, starting with a Type Approval Programme for an Italian Compressor manufacturer in 1984.

This paper will consider the driving forces behind this new approach and detail some history of the performance of conventional seals. It will also look briefly at general sealing principles and provide some detail of metal bellows historic development and usage. Finally, it will cover metal bellows seals dedicated development to industrial compressors, describe in-house testing and external type approval, and comment on the perceived benefits of their use.

2. GENERAL SEALING PRINCIPLES

Mechanical seals are the most versatile type (Ref.1) of seal for rotating shafts. They have a superficial resemblance to thrust bearings. However, the very close running clearance which must be maintained, poor lubricating properties of the "lubricant" and very low lubricant flow combine to make the design of mechanical seals much more difficult than that of thrust bearings.

The problems in designing mechanical seals explain why the reliability is generally worse than for thrust bearings.

In the simplest terms, a mechanical seal is a compromise between high wear and high leakage, Short term leakage will exist when the closing force imbalance produces a condition where the seal face lubricating film is too thick. Conversely, short term wear will result from an imbalance which will not support the fluid film, causing heavy contact between the faces. Seal performance and reliability depends upon seal design, friction face materials, environmental conditions, and quality of fitting.

The major driving force in these programmes was seen to be the deteriorating leakage performance of conventional pusher type seals and rubber bellows seals. Leakage of mechanical seals is notoriously difficult to predict, and proposals are based mainly upon statistical history and test data.

An equation for leakage was developed by Heinze (1949), based on the assumption that a hydrodynamic film exists in face seals and that the leakage can be calculated with the known equation for laminar flow through a radial annular gap in the full fluid lubrication regime.

$$Q = \frac{c\, d_m h_o^3 (P_1 - P_2)}{\eta\, b} \qquad \text{Ref.2.}$$

where Q is leakage flow rate
   C is a constant, dependent upon units
   d_m is mean diameter of interface
   h_o is separation of interface
   P_1 is sealed pressure
   P_2 is atmospheric pressure
   η is absolute viscosity
   b is width of interface

A development of this formula was proposed by Mayer (1977) for a mixed lubrication regime.

$$Q = \frac{K\, dm\, h_o^2 (P_1 - P_2)\, s}{G} \qquad \text{Ref.3.}$$

where K is a constant dependent upon units
   S is a gap factor. Empirical, dependent upon peripheral velocity
   G is net face pressure, dependent upon spring load, pressure differential and hyraulic balance of the seal.

Study of these two equations shows the difficulty in an analytical approach to leakage prediction. Apart from anything else, the actual gap form is difficult to predict and can deviate considerably from the assumed parallel gap because of temperature differences in the ring. Additionally, the h_o term is critical since (Ref.2) predicts a cubed power, and (Ref.3) a squared power.

Other factors which affect leakage are not considered in these models. First, microscopic distortions caused by thermal and mechanical effects will affect leakage performance. Additionally, face material properties will affect

the thermal conditions, as will the seal structural design. Lubricant properties and flow and the geometry of the seal cavity are also all known to affect leakage and life of the mechanical seal. Most important of all is seal deterioration. Whilst many seal products will provide good initial field performance, long term reliability is a different story!

3. BRIEF HISTORY OF METAL BELLOWS SEALS

Welded metal bellows have been used as sealing elements in mechanical seals and valve stems for four decades. The metal bellows seal was originally developed for the defence industries. Duties are typically high speed with little space availability and relatively high vibration levels. Current status can be described by three samples presently in production from the defence industry in the U.K.

	SIZE(mm)	SPEED(r/m)	PRESSURE(bar)	TEMP(°C)
a)	16	140 000	–	180
b)	35	30 000	20	150
c)	20	50 000	2	400

a) Weapon Steam Turbine
b) Aircraft Fuel Pump
c) Aircraft Gas Turbine Starter

Metal bellows seals for Process Pumps were developed in the 1960's, based on the design principles and proven high speed and temperature performance in the defense industries. Standard products in hastelloy (for high corrosion resistance), precipitation hardened stainless steel (for high temperature or high pressure) and inconel (for combinations of corrosion, temperature and pressure) are available, and three samples again describe current status on process pumps.

PRODUCT	SIZE(mm)	SPEED(r/m)	TEMP(°C)
a) Sulphuric Acid	55	1450	+ 60
b) Vac-Gas Oil	75	3000	+410
c) Ethylene	60	4500	–103

MATERIALS OF CONSTRUCTION

a) Hastelloy
b) AM 350
c) Inconel

In addition, edge welded metal bellows seals have been extensively used on Heavy Duty Compressors. The requirements here are quite difficult with shaft sizes up to 200mm plus, and speeds and pressures to 10000 r/m and 20 bars. In these installations, bespoke engineered solutions are required, normally using stationary mounted double seals with an oil lubrication system, at a higher pressure than the gas pressure, supplied to the intercavity.

4. DEVELOPMENT FOR INDUSTRIAL REFRIGERATION COMPRESSORS

These machines have normally used a conventional pusher seal manufactured by the OEM or commercially sourced. A typical pusher seal is shown in Fig.1 and is defined as having a secondary sealing element which must allow axial movement. Since there will always be some axial movement of the front end (machine harmonic, thermal growth, thrust bearing weardown, mechanical seal friction face weardown, etc) there are two real advantages in dispensing with an axially moving sealing member. Firstly, such a member will roll, or even worse, will slide and create a frictional resistance to movement. The level of hysteresis is dependent upon the frictional characteristics of the mechanism - surface finish, tolerancing, rubber squeeze, lubrication, squareness - and is thus uncontrolled. However, the hysteresis-free action of the bellows seal will provide totally free movement of the dynamic working end and give superior performance at higher speeds and will accept higher levels of non-squareness. The metal bellows seal will allow poorer set-up conditions than an equivalent conventional seal with dynamic contacting secondary seals.

A second advantage is more long term but, again, is due to the relative axial movement between the seal front end and the shaft. In addition to the frictional wear that occurs at the point of contact with dynamic secondary seals, abrasive and corrosive wear can result from particle build-up (from leaked product) at the secondary seal and this will give an accelerated failure condition.

Thus, seal deterioration caused by the sliding elastomer can be documented as follows:

*   Fretting, producing microwear of shaft and elastomer, creating more friction and more resistance to sliding or rolling.

*   Causing increasing leakage and product build-up at the sliding interface and eventual accelerated total failure caused by inability of the faces to axially track.

An alternative solution to the pusher seal in many compressors has been the rubber bellows seal (Fig.2.). Whilst this has been a cost-effective solution in many installations, and eliminates the "hang-up" associated with pusher seals, it is well known that quite often the elastomeric diaphragms and gaskets have deteriorated from their exposure to the refrigerant.

For all these reasons, a number of compressor companies began to consider the metal bellows type of seal. A typical seal is shown in Fig.3.

The bellows itself has two functions. Its primary function is to provide a closing force between the rotating element and its stationary counterface. But in so doing, the bellows itself becomes a seal between the semi-dynamic front end of the seal and its rigidly fixed rear end.

Whilst the pusher seal has a secondary sealing element at the front (or dynamic) end of the seal, the bellows seal construction allows the packing to be placed at its rear (fixed end). This allows an inherently hysteresis-free action of the bellows seal. This has no moving parts or sliding elastomer in contact with the shaft or sleeve, and therefore, eliminates wear on these parts. The absence of sliding elastomers

eliminates seal drag or hang-up, which is the major cause of failure in conventional seals with dynamic contacting secondary seals. A bellows seal is inherently balanced and there is, therefore, no need for 'stepping' the shaft or sleeve. The hydraulic balance range of the bellows seal is variable by changing the contact nose profile.

Before looking in detail at some of the developments in this business sector, a review of market differences is considered relevant.

During the development phase of the metal bellows seal for process pumps from existing defense based products, the requirement differences were seen to be:-

*   The seal should be highly standardised to reduce costs.
*   The seal should be usable in a very wide variety of applications with minimal variation of the product (normally limited to elastomers and friction face).
*   The seal should readily accept process upsets.

The products developed for Industrial Refrigeration Compressors are essentially similar to those supplied to the Process Industries, but again some differences in their requirement are apparent.

-   Standardisation for cost even more essential.
-   Establish manufacturing methods for high volume.
-   Leakage requirements more stringent.

5. SPECIFIC DEVELOPMENTS

In the early 1980's, the seal manufacturer was requested to develop better sealing performance by several compressor users, mainly in Italy.

Around 200 metal bellows seal units, identical to conventional process pump seals, were supplied to the users and performance at the plant was carefully monitored.

At the same time the seal manufacturer had been developing a low cost, high volume unit with similar performance characteristics for both the process pump and gas compressor OEM market. This development made it possible for the OEM to consider this technology.

In 1984, compressor manufacturers in 3 EEC countries began type approving this type of product. In parallel, the seal manufacturer conducted a major in-house test programme.

The in-house programme used a production belt driven piston open compressor.

The initial seal arrangement installed into the compressor was in principle a standard type seal product normally supplied to pump installations using a standard carbon graphite rotary friction face against a high chrome cast stainless steel stationary counterface. The shaft size was 40mm diameter, and the test compressor was charged with Refrigerant 502 at 4,5 atmospheres, with an oil pressure of 9 atmospheres.

This particular compressor manufacturer demanded a very low oil leakage level - less than 0.5ml/day. On the preliminary test runs, leakage was erratic and averaged around 5ml/day which was unacceptable. Short term tests on a number of alternative stationary counterface materials were carried out with varying face widths to reduce frictional heat production. The best average leakage rate achieved was 0,9 ml/day.

Further fine tuning of the seal geometry to further reduce heat production and to improve the efficiency of the oil flow yielded an additional improvement to 0,4ml/day.

The total programme involved some 15 changes with typical seal running times of 7 to 10 hours. Since the leakage requirement of 0,5 ml/day had been achieved, and it was felt that initial running would produce higher leakage than a long term leakage rate (from normal running-in experience), an endurance test was performed.

A new seal arrangement incorporating all the small detail changes was manufactured and assembled into the compressor (Fig.4). The compressor was operated for a total of 200 hours. Total leakage was 3,3mls. which converts to 0,4ml/day.

This compressor and seal arrangement was then endurance tested for 32 weeks with numerous (50 plus) starts and stops. The cummulative leakage after 32 weeks of almost continuous running was 12mls. A leakage rate/time plot is shown in Fig. 5, superimposed with typical leakage rate plots for rubber bellows and pusher type seals.

These tests indicated that very low leakage was achievable in controlled laboratory conditions and gave confidence that metal bellows seals were likely to give major improvements for long term leakage in the field.

By the end of this 12 month internal programme, the OEM industry had type approved five compressor models. Since that time a further twenty types have been approved, some of which were very large (100mm plus shaft diameter) multi-piston machines. On these large machines, the seals were subjected to intensive, critical, long term (18 months +) internal testing and were additionally fitted to specific machines in the field with a history of poor seal reliability. In addition to vastly improved performance, the metal bellows seal was seen to have a significant advantage in ease and therefore reliability, of fitting.

Since the seal manufacturer has little contact with the end user market, he relies on feedback on seal performance from the compressor manufacturers. It has been reported generally that leak rates are reduced from the levels which were considered acceptable for the previously installed conventional seal, but the bellows seal has provided significantly better long term leakage and life performance.

For the purpose of this paper, one compressor manufacturer was approached for some detail on a comparative basis. This company is presently evaluating the metal bellows seal type.

In this instance, the metal bellows seal had replaced a "home-made" pusher type seal, with an 'O' ring dynamic secondary seal. He reported a reduction in oil leakage from 0,1/ 0,4ml/hour to .02/.05ml/hour.

The average time to failure in the field for the conventional seal was 300 hours, representing 2 to 4 months compressor operation.

Some 150 metal bellows seals of 2 separate shaft sizes were supplied for evaluation. Around 10 pieces were tested in-house, and the remainder supplied for field evaluation. There has been no real seal failure, and it is understood some 50 installations have run for over 1000 hours representing 6 to 12 months compressor operation.

He reports that the major advantages of the metal bellows seal are the improved carbon graphite seal face material and lack of dynamic secondary seal hysteresis from 'O' ring swell.

6. FUTURE DEVELOPMENTS

The future will depend on the development of the machines that welded metal bellows seals are fitted to. However there are certain aspects that we can anticipate:-

1. In order to obtain more efficiency from the compressor, speeds, temperatures and probably pressures will increase. There have already been significant changes in the performance of air compressors, especially higher speeds.

2. Practical problems in refrigeration compressors such as copper deposition and ease of field maintenance must be addressed.

3. "Cost of ownership", that is increased performance with decreasing cost must follow the trend of almost every other mechanical product.

4. The replacement of CFC's with safer (and probably more expensive) compounds drives the need for better sealing without increasing the cost of the total machine beyond value for money.

On the first issue the experience of the aerospace industry will become the main route i.e. stationary seals with rotating seats. This gives a number of "spin-off" advantages such as compact seal design, capability of much higher speeds and the ability to use one seal for many shaft sizes. The basic welded metal bellows design is an ideal building block for all of these and has been used in these problem areas for over 30 years. New materials and especially non-metallics may lead the way to preventing such phenomenon as copper deposition.

Cost effectiveness is a stronger driving

force than ultimate seal performance, and the
long term requirement is to provide leakage
and life performance which is acceptable to
the compressor user, coupled with practical
benefits of simple fitting.

The practical application of new production techniques should bring the cost of these
products down to levels that rival conventional
seal products without the problems associated
with these conventional techniques.

References

1. Mechanical Seal Practise for Improved
    Performance.
    MEP 1988

2. Heinze, E. Über Gleitringdichtungen, mit
    besonderer Berücksichtigung ihrer Verwen-
    dung im Kältemaschinenbau. Kältetechnik 1
    (1949)

3. Mayer. E. Mechanical Seals. Newnes-
    Butterworths. 1977

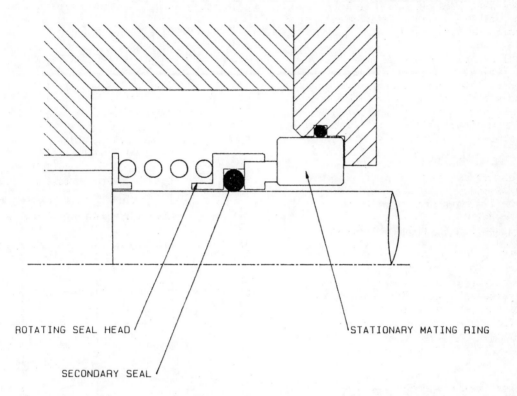

ROTATING SEAL HEAD

STATIONARY MATING RING

SECONDARY SEAL

Fig 1   Conventional pusher seal with 'O' ring secondary seal

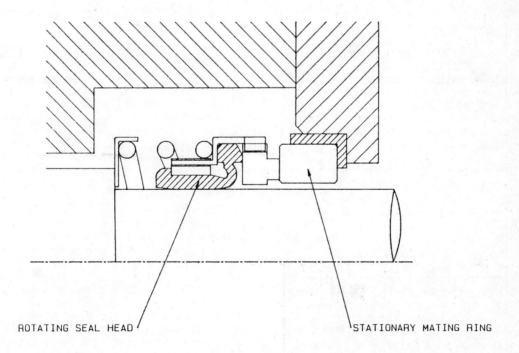

ROTATING SEAL HEAD

STATIONARY MATING RING

Fig 2   Rubber bellows seal

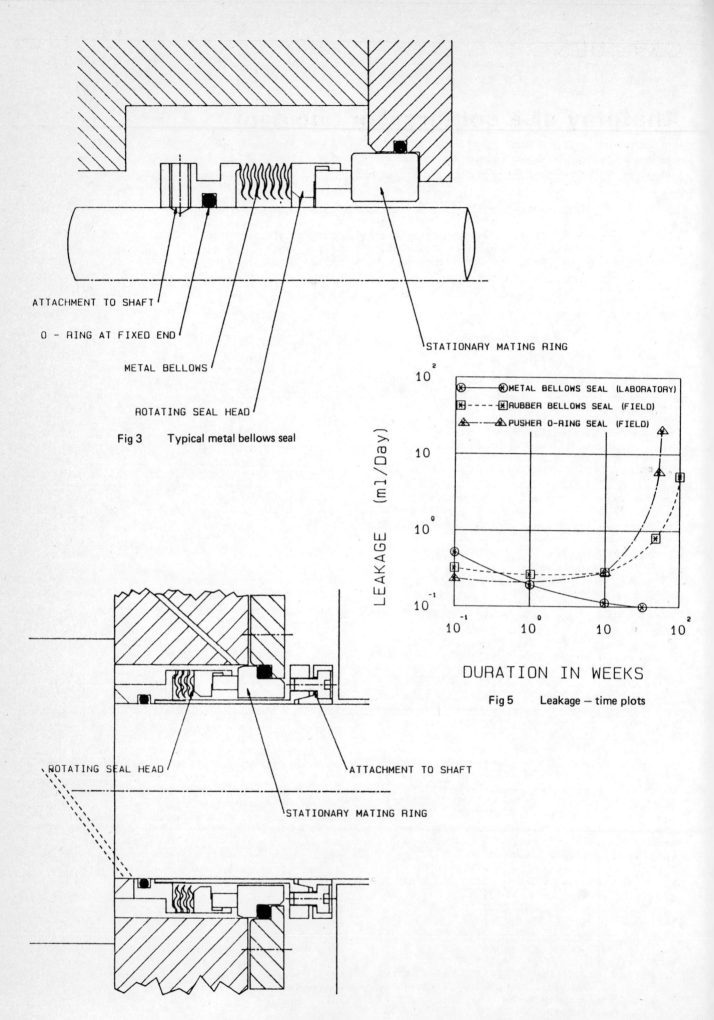

ATTACHMENT TO SHAFT

O - RING AT FIXED END

METAL BELLOWS

ROTATING SEAL HEAD

Fig 3   Typical metal bellows seal

STATIONARY MATING RING

ROTATING SEAL HEAD

STATIONARY MATING RING

ATTACHMENT TO SHAFT

Fig 4   Seal arrangement for in-house testing

LEAKAGE (ml/Day)

10^2

10

10^0

10^{-1}

⊗ METAL BELLOWS SEAL (LABORATORY)
⊠ RUBBER BELLOWS SEAL (FIELD)
△ PUSHER O-RING SEAL (FIELD)

10^{-1} 10^0 10 10^2

DURATION IN WEEKS

Fig 5   Leakage — time plots

C390/025

Anatomy of a compressor accident

E J POOLE, BSc, CEng, FIMechE, MIMarE
CompAir BroomWade Limited, High Wycombe, Buckinghamshire

SYNOPSIS   It seemed impossible that an 18kW air compressor, designed for 10.5
bar.g having operated satisfactorily at 7 bar.g for several years should,
within ten seconds of starting, generate internal pressures greater than 90
bar.g.   It was equally surprising that a cast iron cylinder head designed for
16 bar.g would withstand an internal pressure of more than 70 bar.g.   Finally
it was unexpected that, the motor overload protection would allow the machine
to raise these pressures.

The circumstances of the accident provide cogent support for the new Pressure
System Regulations which are expected to come into force later this year.

1   INTRODUCTION

In July 1984 the two stage air compressor which
is the subject of this paper had been in normal
industrial service for 14 years; albeit in at
least two different locations.   Then within a
period of less than 10 seconds from the machine
being inadvertently started the second stage
cylinder head exploded with fatal consequences
for a bystander.   The sequence of events
leading up to the accident, the circumstances
of the accident itself and the subsequent
investigations comprehensively justified all
the practical precautions and legal constraints
that properly circumscribe the design,
construction, operation and maintenance of
industrial air compressors.

From the aftermath two main features emerged.
Firstly, at a practical level, each of the
several errors subsequently identified to have
been made by the operators and other people
concerned with the machine during the period
before the accident made crystal clear to all
concerned the sense and logic of 'doing things
properly'.   To the manufacturers it also
provided a unique opportunity to analyse
operational features and conditions which had
not been assessed during the original
development of the family of compressors of
which the subject machine was a member.   This
review confirmed that the design was more than
adequately safe under 'all reasonably
foreseeable' operating conditions.   It also
revealed, however, that the ingenuity of a
succession of users and maintainers could
produce a set of circumstances in which a
machine designed and constructed for 10.5 bar.g
maximum operating pressure and originally
fitted with appropriate protective devices
could generate, in a very short time, a
discharge pressure in excess of 80 bar.g.

This paper presents the sequence of events from
original design and manufacture through its
service life, during which 'unofficial'
changes, some unwise, others positively
dangerous had been made, to the accident
itself.   It identifies the series of errors of
commission and omission which taken together
set the fuse for the accident.   Even then it
required grossly incorrect operating procedures
to produce the final catastrophe.

2   BACKGROUND

The machine in question was of the type
illustrated in Figures 1 and 2 being an air
cooled, two stage, single acting piston
compressor directly coupled to and driven by a
18.5kW, 1460 rpm, 415V, 3 phase induction
motor.   The static parts of the compressor -
crankcase, cylinders, cylinder heads etc - were
all made of cast iron to BS1452 (1961) grade 17
and were designed so as not to exceed a set of
allowable stresses which included a maximum
value in direct tension of 4.2 tons/in^2
(65N/mm^2).   The retention of each cylinder to
the crankcase was achieved by sandwiching it
between the cylinder head and the upper face of
the crankcase using four long EN16R tie bolts
having a 0.2% proof stress of 32 tons/in^2
(494N/mm^2).

Figure 3 illustrates how the automatic plate
valves in the first and second stage cylinder
heads were each retained by lanterns inserted
through circular openings in the top of each
cylinder head.   These lanterns, with O'type
sealing rings, served to complete the pressure-
tight enclosure of the cylinder heads and were
themselves held down by external forged EN9
retaining plates each secured by two high
tensile cap screws.   To verify their pressure-
tightness and constructional safety both
cylinder heads, as machined castings, were
hydraulically pressure tested at the time of
manufacture.   In the case of the second stage
cylinder head the test pressure was 24.1 bar.g
being 1.5 times the maximum design pressure of
16.55 bar.g.   That this figure substantially
exceeded the specified maximum compressor
operating pressure of 10.5 bar.g and the actual
working pressure in the particular factory of
6.9 bar.g was due to several factors.   Firstly
the design was intended to cover the eventual
development of the compressor to 13.8 bar.g
maximum working pressure.   On top of this a
further 20% pressure rise was allowed to cover
the setting of the downstream safety valve
which would begin to open at 15.2 bar.g and
then require a further 10% differential to
become fully open and be capable of passing the
full output of the compressor.

As a further protection the discharge pipe from the first stage of the compressor, for which the normal maximum delivery pressure was 2.8 bar.g, was also fitted with a pressure relief valve set to lift at 3.1 bar.g and be fully open at the design pressure of 3.45 bar.g. Accordingly the first stage cylinder components were individually pressure tested to 6.9 bar.g i.e. twice the design pressure.

In standard form the compressor as supplied by the maker was equipped with the following regulation and protective devices and indicators (see Figure 4):-

Interstage pressure relief valve fitted in the compressor's first stage outlet pipe set to open at 3.1 bar.g.

A capillary type over-temperature switch with its bulb inserted in the second stage outlet pipe, normally set at 240 deg C being the maximum acceptable temperature and representative of the combination of highest operating pressure and maximum allowable ambient temperature.

An automatic pressure regulator or governor set to unload the first and second stage suction valves of the compressor and to 'blow-down' the compressed air in the intercooler when the upper set pressure of the regulator is reached. This regulator automatically 'unloads' and 'loads' the compressor when the air pressure in the receiver reaches the upper and lower set pressures while the compressor continues to run.

A fusible plug in the first stage cylinder outlet pipe with a melting point of 210 deg C.

An instrument panel with three gauges indicating respectively the pressure at the outlet from first and second stage cylinder heads and the lubricating oil system pressure.

The system also included a free standing air cooled aftercooler and an air receiver with protective devices and instruments comprising:-

A safety valve in the inlet header of the aftercooler set to open at 10.7 bar.g - this being a standard setting just above the maximum operating pressure but well below the design pressure of the aftercooler.

A safety valve in the air receiver set to open at 6.9 bar. g as determined by the customer's operating requirements and the design of the receiver itself. The receiver also carried a large gauge indicating stored air pressure.

Finally the electrical supply to the motor via a fused circuit breaker and a lever operated star/delta starter was protected against excessive current by fuses in each phase; no thermal over-current protection relay was included. The 50 amp rating of the fuses to match the 38 amp full load current of the motor meant they had the ability to pass approximately 75 amps equivalent to a motor power output of about 35kW) for a short duration.

This comprehensive array of protective and regulation devices should have ensured that no accident could possibly occur as a result of over-pressure conditions. Unfortunately one other device had been installed - a stop valve between the compressor outlet and the aftercooler inlet. Despite the maker's explicit installation instructions that a safety valve must be fitted between any such stop valve, if installed, and the compressor outlet no such additional safety valve was fitted at the time of the accident.

The users of the compressor were at least its third owners. The machine had been manufactured in 1969 and sold to a company in Northern Ireland and nothing is known of its service history there. When the accident occurred the owners were a foundry in the Midlands who had purchased the compressor with its motor and aftercooler in 1976. In 1979 the compressor had been completely overhauled by the manufacturers' local distributor and service agents from whom it had been purchased. Between 1979 and 1984 it was relocated into a lean-to building outside the main factory although the starter and fused switch remained inside the factory and out of sight of the compressor. The distance between the starter and the compressor was approximately 30 feet.

Much doubt existed during the subsequent investigation as to what changes had been made by whom to the compressed air pipework. It seems likely that a non-return valve in the pipe between the aftercooler and air receiver was part of the original installation. The origins of the stop valve situated in the 2.5 inch diameter delivery pipe about 30 inches from the compressor discharge flange were never established. Neither was the reason for the removal of the hand wheel from the spindle of this valve. Immediately after the accident some mole grips were found to be fastened to the valve spindle which bore scars suggesting that this had been the normal method of operation for some time past. In the short pipe between the stop valve and the compressor there was a 'T' piece with its branch plugged. It is possible, but not certain, that this may have carried the appropriate safety valve at some time.

3   CIRCUMSTANCES OF THE ACCIDENT

The introduction of additional production equipment to the site had increased the demand for compressed air beyond the capability of the installed compressor and a portable compressor was hired to augment the supply. This arrived late one morning and the lunch break was taken as an opportunity to connect the hire machine. The plant manager instructed that it should be connected directly to the new equipment and not into the factory compressed air system. This intention was apparently misunderstood and the portable compressor output was in fact connected by the shop foreman into the factory system at a point between the aftercooler and the receiver. To do this the factory compressor was stopped by pressing the stop button on the starter. The fuses were not removed, the electrical supply was not isolated in any way and no warning of the work in hand was displayed or, apparently, communicated to other personnel. Presumably it was at this stage that the mole grips were used to shut the stop valve.

Just at the end of the lunch break the plant manager noticed that his instructions had not been followed and with the foreman began changing the connections. While doing so another employee of the Company returning after lunch noticed there was no compressed air at his work place and on going to discover why he found the compressor stopped. Seeing no reason for this he went inside and operated the starter. Alerted by shouts from outside he left the starter energised and went back outside to join the foreman by the compressor itself.

The subsequent investigation confirmed that about 10 seconds after the compressor was started the second stage cylinder exploded severely injuring the employee and the foreman, one of whom subsequently died of his injuries. A portion of the cylinder head with the valve lantern retaining plate attached was found more than 100 yards away.

4   ON-SITE INVESTIGATIONS

Present at the immediate investigations were representatives of the Health and Safety Executive, the owners, the compressor manufacturers and the police. Soon the following potentially contributory facts were established:-

Apart from the destroyed second stage cylinder head the compressor remained in sound working order.

The fusible plug in the first stage delivery pipe of the compressor remained intact.

The outlet connection from the intercooler blow-down valve had been permanently plugged so preventing discharge of condensate and the de-pressurization of the intercooler during unloaded running.

The interstage safety valve was stamped '100 psi' (6.9 bar). This was subsequently proved to start opening at 3.45 bar.g and become fully open at 3.8 bar.g as opposed to the 3.1/3.45 bar.g setting of the valve originally fitted by the manufacturers.

The stop valve in the discharge pipe was fully shut and subsequently found capable of holding in excess of 70 bar.g pressure without leakage.

The capillary connection of the second stage temperature switch was broken. It was possible that this may have happened at the time of the accident but the fact that it was broken at the switch rather than where the bulb was inserted into the second stage delivery manifold suggests this had occurred some time before the accident.

The fuses in the electrical starter remained intact. Subsequently they were found to operate correctly in relation to their specified current rating.

The starter was in its 'stop' condition and is presumed to have been manually operated immediately after the accident.

The only strange observation was that the internal surfaces of the broken cylinder head were found to be 'dry' and the film of lubricating oil expected in normal service and always found during routine maintenance was not present.

On the face of it there remained little to explain except how the compressor managed to reach a second stage internal pressure capable of destroying the cylinder head without activating one or other of the protection devices. To establish this it was essential to determine as accurately as possible at what pressure the disintegration eventually occurred and the processes by which that pressure was generated.

5   ANALYSIS

Examination of the design of the second stage cylinder head suggested that catastrophic failure would take place when the membrane wall between the suction and delivery chambers (see Figure 5) was no longer able to sustain the loads exerted on it by the internal pressure loading on the upper and lower surfaces. Presuming the normal properties of grade 17 cast iron had been achieved, and examination of the broken components tended to support this, the internal pressure to cause such failure was calculated to be 86.5 bar.g (1250 lbf/in^2g).

To verify this two sample cylinder heads made to the same specification, but 15 years later, were subjected to hydraulic tests whereby the pressures in the inlet and discharge chambers were raised progressively, to 4 bar.g and 70 bar.g respectively. These pressures had been estimated to be representative to the conditions in the subject machine. Difficulties in maintaining leak free conditions at the various blanking plates prevented any higher pressure being reached on the discharge side. Neither cylinder head was damaged or permanently deformed by these pressure tests.

To shed more light on the situation several other questions were asked:-

(1) Bearing in mind the operation of the interstage relief valve, was there a limiting pressure which the compressor was capable of raising against the stop valve in the short discharge pipe?

(2) How long would it take to approach within, say, 5% of this limiting pressure?

(3) Was there any correlation between the period of about 10 seconds from starting the compressor to the explosion mentioned by those involved and the estimated time it would take the compressor to raise failure pressure levels?

(4) Why did the motor fuses not operate to stop the compressor prior to this very high pressure being reached?

Using the known performance characteristics of the compressor type a computer model was established to estimate all relevant operating parameters within the machine after each single revolution of the crankshaft. Certain assumptions were necessary to complete this model. In particular the variation of volumetric efficiency for pressures above those encountered in normal service in both stages was estimated, diminishment of pressure loss due to flow through orifices, pipes, etc. as the pressure increased and the air flow into the sytem reduced virtually to zero. It was also assumed that the mass of air in the intercooler and its connecting pipes remained at constant temperature and that no heat losses occurred from the discharge pipe.

The analysis was subsequently influenced by the effect of the interstage relief valve. The first calculations presumed that the '100 psi' marking on the valve represented its actual setting and the process of pumping-up the closed delivery pipe had three identifiable phases:-

(1) The acceleration of the motor/compressor unit towards full speed with the starter in 'star' mode which was presumed to take approximately 3 seconds during which 36 revolutions of the crankshaft occurred.

(2) Transition to 'delta' and subsequent full speed running with the discharge pressure from both first and second stage cylinders rising in normal relationship to one another until the first stage discharge pressure caused the interstage relief valve to open.

(3) Once the interstage relief valve was open the effect was for the machine to operate in single stage mode with the second stage doing all the work to further increase the delivery pressure. Meanwhile the first stage served only to maintain the inlet pressure to the second stage at the relief valve setting.

For the first analysis the interstage relief valve was assumed to start opening at a pressure above 6.9 bar.g (100 lbf/in^{2}g) and be fully open at 7.6 bar.g (110 lbf/in^{2}g). In this case the calculations indicated that the compressor would have completed approximately 220 revolutions in 10.5 seconds before the relief valve opened at which time pressure at the stop valve would have reached approximately 89 bar.g (1300 lbf/in^{2}g). As this pressure exceeded the value calculated to destroy the HP cylinder head and the elapsed time to reach this pressure corresponded with the reports of the accident it appeared to be an open-and-shut case. There remained doubts concerning the power input to the compressor to achieve these pressures vis-a-vis the over current protection in the electrical supply.

Before this latter factor was examined, however, evidence appeared that the actual setting of the interstage relief valve was 3.4/3.8 bar.g (50/55 lbf/in^{2}g). The calculations were therefore repeated using these values. It was now predicted that the final discharge pressure would be asymptotic to approximately 75 bar.g (1090 lbf/in^{2}g) and that 95% of that value, 71.2 bar.g (1030 lbf/in^{2}g), would be reached in the discharge side of the second stage cylinder head after about 340 crankshaft revolutions in approximately 15 seconds (see Figure 6).

Now we had a situation where the maximum pressure level to have been generated in the second stage cylinder head in more than the reported time only marginally exceeded the static pressure which had failed to cause breakage or distortion under hydraulic test. Clearly other possibilities needed to be examined.

An alternative hypothesis was that ignition of the oil or oil vapour in the discharge pipe or cylinder head had occurred. It was felt that this could have been exacerbated by the long service and poor maintenance of the machine. It would also possibly explain the unusual 'dryness' of the cylinder head surfaces noticed after the accident.

The same modelling procedures yielded an assessment of the compression temperature generated in the second stage cylinder at each stroke of the piston and the resulting increase in temperature of the air stored in the discharge pipe between the compressor and the stop valve. With the 3.4 bar.g interstage relief valve setting the compression temperature in the cylinder increased to 300 deg C after approximately 100 revolutions in 6 seconds and 400 deg C after 190 revolutions in about 9 seconds. Thereafter it increased more slowly reaching 440 deg C after 15 seconds.

With the specified lubricating oil having a closed flash point of approximately 230 deg C the balance of evidence now supported the theory that oil mist detonation in the cylinder or cylinder head after less than 10 seconds had caused a sudden increase of pressure to well in excess of the 90 bar.g probably needed to destroy the cylinder head. It was also considered more likely that the reported 10 seconds between starting the compressor and the explosion was over-estimated rather than under-estimated by those directly involved.

Once the interstage relief valve had opened the input power to drive the compressor at its normal speed would have dropped from a maximum value of about 26kW to an asymptotic condition of 10.5kW after 30 seconds. More interestingly the 18.5kW rating of the motor would have been exceeded only for a period of 6 seconds. Finally the 50 amp rated current of the fuses was probably not exceeded at any time and any excess was certainly within their thermal/time rating.

6   CONCLUSIONS

In the absence of the essential safety valve between the compressor and the stop valve the investigation starkly demonstrated that none of the many protective devices, even if they had been able to operate, could have averted the accident. The second stage temperature trip with its bulb inserted in the delivery pipe was unlikely to have operated even if the capillary had not been broken. Firstly its own thermal inertia was likely to have prevented a sufficiently fast response. More certainly the temperature of the air in the closed volume of the delivery pipe would not have risen significantly above the setting of the switch. The calculations indicated that this temperature would be 220 deg C after 8 seconds with an eventual value of 270 deg C after 30 seconds (Figure 6).

The real lesson, however, came in the demonstration that everyone concerned with compressed air systems must exercise continuous vigilance, discipline and attention to detail if hazardous operating conditions are to be avoided. The compressor manufacturers concerned certainly understood much more about the off-design behaviour of their products and the opportunity that this could provide for unsatisfactory operation. Some of the users of the equipment unfortunately had no opportunity to learn from their experience. It is to be hoped that the other people who represented the owners and users have a better appreciation of the potential for disaster inherent in the stored energy of compressed air further increased by the presence of combustible lubricating oil.

Overriding everything was the recognition that the most important single protective device was not incorporated in the system. The compressor makers were helpless in this respect as they had no control over the installation and no opportunity to present instruction manuals for machines which were purchased second or third hand. The installers said categorically that a safety valve had been fitted upstream of the stop valve and the branch connection for it clearly existed. The users were not specialists in compressed air systems and perhaps might have considered that they were not expected to know about these things. Any one of many different actions could have prevented the accident - removing the fuses, hanging a notice on the starter, communicating with the operator, clearer instructions, etc, etc.

In summary it is unlikely that a better case could be made in support of the Health and Saftey Executive in their preparation of the new Pressure Systems Regulations which are expected to become law this year. Perhaps the emphasis that this will place on the need for competent persons to supervise the design, manufacture, installation, use and maintenance of compressed air systems and their insistence of an explicit scheme of regular examination may hopefully frustrate the future presentation of a similar paper.

The author's acknowledgements are due to representatives of all the companies and organisations involved in the investigation. Most particularly, however, he thanks Mr S J Morris who carried out all the detailed analytical work. His capacity to take pains and the unique accuracy of his mathematical work would serve well as an example to anyone concerned with guaranteeing the safe operation of compressed air systems.

Fig 1   Type V100A 18kW air compressor

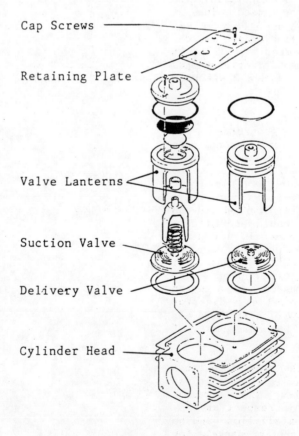

Fig 3   Components of second stage cylinder head assembly

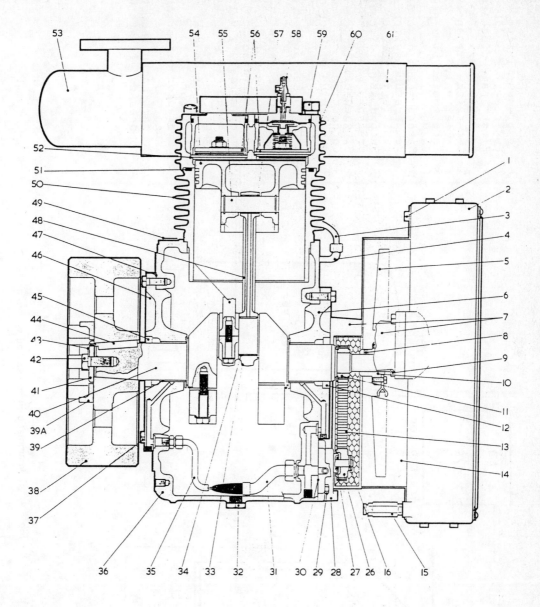

Fig 2   Compressor cross-section

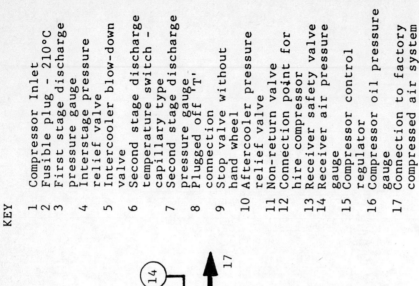

KEY

1 Compressor Inlet
2 Fusible plug - 210°C
3 First stage discharge pressure gauge
4 Interstage pressure relief valve
5 Intercooler blow-down valve
6 Second stage discharge temperature switch - capillary type
7 Second stage discharge pressure gauge
8 Plugged off 'T' connection
9 Stop valve without hand wheel
10 Aftercooler pressure relief valve
11 Non-return valve
12 Connection point for hire compressor
13 Receiver safety valve
14 Receiver air pressure gauge
15 Compressor control regulator
16 Compressor oil pressure gauge
17 Connection to factory compressed air system

Fig 4   Diagrammatic compressed air system

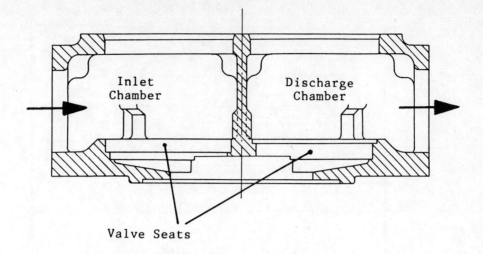

Inlet
Chamber

Discharge
Chamber

Valve Seats

Membrane Wall

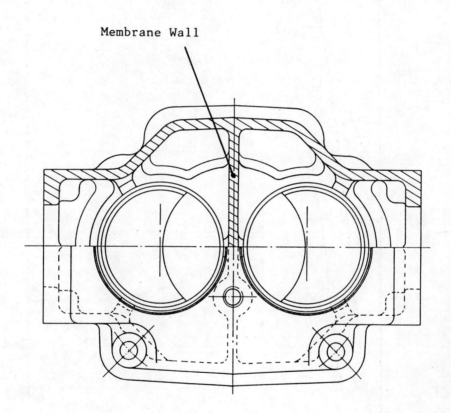

Fig 5   Second stage cylinder head

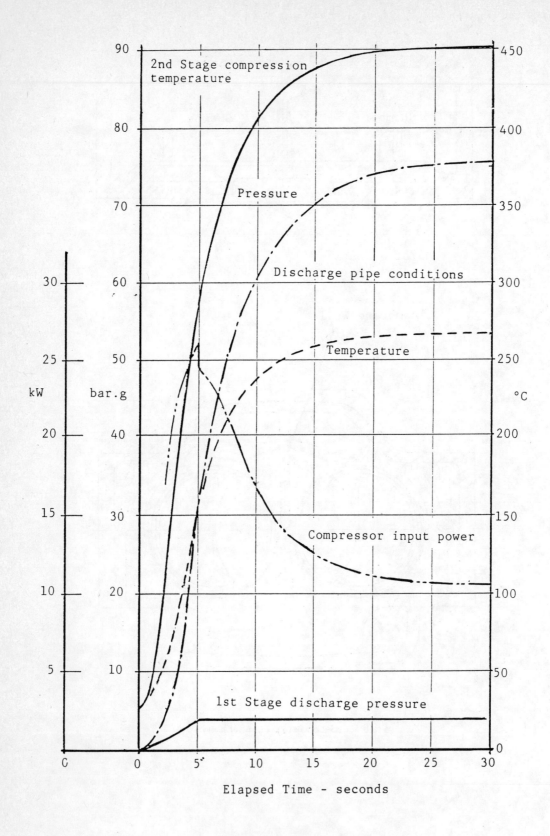

Fig 6   Compressor operating conditions